EFFECTS OF IONIZING RADIATION
ON THE DIGESTIVE SYSTEM

EFFECTS OF
IONIZING RADIATION ON
THE DIGESTIVE SYSTEM

by

I. T. KURTSIN

ELSEVIER PUBLISHING COMPANY
AMSTERDAM / LONDON / NEW YORK
1963

TRANSLATED BY SCRIPTA TECHNICA, INC.

WASHINGTON, D.C. (U.S.A.)

SOLE DISTRIBUTORS FOR THE UNITED STATES AND CANADA

AMERICAN ELSEVIER PUBLISHING COMPANY, INC.

52 VANDERBILT AVENUE, NEW YORK 17, N.Y.

SOLE DISTRIBUTORS FOR GREAT BRITAIN

ELSEVIER PUBLISHING COMPANY LIMITED

12B, RIPPLESIDE COMMERCIAL ESTATE

RIPPLE ROAD, BARKING, ESSEX

LIBRARY OF CONGRESS CATALOG CARD NUMBER 63-19828

WITH 72 ILLUSTRATIONS AND 68 TABLES

Contents

PART II

MECHANISMS OF IMPAIRMENT OF THE ACTIVITY OF THE DIGESTIVE ORGANS DURING RADIATION SICKNESS

To the fond memory of my teacher

Academician Konstantin Mikhailovich Bykov

Note

This book has been written for the general use of physicians and scientists. It deals with an urgent problem in modern medicine and contains a vast amount of varied experimental material on changes in the functions of the digestive organs caused by ionizing radiation, together with an analysis of the mechanism of these changes. Several ways of preventing and treating serious disorders of the digestive organs during radiation sickness are outlined.

Foreword

Physiologists, pathologists, and clinical physicians were first confronted with the problem of radiation lesions of the digestive organs fifteen years ago as a result of the widespread use of atomic energy in various branches of the national economy. It has now become one of the most pressing problems of modern medicine, justifying the intensive experimental work of Soviet and foreign investigators in the field.

For the past eight years, a team of scientists under my direction has been studying in detail; 1) radiation-induced impairment of the secretory function of the salivary glands, stomach, pancreas, liver, and small intestine, 2) motility of the gastrointestinal tract, 3) the structure of the various digestive glands, and 4) certain aspects of the neurohumoral mechanisms regulating digestive functions.

This research has been conducted in conformity with the general theory of I. P. Pavlov on higher nervous activity and the teaching of K. M. Bykov on functional interrelations between the cerebral cortex and the internal organs. Consequently, with respect to method and experimental techniques, it differs radically from a good deal of the work on radiation injury to the digestive organs done by many investigators, particularly those in foreign countries.

The availability of our own experimental data, derived from prolonged chronic experiments on 100 dogs, and the lack of surveys and monographs on radiation injury to the digestive system in world literature encouraged us to systematize our findings and compare them with those of other authors. As soon as we started this work, however, we encountered difficulties familiar to all investigators who have assumed a task of this kind. One can compare and contrast only results obtained on the same animals under identical experimental conditions. The literature contains information on radiation lesions of the digestive tract in man and in a great variety of animals—dogs, cats, rabbits, rats, mice, frogs, pigs, and monkeys—all of which have varying degrees of resistance. Moreover, observations were sometimes made during acute experiments, with all the shortcomings inherent in this type of investigation; sometimes during chronic experiments with "fistula" animals; and sometimes on human patients.

Different authors have used different doses of irradiation, the limits of which have ranged from the maximal permissible dose to several thousand roentgens. Neither the technical conditions of the irradiation nor the dose rate, was found to be constant; hence, the animals' radiation sickness differed in severity and outcome, despite the apparent uniformity of the dose. Furthermore, sometimes total-body external irradiation, chiefly X-rays, was used; at other times, internal irradiation with a variety of radioactive substances of unequal power was used: phosphorus, polonium, strontium, nuclear fission products of uranium, etc. A number of investigators studied functional changes in the digestive organs after external local irradiation with gamma and beta rays, again with different dosages, dose rates, and experimental conditions (acute and chronic).

These authors studied the digestive functions without taking into account the functional state of the higher divisions of the central nervous system and the typological characteristics of higher nervous activity which, in our opinion, largely determine the individual radiosensitivity of the organism and substantially influence the course and outcome of radiation sickness. These investigators often concentrated on changes in the digestive functions while ignoring the general condition of the organism, the clinical picture of the disease, or the stage of development of the pathological process.

Therefore, in systematizing and generalizing these data, we were compelled to rely chiefly on our own factual material. First of all, our data was collected in a single consistent research effort. Secondly, they were obtained by uniform experimental methods. Thirdly, the experiments were on the same kind of animals (dogs) kept under similar conditions of laboratory life and diet. Fourthly, they all pertained to total-body X-irradiation with an RUM-3 apparatus using the same doses (250-350 r) and dose rates. Finally, we took into account, on one hand, the functional state of the higher divisions of the brain (as determined by conditioned salivary reflexes), and the typological characteristics of the animals' higher nervous activity (established by means of the "lesser standard" tests), and, on the other, the activity of the digestive organs (studied by chronic fistulas).

Our data then had to be compared with the clinical picture of radiation sickness. Accordingly, in all investigations of digestive functions, we simultaneously determined peripheral blood changes (leukocyte and erythrocyte counts, hemoglobin content, erythrocyte sedimentation rate), body temperature and weight, food excitability, motor activity, and other indicators of pathological conditions.

It is not for us to judge how successful we have been in our attempt to organize our material and interpret it in the light of modern radiobiology, radiophysiology, and radiopathology. We shall be satisfied if this work helps in promoting further research on the problem, assists clinicians and other physicians in understanding the physiological mechanisms responsible for the development of radiation injury to the digestive organs, and aids in the search for new and more effective methods of preventing and treating radiation sickness. We shall be extremely happy if our modest effort contributes to the advance of Soviet science.

In conclusion, I should like to express my sincere thanks to my esteemed co-workers M. E. Vasilenko, S. V. Voĭnov, A. D. Golovskiĭ, G. Dzhagiik, V. B. Zakharzhevskiĭ, V. N. Zvorykin, A. E. Karpenko, A. G. Korobkina, A. G. Kuzovkov, É. K. Kuznetsova, N. A. Lapshin, A. V. Myasnikov, E. V. Pashkovskiĭ, A. V. Popov, V. L. Popkov, M. S. Seregin, P. V. Simonov, A. A. Fadeeva, Hua Kuan, I. G. Chursin, and N. A. Yaroslavtseva, who took an active part in working out the problem of radiation lesions of the digestive system, and to the technicians who took good care of the surgical and sick animals and were unfailingly helpful in carrying out the physiological observations.

Professor I. T. Kurtsin

May 13, 1959
Leningrad

Introduction

Radiation sickness as an independent human disease has become the object of earnest attention by physicians and clinicians comparatively recently.

Isolated cases of radiation lesions turned up soon after Roentgen discovered X-rays in 1895 and A. Becquerel and M. and P. Curie observed in 1896 that certain substances (compounds of uranium, radium, polonium, chalcocite, autunite) were naturally radioactive. A year after the discovery of X-rays, Becquerel and P. Curie found burns on their hands caused by radium rays. The first case of radiation sickness was described six years later. There were 7 such cases in 1907, 31 in 1908, and 54 in 1911. Later, the incidence of radiation injuries increased considerably following Rutherford's discovery of artificial nuclear fission and Frederick and Irene Joliot-Curie's discovery of how to obtain radioactive substances artificially.*

Nine deaths were recorded between 1922 and 1924 among workers painting watch dials with paints containing radioactive substances. In 1929 Martland described 18 fatalities due to injury by ionizing radiation, and the press published 126 more such cases the next year. Cases of skin cancer and serious blood diseases (leukemia) were observed in roentgenologists and radiologists exposed to external irradiation by roentgen and gamma rays in the course of their work. Lung cancer was found in Yakhimov and Schneeberg miners working in an atmosphere with high concentrations of the radioactive gas radon.**

The extensive use of atomic energy nowadays in various branches of the national economy, technology, and science—biology, physiology, and medicine in particular—has made radiation injury an urgent problem attracting the attention not only of specialists in a variety of clinical disciplines, but also of a vast army of theoretical scientists, from physicists and chemists in various specialties to biologists, physiologists, pharmacologists, histologists, and pathologists.

---

*See Marie Curie. Radioactivity. OGIZ, Gostekhizdat, 1947, pp. 328, 343.
**The Danger of Ionizing Radiation to Man. Izd. IL, Moscow, 1958, p. 27.

Among the numerous problems pertaining to the biological effects of ionizing radiation, which have been thoroughly investigated in recent years in many countries of the world, radiation injury to the digestive system occupies a special place. The reason for this is that the clinical symptoms of radiation lesions of the digestive tract are very pronounced. According to foreign physicians, chiefly Japanese and American, who examined large numbers of people in Hiroshima and Nagasaki, the radiation sickness from which people suffered after explosion of the atom bombs was characterized, among other things, by leukopenia, anemia, leukemia, adynamia, dystrophy, and hemorrhagic tendencies; by nervous, cardiovascular, and sexual disorders; and by marked impairment of digestive functions (Warren, 1946; Dunhan, Cronkite, Leroy, and Warren, 1951; Tsuzuki, 1953; Kusano, 1954; Dambrin, 1955; Sears, 1955; Marhefka, 1955; A. V. Kozlova and E. I. Vorob'ev, 1956).

It has been observed that within a few hours of exposure most persons receiving doses of 300 to 1000 r develop nausea, vomiting, and diarrhea, which disappear in one or two days and then return at the height of radiation sickness. Other symptoms include marked anorexia and progressive loss of weight. A. N. Gamaleya and M. D. Donskoĭ (1954) mention the development of profuse diarrhea, necrotic ulcers of the buccal mucosa, stomatitis, and symptoms of paralytic intestinal obstruction.

Severe lesions of the digestive system were observed during the course of radiation sickness in persons exposed to radioactive fallout after the 1954 hydrogen bomb test on Bikini atoll (Arnold, 1954; Koyama and Kumatori, 1955; Mikamo, 1956; others). Digestive disorders included marked anorexia, nausea, vomiting, meteorism, disturbed secretory and motor activity of the gastrointestinal tract, stomach pain, acute weight loss, exhaustion, and several local and general inflammations in the alimentary canal.

A similar picture has been described by other investigators who observed persons after brief contact with intense ionizing radiation following the breakdown of an experimental reactor at Los Alamos research laboratory and after prolonged contact with such radiation (from being present during treatment with X-rays or radium or from working with isotopes).

According to L. Hempelmann, H. Lisco, and D. Hofman (1954), impairment of gastrointestinal activity in nine persons exposed during the course of an experimental chain reaction manifested itself variously, depending upon the radiation dose received. Seven men exposed to X-ray doses ranging from 31 to 390 r and to 0.18 to 26.6 r of gamma rays suffered only minor disorders. Another man, who received 480 r of X-rays and 110 r of gamma rays, complained of nausea and repeated vomiting the first day after the radiation. The next day he suffered prolonged periods of hiccuping. Two days later, his appetite, which had been absent, returned, but he could not eat owing to inflammation of the buccal mucosa. He became flatulent on the 10th day and his abdomen was tender, especially in the right upper quadrant. From the 12th day until he died 24 days after exposure, he had liquid stools, severe stomatitis, and weight loss. The ninth patient died nine days after exposure to 1930 r. He developed nausea and vomiting soon after exposure and, by the end of the week, anorexia, jaundice, and collapse. At autopsy the intestine was found to be obstructed.

According to A. K. Gus'kova and G. D. Baĭsogolova (1955) who observed two patients with acute radiation sickness after total-body external gamma and neutron irradiation of 300 to 450 r, one man suffered nausea, vomiting, and loss of appetite within 20 seconds of exposure, while the other man showed the same symptoms within a few minutes. These symptoms abated after repeated gastric lavage but returned the next day.

M. N. Pobedinskiĭ (1954), Yu. G. Grigor'ev (1956), and N. A. Kurshakov, and I. S. Glazunov (1955) state that nausea, vomiting, thirst, abdominal pain, diarrhea, tenesmus, and anorexia are the most pronounced symptoms of radiation lesions of the digestive organs. Several of these symptoms were also noted by A. M. Yugenburg, L. G. Peretts, and R. S. Mostova (1933) in patients after external local irradiation.

According to N. N. Rynkova (1956), the impaired gastrointestinal activity observed during acute human radiation sickness is identical with the clinical picture of gastritis and enteritis. Changes in secretion and in enzyme activity of the intestinal juice parallel changes in the dynamics of nervous processes in the cerebral cortex, the extent of the changes varying with the stage of the disease.

We see, therefore, that ionizing radiation injury causes, among other things, serious impairment of activity in the digestive system, the effects remaining to some extent for many months and even years after clinical recovery. Disorders of gastrointestinal activity also occur in chronic radiation disease resulting from the prolonged action of radioactive substances taken into the organism, or from systematic exposure to small but greater than maximum permissible doses of external radiation from gamma rays, X-rays, or neutrons.

With a mild, chronic radiation sickness, the appetite diminishes and dyspeptic symptoms and meteorism appear. After an initial period of hyperfunction, gastric activity is marked by hyposecretion and achylia. In a moderately severe case, there are more marked metabolic disturbances: appetite reduction, regurgitation, pressure and heaviness in the gastric region, occasional diarrhea, decrease in the enzymatic activity of the digestive juices, heightened muscle tone of the large intestine, and stasis of chyme in the ileocecal region. In a severe case, the above symptoms are both more pronounced and more constant.

The chronic course of the disease, according to N. N. Rynkova (1956), is accompanied by decreased gastric and pancreatic secretion, weakened hepatic detoxifying ability, and impaired gastrointestinal motility. Z. A. Zedgenidze (1956) notes a "gastric paresis" during the first 24 hours, which disappears during the latent period of the disease, being followed by normal decreased motility. Paresis of the gastric and intestinal muscles, however, reappears at the height of the disease. Such undulation of the pathological processes has also been observed in the changes in gastric secretion. This reflects the wavelike or cyclic course of radiation sickness in general (N. A. Kraevskiĭ, 1955).

The disruption of digestive activity observed during radiation sickness of varying severity takes place against a background of impaired function of the central and peripheral nervous systems of hematopoiesis, of the cardiovascular system, the endocrine glands, kidneys, skin, and other organs, together with serious metabolic disturbances and dystrophy of cells and tissues. The course of the disease is subsequently complicated by the development of various infectious or septic processes which frequently are the direct cause of death. Autopsy of those dying of radiation sickness reveals the presence of profound injuries to the digestive organs (Bloom, 1947; Tullis and Warren, 1947; Liebow, Warren, and de Coursey, 1949; Brugge, 1952; T. Sears, 1955; N. A. Kraevskiĭ, 1955, 1957). Histological examination reveals evidence of changes in the mucosa of the gastrointestinal tract (the small intestine and ileum in particular), destruction of the glandular apparatus, and intramural nervous and vascular formations.

Vomiting, lowered food excitability, inflammation and ulceration of the gastrointestinal mucosa, and other signs of radiation injury to the digestive system have also been observed in animals exposed to ionizing radiation (P. D. Gorizontov, 1955; Yu. N. Uspenskiĭ, 1957; S. R. Perepelkin, 1957; and others). For example, in a monkey exposed to a single total-body dose of 400 to 800 r, disruption of digestive activity is the clearest sign of radiation sickness.

Severe radiation lesions of the gastrointestinal tract also occur after local irradiation of the abdominal region (Régaud, Nogier, and Lacassagne, 1912; Warren and Whipple, 1922; Graham, 1939; Bond, Swift, Allen, and Fischler, 1950; Quastler, Lanzl, Keller, and Osborn, 1951; Yu. N. Uspenskiĭ, 1957).

In concluding this brief survey, we should like to stress the fact that radiation lesions of the viscera, including the digestive organs, are associated with pronounced symptoms of nervous disorders, especially in the higher divisions of the central nervous system.

In 1957, 354 patients with radiation lesions were observed by M. P. Domshlak, Yu. G. Grigor'ev, N. G. Darenskaya, L. B. Koznova, and G. F. Nevskaya. Besides changes in blood composition,

PART I

Functional Characteristics of the Digestive Organs after Exposure to Ionizing Radiation

CHAPTER I

Salivation

Ionizing radiation produces profound and long-lasting injury to the salivary glands which, depending on the type of radiation, dose and dose rate as well as on the species and individual radiosensitivity of the organism, may at times be limited to impairment of a specific activity (e.g., production or discharge of secretions) with no significant injury to the tissue proper. At other times, radiation may induce morphologic changes in cells and tissues along with the secretory disorders. These changes follow both external and internal irradiation.

EXTERNAL IRRADIATION

Disturbances of salivation following total-body irradiation have been extensively investigated chiefly in research on conditioned salivary reflexes. The pioneers in this field were M. I. Nemenov (1932, 1938, 1955, 1950) and his co-workers, some of whom were students of I. P. Pavlov—P. S. Kupalov and F. P. Maĭorov. More recently, N. N. Livshits (1956), I. T. Kurtsin (1957, 1958, 1960), P. I. Lomonos (1959), and other Soviet investigators have successfully continued their work, which has showed that irradiation causes changes in the conditioned food reflexes and acid-defense salivary reflexes of dogs within a few seconds of exposure. Differences were observed in accordance with the conditions and dose used. Wave-like changes are most typical, with a marked decrease in conditioned salivation during the period of clinical symptoms of radiation sickness. In our experiments cited above, we were able to distinguish four characteristic stages in the onset of changes in conditioned salivation after total-body X-irradiation of dogs with a dose of 250 to 350 r (I. T. Kurtsin, A. G. Kuzovkov, and I. G. Chursin, 1957).*

---

*In these, as in our earlier experiments, the dogs were irradiated from two twin RUM-3 X-ray machines under the following

First, the stage of moderate inhibition persists for one to three days after irradiation and is characterized by a slight decrease in salivation in response to positive conditioned signals and by moderate intensification in response to unconditioned and differential conditioned stimuli (Table 1).

Second, the stage of excitation is longer and more pronounced if conditioned reflexes are formed with acid reinforcement and is less pronounced in conditioned reflexes formed with food reinforcement (Table 2). It is characterized by greater magnitudes of conditioned and, in part, of unconditioned salivary reflexes as well as by salivation in response to inhibitory conditioned stimuli.

Third, the stage of prolonged inhibition is characterized by a progressive decrease in conditioned salivation in response to both positive conditioned and unconditioned stimulation. These changes last 15 to 20 days (Table 3).

Fourth, the stage of normalization lasts from two to two and one-half months. This period features cyclic changes in salivation in response to conditioned stimuli; the salivary glands function normally on some days while on others their response does not equal the intensity of the stimulus (Table 4).

The intensity and duration of these stages of reaction will differ somewhat under other irradiation conditions and doses, but according to the findings of many authors, in general, the activity of the salivary glands at the height of radiation sickness is at a low level, whereas it is at a high level during the latent period and the recovery period of the disease.

Our co-worker, A. G. Korobkina, made a special study of salivation in response to unconditioned stimulation of the tongue receptors in dogs during acute radiation sickness caused by total-body X-irradiation with doses of 250 to 350 r. She observed four dogs with chronic fistulas of the parotid, submaxillary, and sublingual glands. Secretion of saliva was induced by oral administration of powdered biscuit (30 g three times at 3-minute intervals) or hydrochloric acid (50 ml of a 0.125% solution three times at 3-minute intervals). The saliva produced in response to each stimulus was collected for two minutes. In addition, there were experiments involving the subcutaneous injection of 0.2 mg of pilocarpine per kg of body weight. The saliva was collected at 5-minute intervals throughout the period of secretion.

---

conditions: tube voltage on the first machine: 250 kv, current 15 ma, filter 0.5 mm Cu and 1 mm Al, skin focal distance 120 cm, dose rate 3.4 r/min; tube voltage on the second machine: 185 kv, current 15 ma, filter 0.5 mm Cu and 1 mm Al, skin focal distance 120 cm, dose rate 3.7 r/min.

Table 1

Conditioned salivation of the dog Zadornyĭ before and on the first day after total-body X-irradiation with a dose of 350 r.

(Reported by I. T. Kurtsin, A. G. Kuzovkov, and I. G. Chursin.)

Time (hr and min)	Conditioned stimulus	Time of iso-lated action of the conditioned stimulus (sec)	Latent period (sec)	Magnitude of conditioned re-flex (drops of saliva)	Magnitude of unconditioned reflex (drops of saliva)
	Before irradiation				
8:35	Bell	20	4	16	69
8:40	Light	20	2	14	53
8:45	Metronome-120 . .	20	3	15	68
8:50	Metronome-60 (differentiation) .	20	8	3	—
8:55	Bell	20	3	17	65
9:00	Light	20	2	14	57
9:05	Metronome-120 . .	20	3	20	67
	Mean magnitudes* . .	20	2.8	16.0	63.1
	On the first day after irradiation (stage of moderate predominance of inhibition)				
13:20	Bell	20	3	13	78
13:25	Light	20	3	14	79
13:30	Metronome-120 . .	20	4	13	78
13:35	Metronome-60 (differentiation) .	20	5	8	—
13:40	Bell	20	5	12	75
13:45	Light	20	5	10	71
13:50	Metronome-120 . .	20	4	12	75
	Mean magnitudes . . .	20	4	12.3	76

*The values of the inhibitory reflex were not taken into consideration when calculating the mean magnitudes.

Table 2

Conditioned salivation of the dog Zadornyĭ on the fourth day after total-body X-irradiation with a dose of 350 r.

(Reported by I. T. Kurtsin, A. G. Kuzovkov, and I. G. Chursin.)

Time (hr and min)	Conditioned stimulus	Time of iso-lated action of the conditioned stimulus (sec)	Latent period (sec)	Magnitude of conditioned re-flex (drops of saliva)	Magnitude of unconditioned reflex (drops of saliva)
		Stage of excitation			
8:35	Bell	20	2	26	95
8:40	Light	20	2	24	76
8:45	Metronome-120 ..	20	2	21	75
8:50	Metronome-60 (differentiation) .	20	3	8	—
8:55	Bell	20	4	16	80
9:00	Light	20	2	14	70
9:05	Metronome-120 ..	20	3	20	74
	Mean Magnitudes ...	20	2.5	20.1	78.3

The experiments showed that the activity of all the salivary glands changes in radiation sickness; however, different glands showed different response dynamics depending upon the extent of radiation injury. In particular, there were also differences noted between those salivations produced by food and those produced by acid. For example, in the dog Seraya, irradiated with a dose of 250 r, parotid gland salivation in response to a food stimulus remained unchanged until the height of radiation sickness, except for a one-day increase in the amount of saliva (25% of the original level) on the second day after irradiation. Salivation increased from the 22nd to 95th days, after which time the activity of the gland returned to normal. Salivation in response to acid stimulation increased except during the first few days after irradiation, when secretion was actually reduced. This hypersecretory phase developed later, beginning with the eighth day, as did the normalization phase, which set in the 41st day after irradiation.

Thus, these studies showed that the most characteristic disturbance of parotid gland activity in mild radiation disease is

Table 3

Conditioned salivation of the dog Zadornyĭ on the 17th day after total-body X-irradiation with a dose of 350 r.

(Reported by I. T. Kurtsin, A. G. Kuzovkov, and I. G. Chursin.)

Time (hr and min)	Conditioned stimulus	Time of iso-lated action of the conditioned stimulus (sec)	Latent period (sec)	Magnitude of conditioned reflex (drops of saliva)	Magnitude of unconditioned reflex (drops of saliva)
	Stage of prolonged inhibition				
8:10	Bell	20	4	6	62
8:15	Light	20	3	12	59
8:20	Metronome-120	20	6	7	63
8:25	Metronome-60 (differentiation)	20	7	3	—
8:30	Bell	20	5	7	52
8:35	Light	20	6	6	42
8:40	Metronome-120	20	7	7	55
Mean magnitudes		20	5.2	7.5	55.5

hypersecretion; they also revealed the difference in the glandular reaction to stimuli of different biological significance. After the action of food, the hypersecretory reaction of the gland continued for several months; but after the action of acid, it did not persist for more than a month, although in this case it developed sooner after irradiation. The reason for this difference in the glandular reaction to different stimuli is evidently to be sought in biochemical changes taking place in the organs of neurohumoral control. Presumably the early change to hypersecretion in the acid-defense reflex was caused by early activation of this defense mechanism, which acts to produce rapid elimination of a harmful agent—in this case, the acid. Characteristically, hypersecretion continues throughout the course of the disease until recovery sets in, whereupon it returns to normal. This is graphically shown in Figure 1 in which there is a comparison between the curve of leukopenia development as an indicator of radiation sickness and the curve of salivation response to acid stimulation. The prolonged intensification of the food reflex, not only at the height of the disease but also during the period of recovery, is undoubtedly the result of weight loss, emaciation, deterioration of digestion in the gastrointestinal tract, and impaired metabolism.

It seems to us that the role of defense mechanisms becomes more pronounced under those conditions of X-irradiation where the

Table 4

Conditioned salivation of the dog Zadornyĭ on the 30th and 32nd days after total-body X-irradiation with a dose of 350 r.

(Reported by I. T. Kurtsin, A. G. Kuzovkov, and I. G. Chursin.)

Time (hr and min)	Conditioned stimulus	Time of iso-lated action of the conditioned stimulus (sec)	Latent period (sec)	Magnitude of conditioned re-flex (drops of saliva)	Magnitude of unconditioned reflex (drops of saliva)
Normalization stage, experiment of May 10, 1955					
8:40	Bell	20	2	16	63
8:45	Light	20	4	19	74
8:50	Metronome–120	20	5	14	68
8:55	Metronome–60 (differentiation)	20	3	3	—
9:00	Bell	20	4	9	64
9:05	Light	20	3	13	71
9:10	Metronome–120	20	2	14	67
Mean magnitudes		20	3.3	14.2	67.8
Normalization stage, experiment of May 12, 1955					
8:55	Bell	20	3	11	67
9:00	Light	20	9	7	52
9:05	Metronome–120	20	2	14	63
9:10	Metronome–60 (differentiation)	20	3	6	—
9:15	Bell	20	8	6	62
9:20	Light	20	10	4	57
9:25	Metronome–120	20	11	13	65
Mean magnitudes		20	7.2	9.2	61

dose is comparatively small while the resistance of the organism
is high. In cases of severe radiation injury when these mechanisms
deteriorate, it is more difficult to observe the phenomena described
above.

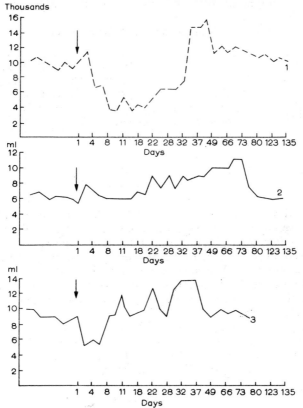

Figure 1. Changes in secretion of the parotid
gland of a dog in response to food and unpleasant substances during acute radiation
    illness. (Reported by A. G. Korobkina.)
    1—Number of leukocytes/mm³ of blood.
    2—Volume of saliva after eating powdered
    biscuit. 3—Volume of saliva after oral
    administration of hydrochloric acid.
    Arrow indicates day of irradiation.

    A comparison of the general efficiency of the salivary glands
in normal organisms and in organisms at the height of radiation
sickness shows that in a mild course of the disease, the activity

Table 5

Change in the efficiency of the salivary glands in a dog at the height of mild and severe radiation sickness.

(Reported by A. G. Korobkina.)

Name of dog	Kind of disease (irradiation) dose in r)	Percentage of increase (+) or decrease (-) from original level (norm) of saliva in response to stimuli		
		powdered biscuit	acid	pilocarpine
Seraya	Mild (250)	+35	+20	+15
Kashtanka	Severe (500)	-55	-70	-40

of the secretory cells during both reflex and humoral excitation is increased to a high level, whereas in a severe course, other things being equal, cell activity is at a very low level (Table 5).

Moreover, if we examine the activity of the individual glands of the same animal in normal and pathological states, we discover that during severe radiation sickness, the greatest decrease in efficiency takes place in the sublingual and submaxillary glands (Table 6).

Since the activity of the salivary glands is regulated chiefly by reflex, the data cited testify to serious impairment of the reflex regulatory mechanism. This is further indicated by the fact—established experimentally on the same animal—that at the height

Table 6

Change in the efficiency of the parotid and mixed (sublingual and submaxillary) glands in severe radiation sickness.

(Reported by A. G. Korobkina)

Stimulus	Percentage of increase (+) or decrease (-) from original level (norm) of saliva in response to stimuli	
	Mixed glands	Parotid glands
Powdered biscuit	-75	-20
Hydrochloric acid	-96	-40
Pilocarpine	-80	+15

of mild radiation sickness, salivation in response to an unpleasant substance (acid) is more marked (20% above normal) from a gland with intact innervation than from a gland partially denervated by sectioning the parasympathetic nerve (10% above normal).

This conception of the nature of secretory disorders of the salivary glands after radiation injury is supported by the following unusual phenomenon. Under normal conditions, the saliva of dogs is known to contain no amylase. Its presence in saliva was discovered in the experiments of I. P. Razenkov (1948) and his co-workers, both when they shifted their animals to a carbohydrate diet and after chronic hypoxia. It has also been found that amylase is present in saliva during radiation sickness. Yu. N. Uspenskiĭ (1957) was the first to note the phenomenon, but he offered no satisfactory explanation. Attempts to link the presence of amylase in saliva to enhanced amylase secretion in the pancreas could not be corroborated experimentally. Only one thing was clear: that, as I. P. Razenkov pointed out, in these cases there was an adaptation by the gland to the type of food used. The appearance of amylase in saliva in pathological states, however, remained unaccounted for.

In our experiments on dogs, Korobkina was never able to detect any amylase in the saliva before irradiation. After irradiation, however, it generally appeared in small amounts (from 2-4 to 16-32 Wohlgemuth units) in the saliva of both the parotid and the mixed glands regardless of whether the innervation was intact or partially impaired. The consistent appearance of amylase in the saliva beginning directly after irradiation and lasting throughout the disease until recovery suggests that this is a regular sign in the disease (Table 7). It might be supposed that radiation injury changes the permeability of the blood vessels of the gland (as has been demonstrated to be the case with the vessels of other organs) so that amylase enters the saliva from the blood. Parallel analyses of amylase concentration in the blood and saliva of dogs before and after irradiation, however, gave no support to this hypothesis. The concentration of the enzyme in the blood during radiation sickness remained virtually unchanged. On the occasional days when the concentration in the blood did change, these blood changes were not equalled by changes in the saliva. In fact, when the concentration of amylase increased in the blood (from 64 to 256 Wohlgemuth units), amylase was actually found to disappear from the saliva.

All these observations suggest that the presence of amylase in saliva during radiation sickness is the result of secretion rather than of excretion, and that the phenomenon should be associated with impaired digestion in the alimentary canal and general exhaustion. Furthermore, amylase also appeared in saliva after the animals were irradiated with a dose of 500 r (which usually caused severe disease with a fatal outcome), but there were days when it

SALIVATION

Table 7

Amount of amylase in the saliva of the parotid gland of a dog
during acute radiation sickness.

(Reported by A. G. Korobkina.)

Experimental conditions	Amylase in Wohlgemuth units			
	Powdered biscuit		Acid	
	Intact gland	Denervated gland	Intact gland	Denervated gland
Before irradiation	0	0	0	0
Days after irradiation				
1	4	2	16	16
2	4	2	32	32
4	4	8	16	32
6	32	16	0	0
9	4	4	32	32
11	8	8	0	0
13	2	4	8	2
18	16	8	32	16
20	4	4	8	2
22	8	8	8	4
24	8	8	8	8
28	4	4	16	4
30	4	4	16	16
32	0	0	8	8
34	0	0	0	0
37	0	0	0	0
39	0	0	4	2
41	0	0	0	0
59	0	0	0	0
62	0	0	0	0
73	0	0	0	0
95	0	0	0	0
123	0	0	0	0
141	0	0	0	0

could not be detected. This happened when the disease was very
severe, so that disappearance of the enzyme may well have been due to
marked inhibition of salivary function.

The activity of the salivary glands during radiation sickness
changes in response to both humoral and reflex stimuli. According

to Korobkina, pilocarpine intensifies salivation from the very first day after irradiation. This intensification takes place during the latent period of the disease and continues during the period of clinical symptoms; it disappears 30 days after irradiation with a dose of 250 r. Sometimes on the first day or two after irradiation, the dogs manifest a decreased glandular response to pilocarpine. This inhibition is more pronounced in dogs irradiated with 500 r. It arises the first day and, with some wavelike fluctuation, remains throughout the disease until the animal dies.

It was also determined that in saliva obtained after pilocarpine stimulation following irradiation and during radiation sickness, amylase is present in the same concentration as it is in saliva produced under similar conditions in response to food and unpleasant substances. A comparison of the change in salivation in response to acid with that following the administration of pilocarpine throughout the disease reveals several common features which suggest injury to the parasympathetic innervation of the salivary glands. On the other hand, since impaired secretion also occurs in glands deprived of parasympathetic innervation, there is reason to regard this impairment as the result of radiation injury to their sympathetic innervation. Involvement of the latter is also attested by the fact that amylase appears in the saliva of irradiated animals.

The experimental findings cited above indicate that the impairment of salivation caused by total-body irradiation results from radiation injury chiefly to the reflex regulatory mechanisms. There is also the possibility, however, that the changes in salivation are the result of direct injury by radiant energy to the cells of the salivary glands. Irradiation of the salivary gland area indeed reduces the magnitude of conditioned food and acid–defense salivary reflexes (Case and Boldyreff, 1925). At the same time, glucose-6-phosphate dehydrogenase activity increases in the submaxillary and sublingual glands (English, 1955).

Since roentgen rays have great penetrating power, they are capable of injuring not only the salivary glands but also other tissues in the path of the rays. Nervous tissue is particularly susceptible. Leopold (1952), for example, observed a decrease in unconditioned salivation and a reduction of solid residue in the saliva after local irradiation of the head in animals. In addition, conditioned salivation is also disrupted after local irradiation of the superior cervical sympathetic ganglia with doses of 1200, 3000, 4500, and 6000 r (F. P. Maĭorov, M. I. Nemenov, and L. S. Vasil'eva, 1949; F. P. Maĭrov, B. V. Pavlov, and N. Ya. Lipatov, 1956). Similar results are also obtained after X-irradiation using fractional doses ranging from 600 to 800 r over 10 sessions.

Thus, these experiments seem to indicate that a reflex mechanism is responsible for the changes of salivary function. The following experimental data also point in this direction.

A. G. Korobkina discovered that at certain times after dogs were irradiated, salivation became impaired only in response to food stimulation, while the reaction of the glands to acid-defense stimulation remained normal. If changes in salivation were caused solely by injury to the secretory cells, this change would be reflected in dysfunction following all kinds of stimulation. Since this was not the case, the secretory disorders were apparently due to radiation lesions of a food center in the brain which regulates the particular type of salivation. Furthermore, the difference which Korobkina discovered in the character of the secretory changes in response to food and unpleasant substances favors the likelihood of injury to the reflex regulatory mechanisms rather than to the secretory cells of the salivary glands proper.

Another of our co-workers, M. S. Seregin, studied salivary reactions to conditioned stimuli during X-irradiation of dogs. He discovered that changes in conditioned salivation arose 10 or 15 seconds after the start of total-body irradiation when the animals had received altogether only about 2 r. It is worth noting here that in one of the dogs, changes in salivation in response to conditioned signals were not accompanied by any noticeable changes in unconditioned salivation.

The results of these experiments suggest that radiation produces injury primarily to the conditioned reflex mechanism governing the activity of the salivary glands rather than direct injury of the secretory cells, which require massive doses of ionizing radiation for injury to occur.

P. I. Lomonos (1959) performed two series of experiments on dogs with previously formed conditioned food and acid-defense reflexes. In one series, she irradiated the entire body with 300 to 2000 r while shielding the head. In the other series, she irradiated only the belly with 700 to 4000 r while shielding the central nervous system. In all cases she observed changes in conditioned salivation, but the direction of the effect was different. For example, with food as reinforcement, irradiation of the belly of dogs decreased the magnitudes of both conditioned and unconditioned salivary reflexes, while with acid as reinforcement, the irradiation increased the magnitudes of conditioned reflexes alone.

Finally, Yu. N. Uspenskiĭ, T. A. Timofeeva, and I. V. Shvartser (1957) obtained significant data in experiments on six dogs whose bellies were irradiated with doses of 660 and 400 r with a focal distance of 30 cm, filter 0.45 mm Cu and 1 mm Al without a tube. Saliva was twice obtained from a chronic fistula of the parotid gland upon oral administration of powdered biscuit. The amount of saliva thus obtained before irradiation ranged from 3.0-3.4 to 4.5-5.0 ml; the first three days after irradiation, it dropped in two dogs to 0.7-1.5 ml and in the other animals to 2.0-3.0 ml. Thereafter, the amount of saliva in response to stimulation rose to 5.7-7.5 ml—i.e., it became abnormally high. By the end of the week, the activity of of the gland declined again; the amount secreted in response to stimulation was 1.5-3.0 ml. During the fourth and sixth weeks salivation rose and fell, and this wavelike phenomenon was noted in individual dogs about two months after irradiation, at which time the secretory function of the salivary glands became normal. In two dogs irradiated with a dose of 400 r, the radiation sickness and salivation changes had the same characteristics as they did after irradiation with a dose of 660 r, except that the latent period of the disease was 10 days instead of 3 to 5 days, the symptoms and changes in salivation were less marked, however, than after irradiation with a dose of 660 r. A relationship was noted among the changes in salivation, stage of the disease, and severity of the pathological processes.

Thus, the results of experiments with total-body and local irradiation given above confirm the view that secretion of the salivary glands is impaired by radiation injury, chiefly to the reflex regulatory mechanisms. This injury may be caused either by the direct action of radiant energy on cell structures of the nervous system or by toxins produced by ionization and resultant chain chemical and biochemical reactions; however, this does not necessarily exclude the possibility of changes of trophic processes in the salivary secretory cells themselves, especially after massive doses of irradiation and at the height of radiation sickness.

Yu. N. Uspenskiĭ, T. A. Timofeeva, and I. V. Shvartser (1957) discovered, after exposing the bellies of dogs to local irradiation, that there were qualitative changes in the saliva along with quantitative changes in secretion (Table 8).

These changes consist of wavelike variations in the content of solid residue and inorganic substances and a resultant modification of the proportion between them and the organic substances—a proportion which is 1:1 during the second and third weeks after irradiation. In addition, on some days during the sickness, the saliva is found to contain 32 to 64 Wohlgemuth units of amylase. The saliva also shows an increase in protein content from 0.41-0.64% to 0.94-1.18%, especially on the 9th and 17th days after irradiation (Yu. N. Uspenskiĭ and A. V. Afanas'eva, 1958).

All these qualitative changes in secretion cannot be ascribed solely to action on the secretory cells by humoral substances formed during the development of radiation sickness. In local irradiation of the abdomen, the nervous system is affected, and qualitative changes in the saliva may arise as a result of the disruption of trophic influences on the salivary glands coming from the central nervous system. This is borne out by Uspenskii and co-workers, who discovered that subcutaneous injection of irradi - ated animals with acetylcholine induced a secretion of 0.8 ml above the normal volume of 3.0 to 3.2 ml, whereas the injection of epinephrine induced salivation 1-1/2 to 2 times greater than usual; at the same time, the solid residue in the saliva decreased from 1.52-1.57% to 1.16-1.24%.

Table 8

Secretion of saliva in dogs before and after irradiation of the abdominal area with a dose of 660 r.

(Reported by Yu. N. Uspenskiĭ, T. A. Timofeeva, and I. V. Shvartser.)

Experimental conditions	Amount of saliva (ml)	Solid residue (%)	Organic substances (%)	Inorganic substances (%)	Amylase in Wohlgemuth units)
Dog No. 2					
Before irradiation	3.0-3.8	0.9-1.2	0.7-0.85	0.2-0.35	0
After irradiation:					
2nd day	0.7	0.16	0.64	0.52	0
3rd day	0.7	0.72	0.46	0.26	0
5th day	2.5	0.60	0.32	0.28	0
7th day	6.7	1.21	0.79	0.42	64
10th day	5.5	0.91	0.47	0.51	0
13th day	2.8	1.31	0.78	0.53	0
15th day	7.0	0.98	0.36	0.62	0
18th day	4.1	1.00	0.38	0.62	0
22nd day	1.2	1.8	—	—	0
Dog No. 4					
Before irradiation	4.0-4.6	1.7-1.6	0.85-0.9	0.25-0.7	0
After irradiation:					
2nd day	3.0	1.8	0.7	0.38	0
4th day	3.0	1.52	0.78	0.74	0
5th day	3.1	1.1	0.54	0.46	0
8th day	3.5	1.11	0.5	0.61	0
10th day	3.5	1.22	0.56	0.66	32
13th day	4.0	1.28	0.52	0.76	32
14th day	4.8	—	—	—	0
18th day	7.5	1.1	0.58	0.53	8
30th day	3.5	—	—	—	0
50th day	3.2	1.15	0.65	0.5	0

The experimental findings thus suggest that during radiation sickness caused by external ionizing radiation, the function of the salivary glands may vary in relation to the biological significance of the
stimulus. It decreases abruptly upon stimulation with food or
appropriate signals thereof, whereas it increases upon stimulation
with unpleasant substances or their signals. This variation in
glandular behavior, however, is not always evident because with
large doses and rates of ionizing radiation, the work of the salivary
glands will drop off markedly, regardless of the kind of stimulus.
Such a decrease in secretory cell function is one of the clearest
indications of severe radiation injury.

The cyclic nature of changes in salivary activity and response
to stimuli of different intensities is characteristic of the way radiation sickness develops. There may be periods when the glands
respond to strong and weak stimuli with identical salivation (equalizing phase) or to strong stimuli with weak salivation and to weak
stimuli with strong salivation (paradoxical phase). Furthermore,
there may be periods when the glands do not secrete in response
to positive stimuli, but do secrete copiously in response to inhibitory stimuli (ultraparadoxical phase). Following profound
radiation injury, the glands do not secrete in response to either
weak or strong stimuli (inhibitory phase).

The different states of salivary performance noted above are
evidently caused by profound functional changes in the cortical
apparatus regulating their activity and by the development of a
parabiotic state in the corresponding centers of the cerebral cortex.
However, the fact that phasic changes also occur with unconditioned
excitation of the glands suggests the possible development of a
similar state in subcortical salivation centers as well, or perhaps
in the secretory cells themselves.

INTERNAL IRRADIATION

Intravenous injection of dogs with 0.15 to 0.70 mc of radiophosphorus (P^{32}) per kg of body weight, with a total dose of 5 to 9
mc, causes changes in the food and acid-defense conditioned reflexes
within 1-1/2 to 2 hours (O. A. Briukhanov, 1954). At first, there is
a decrease in salivation in response to conditioned signals, then
an increase, and usually a decrease. The magnitude of the unconditioned salivary reflexes diminishes after doses of 15 to 20 mc.

According to our colleague Hua Kuan (1955), radiophosphorus,
in doses of 10 μc or more per kg of body weight decreases conditioned salivation in dogs without producing marked changes in
secretion following pilocarpine injection (Figure 2).

P. I. Lomonos (1959) observed conditioned salivation following
intravenous injection of animals with doses of 0.18 to 2.6 mc of

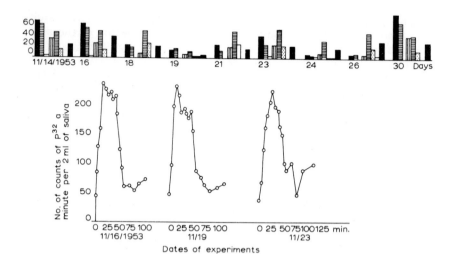

Figure 2. Conditioned salivary reflexes and secretion after pilocarpine injection in the dog Lyuks after injection of 10 μc of radiophosphorus (P^{32}) per kg of body weight.
(Reported by Hua Kuan.)

Columns show magnitudes of conditioned salivary reflexes (scale divisions) in response to a variety of stimuli (from left to right): bell, light, metronome at 120 beats per minute (differentiation), metronome at 60 beats per minute, light, inflation of a balloon in the rectum (12 times per minute), inflation of a balloon in the rectum 24 times per minute (differentiation), and bell. First two groups of columns (from left to right) show reactions before injection; subsequent groups, after injection of radiophosphorus. Curves show secretion of radiophosphorus with saliva secreted after pilocarpine stimulation of the glands: first curve, before injection of phosphorus; the rest, after injection.

radiocobalt (Co^{60}) per kg of body weight.   F. N. Serkov (1955) observed that in dogs salivation increased, decreased, and then increased again after oral administration of radiophosphorus at the rate of 75 μc per kg of body weight.

Studying the effect of chronic action of radiostrontium (Sr^{90}) on conditioned salivation in four dogs, E. N. Klimova (1957) discovered that the stability of positive and inhibitory conditioned reflexes is impaired after small doses (1 μc/kg orally for six months). Beginning with the second half of the first month, salivation in dogs with a strong type of nervous system sometimes increases in response to positive and inhibitory signals; at other times, there is pronounced pathological lability of the cells: an increase in magnitude of conditioned salivary reflexes at the beginning of an experiment and a sharp decrease toward the end. A decrease in conditioned salivation predominates in dogs with a weak type of nervous system; frequently, total inhibition at positive signals is seen. This response is accompanied by salivation disproportionate to the intensity of the stimulus. These phenomena become intensified as radiation sickness progresses, and by the second through the fifth months, and especially during the sixth month after the start of strontium administration, weakening of conditioned salivation and inadequate glandular response are observed more frequently in dogs with either the weak or strong type of nervous system. Termination of strontium injections, however, is not followed immediately by restoration of normal salivation in response to stimuli. Recovery occurs first in dogs with the strong type of nervous system—after 2 to 2-1/2 months. In dogs with the weak type, recovery occurs only after five months, and then not completely.

We would like to direct attention to Klimova's discovery that following the injection of radioactive strontium, dogs suffer marked impairment of salivation in response to conditioned stimuli despite the absence of clinical symptoms of radiation sickness. Consequently, the higher regulatory mechanism of salivation becomes impaired before clinical symptoms of radiation lesions of the internal organs become evident.

The difference in effects obtained by investigators after internal irradiation of animals is evidently attributable to the use of different ionizing substances, doses, and methods of administration, as well as to the individual characteristics of the animals' nervous systems. The important observation to be noted from the experiments described above is that internal irradiation is followed by the same changes in salivation that occur after total-body or local external irradiation. Thus, regardless of the irradiation method used, development of the pathological condition involves common physiological mechanisms, the most important of which is that regulating the reflexes.

The experimental findings cited indicate that impairment of salivation by ionizing radiation is responsible for abnormal chemical processing of food at the very beginning of the alimentary canal. The mechanical processing of food is disturbed by the development of numerous hemorrhages and trophic disorders in the mucosa of the gums, cheeks, lips, palate, and tongue at the height of radiation sickness and by radiation lesions of the jaws and teeth. There are published reports on extensive necrosis of tooth enamel ("radiation caries") in persons exposed during the atom bomb blasts over Hiroshima and Nagasaki. A. V. Kozlova (1957) observed loose teeth and extensive caries in patients after roentgen therapy for tumors of the maxillofacial region. Several investigators have observed postradiation inhibition of tooth buds, suppression of tooth growth and development, and deviation and abnormal position of teeth (M. N. Pobedinskiĭ, 1954). A. A. Prokhonchukov (1957) described disturbed phosphorus–calcium metabolism of a dystrophic nature in the solid tissues of rat teeth after multiple X-irradiation for 10 weeks with a total dose of 700 r.

Thus, prolonged functional disorders of the salivary glands arise after external or internal, total-body or local, irradiation if the dose and rate of ionizing radiation exceed maximum permissible amounts. Both the quantitative and qualitative aspects of secretion are affected. Profound trophic changes take place in the secretory cells with alterations in the production of secretions in general, and of enzymes in particular. Amylase appears in the saliva of dogs; the enzyme is absent when the organism is normal.

Salivary gland disorders are caused both by direct action of ionizing radiation on the neurosecretory apparatus of the gland and by indirect action through the nervous and humoral systems of regulation. The changes undergone by the conditioned–reflex mechanism controlling salivation are especially pronounced. The subcortical salivation centers are also severely impaired.

Secretory disorders of the salivary glands arising after irradiation are phasic in character, for there are periods when the amount of saliva increases or decreases in response to constant food stimuli or their signals. Aside from the wavelike course of the pathological process, however, the most characteristic phenomenon is an intensification of secretion after comparatively small doses of irradiation and suppressed secretion after large doses. After substantially increased doses and dose rates of ionizing radiation, this depression of salivation and decrease in the amount of secretion in response to food begins immediately after irradiation and continues thereafter throughout the sickness until the animal recovers or dies.

CHAPTER 2

Gastric Secretion

Modern knowledge of gastric secretory disorders following radiation injury is derived from clinical observations and the findings of experimental physiology and pathology.

CLINICAL OBSERVATIONS

The clinical material is based largely on data obtained, first, after local X-irradiation of the abdominal area of persons suffering from a variety of gastric diseases; secondly, after local ionizing irradiation of other parts of the body; and thirdly, during acute radiation sickness arising after external total-body irradiation and chronic radiation sickness resulting from prolonged contact with ionizing radiation. Although this material is not uniform in quality and does not provide a comprehensive view of the changes in gastric secretory disorders, not to mention the physiological mechanisms responsible for the origin and development of these disorders, it nevertheless is of great clinical and theoretical interest.

Irradiating the abdominal area for therapeutic purposes, Brügel (1916, 1917) noted a reduction in gastric secretion in patients with hyperacid gastritis. Other clinicians observed the same phenomenon after roentgenotherapy of gastric diseases, peptic ulcer in particular (Kothmejer, 1922; S. A. Molchanov, 1923; Bensaude, Solomon, and Oury, 1925; A. A. Bagdasarov and S. L. Kopel'man, 1929, 1930; V. A. Ioffe and G. G. Zal'tsman, 1934; Palmer and Templeton, 1939; A. Ya. Popov, 1946; Lewin, Haman, and Palmer, 1947; Ricketts, Kirsner, Humphreys, and Palmer, 1948).

Ya. S. Korneeva (1928) irradiated gastric patients with large doses of ionizing radiation for two to six months and, after analyzing their gastric juice, concluded that minimum doses exert a stimulating effect on the secretory cells in anacid and hypoacid gastritis but an inhibitory effect in hyperacid gastritis. Intensification of gastric acid production after roentgenotherapy was noted by

A. M. Yugenburg and R. G. Gurevich (1933); however, although they kept more than 100 patients under observation, they did not detect as frequent a reduction in gastric juice acidity in patients with gastric or duodenal ulcers as did Ya. S. Korneeva and other investigators. According to M. I. Nemenov (1938), roentgenotherapy of gastric ulcers increases the secretion of juice in 75% of the patients.

M. M. Mints (1928) noted distinct changes in gastric secretion in 19 patients with acromegaly after irradiating the hypophyseal thalamic region with doses of roentgen rays ranging from 4/5 to 1 erythema dose. In most cases there was a decrease in the secretion and acidity of the gastric juice.

A. V. Kantin (1938) noted an increase in juice acidity with hypo-acid types, a decrease with hyperacid types, and an absence of any changes with normal juice acidity while treating 55 ulcer patients with radium preparations placed on the neck. He ascribed these changes to the effect of ionizing radiation on the autonomic mechanisms regulating gastric function.

Similar influences on the stomach were observed by I. A. Oksenov (1932) during X-ray treatment of patients with uterine tumors. Like Kantin, he believed that the changes in secretion are brought about through the nervous system.

Assessing these clinical findings, we came to the conclusion that the lack of uniformity in results was due to many factors, as pointed out above. Of no little significance is the fact that gastric secretion was analyzed on the basis of degree of acidity without considering the quantitative aspect. Moreover, the method of obtaining juice from patients permitted the investigators to appraise essentially the second, or neurochemical, phase of secretion while the first, or complex reflex, phase of secretion remained outside their purview. Analysis of the first phase, however, is highly important in characterizing gastric gland activity. Then too the ambiguity of the information on the nature of secretory disorders may be partially due to the use of different doses of irradiation and methods of application.

Despite the disparity in findings and the difficulty of comparing them, however, the clinical material supports the following three theoretical positions: (1) ionizing radiation, regardless of the part of the body exposed (stomach, sex organs, neck, hypophysis, etc.), invariably changes gastric secretion; (2) ionizing radiation in comparatively small doses chiefly stimulates the gastric glands when their activity is low and inhibits them when their activity is extremely high, i.e., it effects different changes in secretion, depending on the original functional state of the neuroglandular apparatus of the stomach; (3) the nervous system, particularly its autonomic division, and the endocrine glands are involved in the causation of functional changes of the gastric glands caused by ionizing radiation.

More recent clinical evidence would be highly interesting in this connection were it not so incomplete, fragmentary, and imprecise. Even in the mass of material collected by Japanese and American physicians after the Nagasaki and Hiroshima atom bomb blasts, there is no detailed information on radiation injury to the secretory cells of the stomach. Meager data on this question were also presented by authors who studied the course of radiation sickness in people exposed to the acute action of penetrating radiation (L. Hempelmann, H. Lisco, and D. Hofman, 1954; A. K. Gus'kova and G. D. Baĭsogolov, 1955; V. G. Piskunova and A. M. Vychegzhanina, 1955; N. N. Rynkova, 1956).

The data on changes in gastric secretion following prolonged contact with small doses of ionizing radiation are unusually interesting. Our colleague V. N. Zvorykin (1957, 1960) used the Bykov-Kurtsin method to study the condition of gastric secretory cells in 65 persons admitted to the clinic for the aftereffects of contact with gamma radiation, neutrons, and aerosols (in combination more frequently than in pure form). The patients had been in contact with radiation between 1 and 21 years, 14 of them with stages I and II of chronic radiation sickness, the others with individual symptoms. Analysis showed that most patients were suffering from impaired gastric secretion reflected chiefly in inhibition of glandular activity. It was manifested by inhibitory, inert, and asthenic types of secretion. An hour's secretion was below normal in 52% of the cases during the complex-reflex phase and in 50% of the cases during the neurochemical phase. It was normal in 35% and 40%, respectively, and above normal in 13% and 10% of the cases. In some persons, inhibition of secretion was so marked that only 5 or 10 ml of juice could be obtained during the investigation (Figure 3).

The gastric juice obtained frequently had low acidity and often was completely lacking in free hydrochloric acid. Total acidity was low during the first phase in 58% of the cases and in 51% of the cases during the second phase. It was within normal limits in 29% and 27% of the cases, respectively, and above normal in 13% and 22%. In the majority of cases, the acidity was lowered to 5 to 10 titration units. Free hydrochloric acid of the juice was low in 46% of the cases during the first phase and in 47% of the cases during the second phase. It was within normal limits in 34% and 22% of the cases, respectively, and above normal in 20% and 31%. Achlorhydria in the juice was common.

The digestive activity was low in the juice secreted during the complex reflex phase of secretion in almost 50% of the cases, and in 25% of the cases during the neurochemical phase. In some individuals the gastric juice was wholly lacking in enzymatic activity. In most cases the juice contained a good deal of mucus.

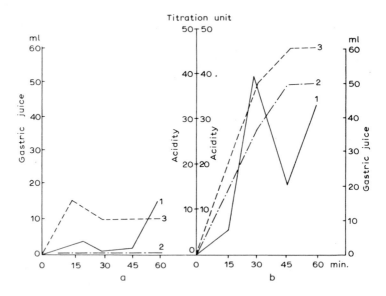

Figure 3. Gastric secretion in man during chronic
radiation sickness.
(Reported by V. N. Zvorykin.)
1 - Amount of juice secreted after mechanical
(a) and chemical (b) stimulation. 2 - Free hydrochloric acid. 3 - Total acidity of juice.

Thus, the most characteristic symptom of impaired gastric
secretion in persons who have had prolonged contact with small
doses of ionizing radiation is marked inhibition of glandular
secretion.

A comparison of Zvorykin's data with those on changes in gastric
secretion in persons with pronounced radiation sickness (N. A.
Kurshakov, 1954; A. K. Gus'kova and G. D. Baĭsogolov, 1955) shows
a common tendency in secretory dysfunction both in cases of early
radiation lesions and during subsequent development of radiation
disease.

The immediate cause of early radiation impairment of gastric
function is not morphologic changes in the mucosa but disorders
of the complex reflex mechanism regulating secretion; this is
attested by: (1) X-ray evidence on the absence of any structural
changes in the stomach, and (2) impairment of the secretory function
chiefly during the complex reflex phase. Frequent functional disorders of the central nervous system such as heightened reactivity, emotivity, poor sleep, memory lapses, easy fatigability,
anorexia, neurasthenia, autonomic weakness, neurocirculatory
asthenia, and the like also tend to support this view.

Other investigators also have observed disorders of higher nervous activity along with visceral changes in persons exposed to ionizing radiation; some of their findings were cited above. I. D. Makulova (1957) called attention to this in her recent study of persons working on gamma-ray flaw detection. V. N. Zvorykin made a similar discovery in connection with gastric secretion and higher nervous activity using objective recording. Besides determining gastric secretion in the patients under his observation, he investigated the condition of the cerebral cortex by means of conditioned blink reflexes formed upon strong and weak sounding of a buzzer or a 50-cps tone, flashing of an electric bulb (achromatic or blue), and a red light (differentiation). It turned out that in the majority of persons with impaired gastric function, positive conditioned reflexes were formed very quickly, frequently on the fifth combination; they were stabilized fairly rapidly and later remained constant. The latent period of the conditioned reflexes lasted no more than a second. The rule of "intensity relations" was fairly well marked. In only two out of 15 persons did it prove impossible to form stable conditioned reflexes despite the great number of combinations. All this testifies to the strength of the excitatory process in most of the persons examined. Attempts to form a differential reflex were unsuccessful, however, even though isolated application of the stimulus without reinforcement was repeated 30 to 40 times. It was just as difficult to extinguish positive conditioned reflexes, which showed the weakness of conditioned, active inhibition. Furthermore, phasic states of cerebral cells were discovered in some of the persons examined.

A comparison of the data on gastric function and conditioned activity obtained at the same time in a single investigation (V. N. Zvorykin and I. T. Kurtsin, 1960) revealed that a shortening of the latent period of positive conditioned reflexes and an increase in their amplitude sometimes coincided with decreased gastric secretion and lowering of its acidity. This suggests that inhibition of secretion here may have been caused by negative induction from the excited cerebral cortex (or from certain portions of it) to the closest subcortical formations, probably the autonomic centers of the hypothalamic region and the medulla oblongata. In other cases, a shortening of the latent period and an increase in the magnitude of conditioned reflexes coincided with an increase in the amount and acidity of gastric juice secreted, which was apparently due to the irradiation of excitation from the cerebral cortex to the subcortical autonomic centers. It was impossible to discover any clear-cut relationship between conditioned activity and gastric secretion in several persons who had had contact with ionizing radiations.

In summary, impairment of gastric secretion in man following radiation lesions may be both primary, caused by the direct action

of ionizing radiation on the secretory cells, and secondary, caused
by disturbances in the peripheral and central nervous mechanisms
that arise as a result of direct and indirect radiation. It is quite
apparent that the resultant disorders of the regulatory mechanisms
are reflected in the activity of the stomach and other organs and
organ systems, which in turn may play a definite part in the disorders of gastric secretion in man.

EXPERIMENTAL OBSERVATIONS

Compared with clinical observations, experimental radiophysiology and radiopathology now has at its disposal a substantial number
of observations on the characteristics of impairment of gastric
secretion caused by ionizing radiations. They may be divided into
four groups: (1) secretory disorders of the stomach after local
irradiation of the stomach proper; (2) secretory disorders of the
stomach after local irradiation of other organs and parts of the body;
(3) secretory disorders of the stomach after total-body external
irradiation; (4) secretory disorders of the stomach after total-
body internal irradiation.

The findings on all four groups are not, of course, identical.
Aside from the irradiation conditions (local, total), the kind and
characteristics of the ionizing radiations, and the dose and dose
rate, we find that other factors are also significant—namely, 1)
the species and individual radiosensitivity of different animals,
2) typological features of the nervous system, and 3) the functional
state of the nervous system at the time of irradiation. Even with
these varying factors in radiation injury, however, it is still
possible to form some general idea of disturbances which occur in
different stages of secretion, of the character and dynamics of functional disorders in individual secretory areas of the stomach, and
of disturbances in the neurohumoral mechanisms regulating the
activity of the gastric glands.

It is more convenient, we believe, to consider the available findings individually by secretory areas of the greater and lesser curvature since K. M. Bykov (1941), his colleagues (G. M. Davydov,
1950; I. T. Kurtsin, 1952; A. V. Solov'ev, 1959), and B. P. Babkin
(1944, 1960) found that the gastric mucosa differs functionally in
different areas. Besides the fundic and pyloric areas discovered
and described in detail by I. P. Pavlov (1897) and his co-workers
(P. P. Khizhin, 1894; I. O. Lobasov, 1896; A. I. Shemyakin, 1901;
A. P. Sokolov, 1904), we must distinguish still a third distinct
secretory area located in the lesser curvature. This area is characterized by copious secretion, a short latent period of juice
secretion, a rapid development of the secretory process, and secretion of a juice high in acidity and digestive activity. As shown by

the recent studies of A. V. Solov'ev (1959), the lesser curvature has mostly parasympathetic innervation while the greater curvature has mostly sympathetic innervation.

All these functional characteristics of the secretory areas of the stomach justify a separate analysis of radiation lesions in each area, particularly since this aspect of the problem has been investigated by a number of authors.

Greater Curvature

In one of the earliest studies on gastric secretion following irradiation,. Szegö and Rother (1921) discovered that there were no significant changes in gastric secretion in dogs after local irradiation of the abdominal area with small and moderate doses. They found that large doses, however, caused hypersecretion and increased the acidity and digestive activity of the juice after food was ingested. Miescher (1923) used small doses of roentgen rays on a dog with a Pavlov pouch seven times during the course of a year and noted after each session of irradiation that the secretory activity of the gastric glands rose briefly and then became inhibited for a long time. Portis and Ahrens (1924) also observed inhibition of secretion in dogs after the abdominal area was irradiated.

It was further noted that after irradiation of the thoracic region the activity of the gastric glands became intensified rather than inhibited. According to A. M. Yugenburg (1925), who studied three dogs with chronic gastric fistulas, local irradiation of the abdominal region in amounts of 0.25 to 5 erythema doses had a stimulating effect on gastric secretion, the extent increasing with the dose. However, after the initial stimulation, even small doses produced a subsequent stable decrease in secretion, at times associated with ulcers of the gastric mucosa. The results were similar in dogs after irradiation of the stomach with radon introduced into the submucosa (G. Auer and A. Chechulin, 1929). Gastric ulcers were formed; "spontaneous" secretion took place; and when food was ingested, a great quantity of juice was secreted with abundant mucus. Within a few months, however, there was a lowering of glandular activity and a sharp decrease in juice acidity. After surveying the literature, Friedman (1942) also noted the decrease in gastric secretion following exposure to ionizing radiation.

Hedin, Miller, and Jelatis (1950) observed a prolonged and substantial decrease in gastric acidity in dogs after local beta-irradiation of the stomach. A decrease in secretion and juice acidity was also observed in dogs after intragastric irradiation of the mucosa with radium in doses of 1500 to 9000 mg/hr (McKendry, 1950; Fox, Littman, Lash, and Grossman, 1952). Like results were obtained after irradiation with strontium and ruthenium (Fox,

Grossman, Littman, and Ivy, 1953; Littman, Fox, Schoolman, and Ivy, 1953). Other authors also observed a change in the secretory process after irradiation of the gastric mucosa (Douglas, Ghent, and Rowlands, 1951). Simon (1949) irradiated the mucosa of five dogs with a Heidenhain pouch using 1800 to 25,000 r of beta particles and discovered a decrease in secretion which was particularly pronounced after large doses.

As the research mentioned above indicates, local irradiation of the stomach with ionizing radiation results initially in intensification of gastric secretion, which later gives way to inhibition. The nature of the effect observed depends largely on the type of radiation and the dose used. Accordingly, the reverse effect is also possible; i.e., initial inhibition may be followed by intensification of glandular activity. This was demonstrated by other experiments in which different doses of ionizing radiation had different effects and when local and total-body irradiation caused intensification in some cases and weakening of gastric secretion and wavelike secretory disorders in others (Ivy, Orndorf, Jacoby, and Whitelow, 1923, Engelstad, 1938; Fox, Littman, Lash, and Grossman, 1952; Yu. N. Uspenskiĭ, 1957).

Certain investigators attach considerable importance to the site where radiation is applied (Portis and Ahrens, 1924). Ivy, McCarthy, and Orndorf (1924) performed experiments on 23 dogs with a Pavlov pouch and discovered that irradiation of the thoracic region with doses below the erythema dose had scarcely any effect on the nature of gastric secretion, whereas irradiation of the abdomen with the same doses resulted in slight, temporary inhibition of secretion. Irradiation of the abdomen with massive doses caused hypersecretion the first two days but sharp inhibition of glandular activity thereafter. These changes in secretion, however, do not last very long, not more than five days.

Case and Boldyreff (1928) observed decreased gastric secretion in dogs with a Pavlov pouch after irradiation of the abdomen. After irradiating the abdomen of dogs with a Pavlov pouch with doses of 600 to 800 r, A. M. Vorob'ev, E. M. Krasina, and N. G. Lesnoĭ (1939) noted increased cell activity in response to food stimuli (meat), particularly during the first hour after eating. Inhibition of gastric secretion and reduction of acidity and digestive activity of the juice after total-body irradiation of dogs were recently observed by S. A. Akopyan, E. Arutyunyan, Zh. Govorkyan, and A. Zakharyan (1959). Additional irradiation, according to their data, produced less pronounced inhibition of gastric secretion. Detrick, Upham, Highby, Debley, and Haley (1954) observed decreased gastric activity in dogs after a single exposure to a dose of 600 r.

Ionizing radiation then, changes not only the amount of secretion and acidity of the juice but also its digestive activity. Many investigators believe that the gastric chief cells are more radiosensitive

than the parietal and accessory cells. This view is disputed by
G. A. Revnivykh (1959) who contends that during acute radiation
sickness in dogs, the enzymatic activity of gastric juice either
does not change at all or decreases slightly; sometimes it remains
at a high level until the animals die.

P. D. Gorizontov (1958) mentions the possibility of a decrease
in Castle's intrinsic factor in gastric juice after chronic irradiation
of dogs with small doses of penetrating radiation. But according
to Hueper and Carvajal-Ferero (1944), who irradiated the abdomen
daily for a considerable period of time with a total dose of over
400 r, X-rays have no influence on the formation of this factor.

Some information on changes in the secretory function of the
fundic portion of the stomach were obtained by Yu. N. Uspenskiĭ
(1956, 1957), who experimented on 10 dogs, of which 6 had a Pavlov
pouch and 4 a Basov gastric fistula. Secretion was studied after
100 g of bread or meat was eaten and after 100 ml of 5% alcohol
was injected into the rectum. There was an hour of observation
without food stimulation, whereupon the animal was given food
and the juice secreted was collected for two hours. The abdominal
region was locally irradiated with doses of 400 to 660 r. All the
animals developed radiation sickness with impairment of gastric
secretion. This impairment was characterized by juice secretion
without digestion ("spontaneous" secretion), a decrease in the
volume of juice secreted in response to the food stimulus, a reduction of acidity and digestive activity of the juice, and lengthening
of the latent period before juice secretion.

Unfortunately, the brief observation of the secretory process
(only the first two hours after ingestion of food) and the short
duration of the experiments on the dogs (because they died soon
after being irradiated) prevented the author from giving a comprehensive description of gastric dysfunction during the entire period
of secretion, at various stages in the development of radiation sickness, and in the recovery period. The only conclusion to be drawn
from his findings is that abdominal irradiation is followed by radiation sickness and that gastric activity is inhibited from the first
day after irradiation until the animals die. This inhibition affects
both the quantitative and qualitative aspects of secretion, its acidity
and digestive power. The degree of inhibition varies with the
severity of the disease. The occurrence of "spontaneous" secretion suggest a serious disturbance of autonomic innervation of the
stomach.

Our colleague I. G. Chursin (1957, 1958) made a thorough study
of gastric dysfunction after total-body irradiation of dogs with a
Pavlov pouch. In an effort to exclude secondary factors that
might affect the results, he standardized the experiments by using
similar radiation conditions with dogs of a single sex (male),
weighing between 13 and 18 kg, of approximately the same age.

He evaluated the clinical signs of radiation sickness by changes in blood composition (chiefly in the leukocyte and erythrocyte counts), erythrocyte sedimentation rate, hemoglobin concentration, body temperature, pulse rate, body weight, general behavior of the animals, food excitability, vomiting, diarrhea, and hemorrhages in the visible mucosa. Another important indication of the course of the disease was the condition of the higher divisions of the central nervous system, which was determined daily or every other day by conditioned salivary reflexes according to Pavlov's method.

Chursin observed that while the gastric disorders had some features in common, they nevertheless had several individual peculiarities varying with the severity of the radiation sickness, with the nature and extent of changes in higher nervous activity, and with the typological characteristics of the animal's nervous system. The following representative findings obtained in experiments on the dogs Volchok, Seryĭ, Medved', and Chernyĭ are illustrative.

During the two weeks after irradiation with a dose of 350 r, Volchok's behavior was normal, but there were some sharp changes in the peripheral blood composition: on the day of irradiation, the leukocyte count rose from 11,000 to 23,000/mm^3 of blood; on the next day it rose to 24,000, then dropped to 7000 by the fourth day, and to 2000 several days later. The erythrocyte count fell from 5.5 to 4.1 million/mm^3 of blood. The hemoglobin content decreased by 20%. The erythrocyte sedimentation rate rose from 3 to 7 to 27 mm/hr. Body temperature rose to 39.0 to 39.5° beginning with the 15th day. There was a marked lowering of food excitability. Petechial hemorrhages were found in the mucosa of the tongue and gums. Diarrhea mixed with blood developed at the height of the disease. Body weight of the animal fell by 0.4 kg.

Changes in higher nervous activity set in immediately after irradiation and were characterized during the first three days by prolonged, successive inhibition and during the next seven days by an increase in the positive conditioned reflexes with preservation of "intensity relations." At the height of the disease, i.e., between the 15th and 30th days, both conditioned and unconditioned salivary reflexes decreased and equalizing and paradoxical phases appeared.

The dog recovered in 1-1/2 months and, judging by clinical indications, exhibited virtually no abnormalities. Higher nervous activity by this time had also returned to normal. Secretion in response to food stimulation increased markedly. During six hours of observation, the eating of meat resulted in the secretion of 43 ml of juice instead of the normal 27 ml; the content of free hydrochloric acid rose from 0.16 to 0.36% while digestive activity remained unaltered. The next week secretion of the glands fell to the original level; but starting with the 15th day, which coincided with the onset of clinically pronounced signs of the disease, gastric secretion in response to stimulation again rose. On certain days of experimentation, the juice secreted in six hours was double the original volume. There were also qualitative changes in the secretion: its acidity rose while its digestive activity fell. The latent period before secretion lengthened from 6 or 7 to 8 or 9 minutes. Secretion returned to normal at the same time that higher nervous activity, hematopoiesis, and body temperature did, i.e., within 1-1/2 months of irradiation.

Radiation sickness followed a more severe course in the dog Seryĭ, although he was irradiated with the same dose (350 r) and under the same conditions. The animal's behavior was normal during the first nine days after irradiation. General depression then set in, body temperature rose to 40.2°, the pulse quickened from 90 to 100 beats per minute, intestinal disorders developed, and the time required to eat 200 g of meat lengthened from 20–35 seconds to 2 minutes. The feces were of liquid consistency and contained blood. Body weight fell by 0.9 kg. Blood composition changed markedly. The leukocyte count after irradiation rose from 11,000 to 23,000/mm³; as early as the third day, however, it began to drop, and by the 13th day of sickness it was 100/mm³. The erythrocyte count dropped from 5.15 million to 3.45 million; the hemoglobin content dropped from 65 to 50%; and the erythrocyte sedimentation rate increased from 4 to 60 mm/hr.

Changes in higher nervous activity were observed within 30 minutes of irradiation; they were characterized by an increase in the magnitude of the positive conditioned reflexes to 19% above the original levels. During the next three days, the conditioned reflexes decreased, and there was successive inhibition. The average magnitude of unconditioned salivation, meanwhile, rose from 65 to 73 drops per experiment. Between the 5th and 11th days of the sickness, the conditioned reflexes again increased, while the unconditioned reflexes decreased to the original level. On the 12th day, however, the magnitude of the conditioned reflexes was two to three times below the original level, while the latent period lengthened from 3 seconds to 12–15 seconds. There was no reflex at all in response to a weak conditioned stimulus. The magnitude of the unconditioned reflexes decreased about 1-1/2 to 2 times. On the 16th day after irradiation, the dog was in agony and was killed. At dissection, numerous hemorrhages were found in the mucosa of the tongue and gums, in the skin, diaphragm, kidneys, myocardium, tonsils, thyroid gland, and digestive organs. Histological investigation of the stomach revealed focal varices in the necks of the gastric glands and changes in the secretory cells in the mucosa of the lesser and greater curvatures.

The most striking thing about the changes in gastric activity during the two weeks that the animal lived after irradiation was the cyclic character of juice secretion on different days after ingesting food. On the fourth day after irradiation, when changes in the blood and higher nervous activity had already become clearly manifested, gastric secretion after eating meat increased 10% above the original volume, but there were no qualitative changes in the juice. On the 8th and 10th days of the sickness, the total volume of juice secreted during an experiment decreased by 12 to 20% of the original level; its acidity and digestive activity were virtually unchanged. On the 12th day, however, average gastric secretion per experiment rose to 61.8 ml, compared with 51.4 ml before irradiation. At the same time, juice acidity fell below the original level. The day before the animal died, the volume of gastric juice decreased to 35.4 ml, the degree of acidity fell from 0.37 to 0.26%, the digestive activity fell from 7.0 to 4.3 mm, and the amount of pepsin fell from 2579 to 554 units (as calculated according to the Schütz-Borissov rule). The latent period of secretion throughout the sickness lengthened from 7-9 to 10-11 minutes. The day before the animal died, it secreted juice continuously at the rate of 1 ml per hour.

The dog Medved', unlike the other two animals, was irradiated with a dose of 250 r. Within two hours, the animal began to vomit. The disease followed a mild course, and body temperature did not exceed 39.0°. All the other signs of the sickness were less pronounced than in Volchok or Seryĭ. Weight loss was no more than 9% of the original level. Changes in higher nervous activity were likewise less marked. During the first few days after irradiation, there was an increase in the conditioned reflexes, but they decreased at the height of the sickness. On some days phasic states of the cortical cells were noted. Significant changes were found only in the peripheral blood: the leukocyte count fell from 10,5000 to 1,250/mm^3; the erythrocyte count fell from 4.6 million to 3.4 million; and the hemoglobin concentration fell from 72 to 50%. All these changes had disappeared two months after irradiation.

Changes in gastric secretion were also less pronounced. At the height of the disease, the total volume of juice secreted during an experiment rose 10 to 30% above the original level, although on certain days it was low (Table 9).

Irradiation of the dog Chernyĭ with a dose of 350 r caused radiation sickness of moderate severity. Changes in gastric secretion were comparable to those associated with hypersecretory disorders. During the latent period of the sickness, the ingestion of 200 g of meat produced 60 to 70% more juice than before irradiation. At the height of the sickness and during recovery, the increase in secretion was even more substantial. On some days the volume of juice secreted on eating was double that secreted during the original experiments. Meanwhile, there was a change in secretion at hourly intervals, which deviated from the normal secretion curve. The secretory function became normal by the end of the second month after irradiation (Table 10).

Table 9

Nature of secretion of the greater curvature after the dog Medved' (with a mild form of radiation sickness) ate 200 g of meat.

(Reported by I. G. Chursin.)

Indices of gastric secretion	Before irradiation	Days after total-body irradiation with a dose of 250 r							
		2	13	20	32	45	47	54	75
Latent period (min)	8—9	7	10	10	9	9	9	8	8
Amount of juice during 6 hours (ml)	68.5	70.6	77.0	81.0	77.7	69.5	64.3	69.4	70.6
Juice acidity (%)	0.40	0.35	0.37	0.36	0.34	0.36	0.36	0.40	0.40
Digestive activity of juice (mm)	7.0	5.3	5.8	7.7	5.3	4.2	5.5	5.3	6.8
Amount of pepsin (units)	3384	1984	2590	4802	2182	1227	1945	2085	3262

The experimental findings set forth above indicate that impaired glandular activity of the greater curvature of the stomach arising after radiation lesions has the following characteristics: cyclic appearance of secretory disorders; quantitative and qualitative changes in secretion (pepsin, acidity); lengthening of the latent period of stomach excitation; changes in the secretion curve and the duration of secretion in response to stimulation; the appearance of juice lacking digestive activity (the extent of secretory disorders being dependent on the severity of radiation sickness) and simultaneously developing disorders of higher nervous activity.

Table 10

Nature of secretion from the greater curvature after the dog Chernyǐ (with moderately severe radiation sickness) ate 200 g of meat.

(Reported by I. G. Chursin.)

Indices of gastric secretion	Before irradiation	Days after total-body irradiation with a dose of 350 r									
		5	12	19	28	37	48	55	72	91	105
Latent period (min.)	6	9	9	6	13	7	6	6	6	7	6
Amount of juice during 6 hours (ml)	26.3	43.9	40.3	34.2	58.8	61.6	27.7	23.3	27.1	26.6	28.2
Juice acidity (%)	0.20	0.18	0.21	0.20	0.31	0.27	0.22	0.23	0.23	0.24	0.24
Digestive activity of juice (mm)	6.5	5.9	7.1	6.6	6.3	5.8	5.2	6.0	6.0	6.3	6.8
Amount of pepsin (units)	1080	1528	2031	1490	1318	2072	749	839	976	1064	1304

Lesser Curvature

The initial data on changes in glandular secretion of the lesser curvature of the stomach were obtained in the experiments of A. V. Solov'ev, N. A. Solov'ev, and O. V. Solodkina (1956) on dogs with two isolated pouches, one on the lesser curvature, the other on the greater curvature. After total-body external X-irradiation of the dogs with a dose of 200 r, the authors observed changes in the secretion of both pouches. The changes were phasic: a period of hyposecretion (first period) alternated with a period of hypersecretion (second period); this cycle continued throughout the sickness. Some other peculiarities were noted in the secretory cells of the lesser and greater curvature after ingestion of various kinds of food. During the first period, the cells of the lesser curvature secreted more juice than usual after the ingestion of meat; during the second period, however, the cells of the greater curvature secreted less juice than usual after the ingestion of meat and milk (Table 11).

Table 11

Changes in gastric secretion in the lesser and greater curvatures of the dog Arno after irradiation.

(Reported by A. V. Solov'ev, N. A. Solov'ev, and O. V. Solodkina.)

Kind of food	Volume of juice (ml) during 6 hours					
	Before irradiation	After irradiation		Before irradiation	After irradiation	
		1st period	2nd period		1st period	2nd period
	Lesser curvature			Greater curvature		
Milk	24.5	20.7	32.0	2.0	0.6	1.5
Bread . . .	18.8	16.8	25.5	1.1	0.4	1.3
Meat. . . .	33.6	36.1	41.3	3.1	1.3	2.7
Total. . .	76.9	73.6	98.8	6.2	2.3	5.5

Analysis of the secretory changes revealed that during the first period after irradiation secretion decreased chiefly in the complex reflex phase, while during the second period secretion increased both in the complex reflex and in the neurochemical phases. At the same time, qualitative changes in the juice did not equal the quantitative changes. The digestive activity of the juice in the two periods decreased, on the average, from 4.8 to 3.9 mm, although the acidity remained high throughout the sickness.

I. G. Chursin (1958) made a further investigation of secretory disturbances of the lesser curvature after external total-body irradiation of dogs with a Pavlov pouch. After determining the usual level of secretion upon eating meat, Chursin exposed the dogs to 350 r and then kept them under daily observation throughout the ensuing sickness. The results of the experiments on the dogs Zadornyĭ, Sedoĭ, and Udachnyĭ are described below.

Zadornyĭ's body temperature rose to 39.0° immediately after irradiation. The animal began to vomit the day after. Adynamia developed between the 12th and 29th days, food excitability decreased, vomiting and diarrhea were frequent, and the stools were bloody. By the 12th day the leukocyte count had dropped from 12,000 to 1,200/mm^3, the erythrocyte count from 5.1 million to 3.81 million, and the hemoglobin concentration from 72 to 53%; the erythrocyte sedimentation rate had risen to 43 mm/hr. Body weight had fallen by 3% of the original weight. Changes were observed in higher nervous activity as well. During the first three days, the positive salivary conditioned reflexes decreased while the unconditioned reflexes increased. The following week both sets of reflexes increased. At the height of the disease, between the 12th and 25th days after irradiation, the conditioned reflexes decreased to one-quarter to one-half of the original level. On some days the unconditioned reflexes also decreased. Equalizing and paradoxical phases were noted in the activity of the cortical cells. Conditioned activity was unstable during the period of recovery, but normalcy was restored by the 45th day. By this time, the other organs functioned normally. Radiation sickness in this dog was moderately severe, judging by the general course of the pathological processes and by the extent of the functional changes investigated.

Gastric activity was characterized by the following changes. During the first five days after irradiation, secretion was increased by food stimulation. The volume of juice secreted in six hours was 12% more than that in the control experiments, but during the next three days the reaction of the glands was normal. All this paralleled the latent period of the sickness. At the height of the disease, there was hypersecretion; the ingestion of meat caused the secretion of 47% more juice than normal. Secretion was elevated in all the experiments until the start of the recovery period, but by the 40th day the reaction of the glands had become normal. The quality of the juice likewise changed during the sickness (Table 12).

Significant changes took place in the secretory process itself. Before the sickness, the volume of juice secreted during the first

Table 12

Nature of secretion in the lesser curvature of the dog Zadornyĭ after eating 200 g of meat during radiation sickness of moderate severity.

(Reported by I. G. Chursin.)

Indices of gastric secretion	Before irradiation (mean data of 4 experiments)	Days after total-body irradiation with a dose of 350 r						
		2	9	17	34	41	54
Latent period (min)	2	3	2	2	2	2	3
Amount of juice during 6 hours (ml)	147.0	165.5	146.3	216.2	188.6	150.3	150.9
Juice acidity (%)	0.46	0.43	0.43	0.42	0.43	0.43	0.44
Digestive activity of juice (mm)	7.2	6.3	7.6	5.7	6.9	6.8	7.3
Amount of pepsin (units)	7674	6567	8470	7024	8979	6950	7508

few hours after eating exceeded that during the next few hours. During the sickness, however, the reverse was true; the amount of juice at the end of the experiment was more than at the beginning, i.e., the secretion curve was disturbed (Fig. 4).

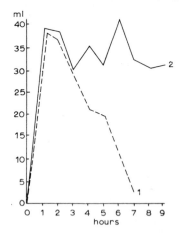

Figure 4. Secretory changes in the glands of the lesser curvature of the dog Zadornyĭ in response to eating 200 g of meat during acute radiation sickness. (Reported by I. G. Chursin.)
1 - Normal secretion. 2 - Secretion on the 17th day of the sickness.

The dog Sedoĭ was irradiated with a dose of 350 r and the disease followed a severe course, killing the animal on the 19th day. Autonomic changes began immediately after irradiation; there was a rise in temperature to 39.9° and vomiting. On the 13th day, movements of the hind paws became disturbed, and there were a great many petechial hemorrhages in the buccal mucosa. On the next day, paresis of the hind paws, ulceration of the tongue covering an area of 0.7 to 0.8 cm^2, diarrhea, and bloody stools were noted. Adynamia became manifest two days before death.

Changes in the blood began the first day after irradiation in the form of mild leukocytosis; subsequently, there was a marked drop in the leukocyte count. After 13 days leukopenia was pronounced, 650/mm^3. The day before the animal died the leukocyte count fell to 100/mm^3. The dog had hypochromic anemia concurrent with the leukopenia: the erythrocyte count fell from 5.2 to 4.05 million, and the hemoglobin content from 78 to 49%. The erythrocyte sedimentation rate increased from 7 to 69 mm/hr. Autopsy disclosed multiple hemorrhages, ulcers, and necrotic areas in the viscera, muscles, and skin.

Conditioned salivary reflexes during the first five days after irradiation increased 10 to 20%, but decreased, starting on the 7th day, to one-half the original level. The unconditioned reflexes decreased 10 to 15%. Hypnotic phases appeared and the latent period of the reflexes was prolonged. Irradiation, then, was followed first by an increase, then by a decrease in the conditioned reflexes, i.e., by intensification of inhibition in the cerebral cortex.

The pattern of gastric secretory changes following food stimulation was cyclic throughout the sickness. During the first five days, secretion increased 10 to 20% and then became almost normal. At the height of the sickness, however, it again increased (by 50%); it remained at this level for several days and then decreased sharply three days before the animal died. This was also the period of the greatest qualitative changes in secretion: both acidity and digestive activity of the juice were diminished (Table 13).

Table 13

Nature of secretion in the lesser curvature of the dog Sedoĭ after eating 200 g of meat during severe radiation sickness.

(Reported by I. G. Chursin.)

Indices of gastric secretion	Before irra-diation	Days after total-body irradiation with a dose of 350 r						
		2	3	7	9	13	15	17
Latent period (min)	4	5	5	4	—	5	—	—
Amount of juice during 6 hours (ml)	42.7	51.8	51.4	45.3	48.4	63.3	39.2	44.0
Juice acidity (%)	0.38	0.35	0.33	0.35	0.34	0.31	0.30	0.20
Digestive activity of juice (mm)	6.9	7.3	7.0	7.3	6.4	5.7	6.0	6.1
Amount of pepsin (units)	2063	2762	2519	2414	1982	2060	1411	1283

The same severe radiation sickness, with similar clinical and pathologicoanatomical changes, was noted after the dog Udachnyĭ was irradiated with a dose of 350 r. The animal died on the 15th day after irradiation with pronounced hemorrhage. In this dog, an animal with a weak type of nervous system, changes in conditioned reflexes occurred on the second day after irradiation, but distinct impairment of gastric secretion did not become manifest until the fourth day, as shown by the fact that the juice secreted after eating meat increased from 39.4 to 47.7 ml, i.e., by more than 20% of the original level. On the following days, secretion sometimes decreased and sometimes increased, and "spontaneous" secretion developed. There were great day–by–day variations in secretion after ingestion of food; a sharp decrease (almost 50% of the original level) was observed three days before the animal died (Table 14).

Table 14

Nature of secretion in the lesser curvature of the dog Udachnyĭ after eating 200 g of meat during severe radiation sickness.

(Reported by I. G. Chursin.)

Indices of gastric secretion	Before irra- diation	Days after total–body irradiation with a dose of 350 r						
		4	6	7	8	10	12	14
Latent period (min)	3	4	3	4	3	3	—	17
Amount of juice during 6 hours (ml)	39.4	47.7	42.3	40.0	54.5	50.5	28.8	21.9
Juice acidity (%)	0.42	0.46	0.45	0.45	0.46	0.44	0.36	0.24
Digestive activity of juice (mm)	4.9	5.6	5.9	6.5	5.1	5.0	3.9	2.9
Amount of pepsin (units)	1037	1756	1372	1680	1417	1262	438	184

Thus, experiments on dogs with isolated pouches of the lesser curvature showed that secretory changes in this region of the stomach have the same characteristics as those exhibited by the cells of the greater curvature, but in less pronounced form. In summarizing the secretory disorders of the greater and lesser curvatures of the stomach of dogs after external irradiation, we may distinguish the following main features.

Most noteworthy is the wavelike or cyclic nature of the changes in gastric secretion after irradiation. At the beginning of the latent period of the sickness, secretory activity is high; gastric juice acidity is unaltered while its digestive activity increases rather frequently. Then the secretory function becomes normal later on in the latent period. When the signs of the sickness are clinically pronounced, secretion again rises, sometimes with great intensity. But along with the increase in volume secreted after ingesting food, the acidity and digestive activity of the juice decrease. Glandular activity usually becomes inhibited two or three days before the animal dies. If the animal recovers, the activity of the glands gradually becomes normal with periods of hyposecretion alternating with periods of hypersecretion. The formation of pepsin by the chief cells is the last gastric function to become normal.

Impairment of secretion following radiation lesions is observed throughout the digestive process in the stomach, being more marked in the glands of the lesser curvature. In some instances glandular activity is at a uniformly high or low level throughout the secretory cycle; in others, dissociation takes place in the secretory process when, during the first few hours after eating, secretion drops sharply, but later reverses itself to rise substantially. This suggests that neurohumoral regulation of gastric activity is severely deranged during radiation sickness. At certain stages of the sickness, the glands are evidently excited by histaminelike products of tissue decay. The presence of these substances in the body partly accounts for the development of "spontaneous" secretion.

Total-body X-irradiation with doses ranging from 250 to 350 r disturbs gastric secretion for about two months. This period coincides with the duration of radiation sickness. Gastric secretion becomes normal simultaneously with the normalization of higher nervous activity. More or less similar phenomena are also observed after local irradiation, e.g., of the abdominal cavity.

GASTRIC SECRETION AFTER INTERNAL IRRADIATION

As in the case of external ionizing radiation, marked impairment of gastric secretion follows internal irradiation, i.e., intake of radioactive substances through the gastrointestinal tract or respiratory system.

According to I. A. Pigalev (1954), who experimented on dogs with a Pavlov pouch, radioactive poison has a drastic effect on gastric secretion in addition to causing spastic contraction of the intestine. The first few days of poisoning are characterized by hypersecretion in the complex reflex phase and hyposecretion in the neurochemical phase, which reflects the asthenic state of the secretory cells. Thereafter, the secretory process remains normal for some time; but by the 8th day of the sickness, hypersecretion again develops, remaining during the first and second phases of glandular activity. Starting with the 12th or 13th day, "spontaneous" secretion occurs in hungry animals, sometimes increasing, sometimes decreasing after the ingestion of food. This wavelike development of gastric malfunction lasts for some time, as was earlier observed by Ivy, Orndorf, Jacoby, and Whitelow (1923).

Of special interest to radiation physiologists and pathologists are the findings pertaining to the effect of uranium fission products and such toxic substances as uranium nitrate on the gastric glands. Published reports indicate that uranium forms complex compounds with bicarbonates and proteins in the body, the hexavalent form being concentrated principally in the kidneys, the tetravalent form in the liver. These compounds are also concentrated in other organs, bones, and tissues. Regardless of valence, however, uranium is highly toxic and causes a number of functional and structural changes in body cells, including those of the digestive organs. Detailed information on gastric disorders following the intake of uranium was obtained by S. R. Perepelkin (1955, 1957, 1960) from experiments on dogs with a Pavlov pouch. The results are as follows.

Intoxication induced by subcutaneous injection of 2.5 to 5.0 mg/kg doses of uranium nitrate has acute, subacute, and chronic forms. The acute form, observed by the author in six dogs, is characterized by general adynamia, disruption of motor coordination, paresis of the hind paws, sometimes convulsions, decreased food excitability, vomiting (sometimes uncontrollable), occasional slight elevation of body temperature, increase in pulse and respiratory rates, wavelike changes in the formed elements of the blood, leukocytosis, albuminuria, glucosuria, and loss of body weight.

The first day that uranium was injected, gastric secretion was inhibited in all the animals after they ate 200 g of meat. On the ensuing days, inhibition of gastric activity was predominant in some dogs, excitation predominated in others, and a mixed form in still others, as when glandular hypofunction gave way to hypersecretion (Table 15).

Changes in juice acidity were directly related to the rate of secretion. There were also some changes in the digestive activity of the juice. For example, the amount of free hydrochloric acid in the juice of the dog Pesochnyĭ rose from 0.39 to 0.55%, while its digestive activity sometimes increased from 3.9 to 4.8 mm or decreased to 3 mm. In the dog Zheltyĭ, acidity rose from 0.30 to 0.36% on the first day of uranium action and fell on the second and third days to 0.20 to 0.29%, while the digestive activity of the juice decreased from 3.5 to 2.6 mm. In the dog Zhuchka, acidity decreased

Table 15

Changes in gastric secretion during acute uranium intoxication in dogs.

(Reported by S. R. Perepelkin.)

Name of dog	Before injection of uranium	Volume of juice (ml) secreted from a Pavlov pouch for six hours after eating 200 g of meat													
		Days after injection of uranium													
		1	2	3	4	5	6	7	8	9	10	11	12	13	14
Pesochnyĭ .	33.4—31.2	25.7	32.2	49.6	31.3	—	49.6	—	68.6	—	44.9	—	5.3	105	16.6
Barbos. . .	2.9— 3.3	0.0	6.2	8.3	3.5	—	1.2	1.9	4.6	2.1	—	1.0	—	—	—
Zheltyĭ. . .	17.7—19.0	15.8	30.8	35.8	25.3	—	—	—	30.7	Dog died					
Zhuchka . .	51.6—58.2	31.1	40.3	44.7	27.9	20.0					Dog died				

from 0.33 to 0.27%, while the digestive activity of the juice decreased from 4.1 to 2.0 mm.

Changes in gastric secretion were observed in an isolated pouch with intact innervation. According to Perepelkin, however, such secretory disorders also occur in dogs with almost completely denervated pouches. For example, in two dogs with denervated pouches, gastric secretion was characterized by periodic alternation of hyposecretion with hypersecretion, even though the normal secretion curve was retained in the process. Wavelike gastric secretion is also found in chronic uranium intoxication (Table 16).

Table 16

Quantitative and qualitative changes in gastric secretion in dogs with chronic uranium intoxication.

(Reported by S. R. Perepelkin.)

Name of dog	Volume and acidity of juice from Pavlov pouch during six hours of experimentation					
	Before injection of uranium		After injection of uranium			
			On the 166th and 172nd days		On the 176th and 217th days	
	Volume of secretion (ml)	Acidity (%)	Volume of secretion (ml)	Acidity (%)	Volume of secretion (ml)	Acidity (%)
Ryzhiǐ	17.6	0.39	12.3	0.40	10.2	0.33
Kurchavyǐ	18.3	0.40	10.8	0.33	11.9	0.37

Wavelike changes were also noted after oral administration of the products of nuclear fission of uranium in doses ranging from 1 to 5 mc/kg. As a result, four dogs observed by Perepelkin developed radiation sickness which ended in the death of one dog on the 20th day and in the death of another dog on the 26th day after the radioactive substance was first administered. The other two animals remained under observation 513 and 563 days, respectively.

The clinical signs manifested during an acute course of the sickness are pronounced, leukopenia developing after brief leukocytosis, both pallor and hemorrhage of the mucosa, lowering of food excitability, salivation, vomiting, bloody diarrhea, and adynamia. Changes in gastric secretion are shown by alternation of hyperfunction and hypofunction (Table 17).

Table 17

Changes in gastric secretion in dogs with acute radiation sickness caused by oral administration of the products of nuclear fission of uranium.

(Reported by S. R. Perepelkin.)

Name of dog	Volume of juice (ml) secreted from a Pavlov pouch for six hours after eating 200 g of meat										
	Before injection of uranium	Days after administration of uranium									
		1	3	6	8	10	13	15	17	20	24
Krasivyĭ . .	2.4—3.6	5.2	12.3	0.4	6.6	2.6	2.2	1.3	Dog died on the 20th day		
Dozor . . .	6.2—7.6	6.9	7.7	5.0	8.5	10.0	8.8	12.3	8.6	4.6	0.6

An increase or decrease in the volume of juice secreted after eating food was observed in both phases of secretion. The digestive activity of the juice changed in different ways: in one dog it was very low only on the first day; thereafter, it exceeded the original level 1.4 and even 9.3 times. (In absolute figures it rose from 57.8 to 538.8 enzymatic units as calculated by the Schütz-Borissov rule.) In another dog the digestive activity was very low throughout the disease (72.5% of the original level). The latent period of juice secretion lengthened somewhat—20 minutes during the last days of life of the animals, compared with the normal average of 10.4 minutes.

In chronic radiation sickness, the volume of juice secreted in response to a standard food stimulus was somewhat high during the first 1-1/2 months, but low thereafter. Digestive activity was sometimes higher and sometimes lower than the original level. The latent period of secretion lengthened somewhat. The secretory changes throughout the sickness had the same wavelike pattern as in acute radiation sickness (Table 18).

Hyposecretory cyclic changes in gastric secretion were also observed after the administration of radon. Perepelkin administered a dose of 0.3 to 0.86 mc/1 of radon to two dogs through the respiratory tract (Table 19).

Table 18

Changes in gastric secretion in dogs with chronic radiation
sickness caused by oral administration of the products of nuclear
fission of uranium.

(Reported by S. R. Perepelkin.)

Name of dog	Before administration of uranium	Amount of juice (ml) secreted from a Pavlov pouch for six hours after eating 200 g of meat										
		Days after administration of uranium										
		1	6	10	27	54	115	192	215	284	511	560
Shus-tryĭ	4.3—5.2	5.0	3.8	6.7	6.6	2.6	3.6	4.5	4.0	4.8	5.6	5.0
Lokh-matyĭ	8.6—6.3	9.1	6.0	6.5	12.5	7.5	6.5	6.6	12.7	6.0	10.0	—

Perepelkin (1958) observed similar changes in gastric secretion
in dogs poisoned by doses of 0.4 to 0.235 mc/kg of radioactive
polonium (Table 20).

A detailed analysis of the data showed that after polonium poisoning, the acid-forming and pepsin-forming functions were not only
preserved, but were above normal. In addition, there was a sharp
decrease in the amplitude of fluctuations in gastric juice acidity
on certain days. Whereas the fluctuation in juice acidity before
poisoning was approximately 0.30%, these fluctuations decreased to
0.10% after poisoning. Since this phenomenon was noted in gastric
activity when the neural connections with the central nervous
system were preserved, and was absent in the activity of the denervated stomach, it is a fair assumption that nervous stimulation
of the gastric parietal cells is intensified during certain periods
of polonium intoxication.

Gastric secretory disorders arising from internal irradiation
and intoxication involve not only the disruption of complex reflex
and humoral regulation of glandular activity but also disturbances
caused by the direct influence of the toxins on the secretory cells
themselves and on the intramural nervous formations closely associated with them. The direct action of toxins plays an important
role in these cases of injury because the chemical and radioactive
substances are eliminated largely through the gastrointestinal

Table 19

Changes in gastric secretion in dogs poisoned with radon.
(Reported by S. R. Perepelkin.)

Name of dog	Before administration of radon	Volume of juice (ml) secreted from a Pavlov pouch for six hours after eating 200 g of meat											
		Days after administration of radon											
		1	3	6	11	13	26	34	46	50	88	102	105
Astra . . . . :	18.4–18.0	12.7	11.7	8.7	13.0	6.1	17.9	9.8	18.1	7.9	11.0	19.2	11.5
Dzhek . . . :	25.0–29.7	22.8	36.3	19.9	27.6	24.7	25.9	18.1	16.6	18.4	19.9	20.1	23.7

Table 20

Changes in gastric secretion in dogs poisoned by polonium.
(Reported by S. R. Perepelkin.)

Name of dog	Before administration of polonium	Volume of juice (ml) secreted from a Pavlov pouch for six hours after eating 200 g of meat												
		Days after administration of polonium												
		1	2	3	5	9	12	15	17	21	25	28	42	51
Trezor . . :	24.6–35.6	25.8	36.6	30.8	33.9	39.1	48.2	35.7	9.7	43.5	47.7	51.8	35.0	29.9
Al'ma . . :	30.5–26.1	43.9	35.2	30.2	29.5	41.6	10.7	Dog died on 14th day						
Belka. . . :	43.7–46.2	55.1	64.0	66.0	60.6	51.3	55.3	34.6	20.8	Dog died on 19th day				

tract, as shown by the experiments of Perepelkin and other investigators, and thus they aggravate the vulnerability of this part of the
body.

EFFECT OF DIFFERENT DOSES OF IONIZING
RADIATION ON SECRETION

The nature and duration of radiation impairment of gastric
secretion is dependent on many factors, primarily the dose of
ionizing radiation (Ya. S. Korneeva, 1928; A. M. Vorob'ev, E. M.
Krasina, and N. G. Lesnoĭ, 1939; Fox, Littman, Grossman and Ivy,
1953; Yu. N. Uspenskiĭ, 1956; S. A. Akopyan, E. Arutyunyan, Zh.
Gevorkyan, and A. Zakharyan, 1959). It has been observed that
single total-body X-irradiation of dogs with doses of 25 to 50 r
has no perceptible effect on gastric secretion, whereas doses in
excess of 100 r do have an effect in most cases.

N. F. Nesterin (1956, 1957, 1960) and N. S. Boĭko (1957, 1960)
studied the significance of dose size, Nesterin in connection with
external irradiation, Boĭko in connection with internal irradiation.
Nesterin exposed dogs with a Pavlov pouch to 200, 400, and 600 r
under the following conditions: voltage 180 kv, current 2 ma,
filters 1 mm Al and 0.5 mm Cu, distance 90 cm, rate 13.8 to
16.7 r/min.

The 200-r dose produced no clinically pronounced signs of radiation sickness. Irradiation with a dose of 400 r resulted in radiation
sickness after a latent period of 13 days. The dogs became sluggish,
passive, were less easily excited by food, lost weight, and had
occasional diarrhea and bloody vomiting; leukopenia and erythropenia were noted in the peripheral blood. After irradiation with a
dose of 600 r, the animals developed severe radiation sickness and
died between 10 and 18 days later.

Although the author was unable to detect any clinically pronounced
signs of sickness with the 200-r dose, he did note in most cases
an increase in secretion after the ingestion of food that persisted
for two weeks. For example, before irradiation, 54 to 88 ml of
juice was secreted for five hours after eating meat; but between
the 1st and 14th days after irradiation, the volume of juice increased
to 93.5 and even 134.0 ml. Before irradiation, after the animals
drank milk, 48.3 to 62.5 ml of juice was secreted compared with
82.0 to 111.5 ml following the milk ingestion after irradiation. After
the animals ate bread, before irradiation, 37.3 to 42.0 ml of juice
was secreted compared with 30.0 to 90.5 ml of juice after irradiation. Generally speaking, there were no changes in acidity or digestive activity of the juice under these conditions of irradiation.

Irradiation with a dose of 400 r caused marked secretory changes
that persisted for 2-1/2 months. For example, the reaction of the

gastric glands to meat was strong for 83 days, rising from a pre-irradiation level of 9.7-13.6 ml to 44.0 ml of juice. There were also qualitative changes; the acidity and digestive activity of the juice increased, especially during the first few days after irradiation.

Irradiation with a dose of 600 r caused extremely severe radiation sickness and death of the animal soon thereafter, thus preventing the author from observing long-range effects. Judging by the data obtained, however, impairment of gastric secretion was profound.

Boĭko investigated changes in the gastric function of dogs with a Pavlov pouch following intravenous injection of a mixture of uranium nuclear fission products (0.5, 0.3, and 0.025 mc/kg body weight) with simultaneous determination of the electromotive force (EMF) of the gastric mucosa according to a method worked out by A. I. Venchikov. The EMF determination made it possible to observe functional gastric disorders before pronounced morphological changes appeared in the mucosa. The EMF was determined on an empty stomach, again after the animals were given 200 g of force-meat or 500 ml of milk, and again after subcutaneous injection of 1.2 mg of histamine.

The experiments showed that injection of uranium nuclear fission products in the aforementioned doses produced acute, subacute, and chronic radiation sickness in six dogs, as determined from changes in peripheral blood composition, body temperature, respiration, and morphology of the gastric mucosa.

Changes in the EMF exhibited a common pattern, although there were some differences in details. With the acute form of the disease induced by injection of 0.5 mc/kg of the substance, the EMF of the mucosa increased during the first two or three days thereafter at times other than during digestion. Beginning with the fourth day however, it decreased, achieving a minimal level at the height of the sickness. The day before the animals died, there were extreme fluctuations in the EMF. Boĭko observed that changes in the EMF of the mucosa appeared four days before the first clinical signs of the sickness became manifest, whereas both changes in the mucosal EMF and clinical signs occurred simultaneously at the height of the sickness. After the ingestion of forcemeat two, five, and eight days after injection of the uranium decay products, the EMF increased, something that was never observed when the animal was normal; in fact, it usually decreased when the animal was normal.

At the start of secretion, the number of "spontaneous" fluctuations in the EMF doubled and tripled. These changes were noted within 24 hours of exposure to ionizing radiation. Similar changes also took place after the glands were excited by the drinking of milk. In cases of histaminic stimulation, such abnormalities were noted only on the fifth day.

The reflex nature of the EMF changes after placing a functional load on the gastric glands was determined in experiments involving the injection of animals with atropine. Following the action of atropine, the latent period of secretion upon ingestion of meat or milk lengthened to 77 minutes, during which time the magnitude of the EMF of the gastric mucosa remained unaltered.

In radiation sickness caused by injection of 0.3 mc/kg of uranium fission products, the changes in the EMF were as follows. The first day there was no change. After two days there was an increase in the original potential difference which persisted for five days. Starting with the sixth or seventh day, the positiveness of the electrical activity of the mucosa grew. Changes in the EMF in these cases preceded the appearance of clinical signs of radiation sickness by five or six days. EMF changes after the eating of force-meat began much later than with doses of 0.5 mc/kg, being noted only on the sixth day. The number of "spontaneous" fluctuations in the potential difference during gastric secretion, however, did not differ from that observed with large doses of radiation and exceeded the original level two- or threefold. In this case, atropine nullified the effect.

With a small dose (0.025 mc/kg), EMF changes in the mucosa at times other than during digestion were wavelike in character, with a tendency for the potential difference to decrease. The frequency of "spontaneous" fluctuations remained unaltered during the first two months; it decreased only toward the end of the third month. Even with these small doses of radiation, however, EMF changes in the mucosa developed before clinical signs of radiation sickness appeared. Following the placing of a functional load on the gastric glands, the EMF changes were not as pronounced as they were after large doses of ionizing radiation. After the animals ate force-meat, for example, days on which the EMF was distorted alternated with days on which it was normal. The same phenomenon was observed after the drinking of milk and the injection of histamine.

The depth of radiation injury to the gastric glands, then, determined from the nature and degree of changes in the electromotive force of its mucosa, was found to be directly related to the dose of ionizing radiation. After large doses, the changes in bioelectric activity of the stomach (frequency of "spontaneous" EMF fluctuations, distorted electric reaction) took place the first few days after irradiation and persisted throughout the period of sickness; but after small doses, they developed much later and were inconstant, alternating with normal bioelectric phenomena. In both cases, however, the changes in bioelectric activity of the gastric mucosa appeared long before the first signs of the sickness became clinically pronounced.

Boĭko then discovered another important feature of gastric dysfunction following radiation lesions caused by different doses.

Secretion in response to food stimuli of different intensity resembled parabiotic reactions: a strong stimulus (meat) caused secretion of the same (equalizing reaction) or smaller (paradoxical reaction) volume of juice as compared with secretion following application of a weak food stimulus (milk).

Parabiotic reactions originated and became manifest sooner after large doses of ionizing radiation than after small doses. Impairment of secretion as reflected in the volume of juice, type of secretion curve, acidity, and digestive activity also set in sooner when large doses were used. For example, with doses of 0.5 mc/kg, disturbances were noted within a day after the uranium fission products were injected; whereas with doses of 0.025 mc/kg, they developed only by the 13th day.

The initial changes reflected functional disorders of the gastric glands; later, however, the substrate suffered organic injury. The absence of free hydrochloric acid and pepsin in the juice signified true achylia. Histamine tests were negative. These findings were confirmed by histological examination of the gastric mucosa. The injection of large doses of uranium decay products resulted in degeneration of gastric gland epithelium, decreased granularity in the secretory cells, a reduction in the amount of mucus in the cells of the pyloric glands, changes in the shape of the parietal cell nuclei, an increase in the number of other cells, erosion and edema in the submucosa and mucosa, and swelling of collagenous fibers in the vascular walls. Profound structural changes in the cells and tissues of the stomach were observed after doses of 0.5 mc/kg and 0.3 mc/kg.

Changes in the chief, parietal, and other cells were particularly marked. A dose of 0.025 mc/kg resulted in minor changes, mostly in the chief cells.

The structural changes in the gastric mucosa described above coincide with the functional disorders of the gastric glands observed after the corresponding doses of ionizing radiation, thereby confirming the importance of irradiation dose as a factor in determining the degree of radiation injury to the secretory process.

MECHANISM OF SECRETORY DISORDERS OF THE STOMACH IN RADIATION SICKNESS

Many aspects of the mechanism governing gastric secretion following radiation lesions have not yet been fully investigated. We do have some factual material, however, that sheds light on the physiological systems significantly involved in the development of radiation disease of the stomach. Published experimental and clinical data make it possible to discuss the nature of impaired secretion during individual phases of the process, particularly the work of the gastric glands during the complex reflex and neurochemical phases in relation to the severity of radiation sickness. Also of special interest in this regard are 1) the part played by radiation lesions of the complex reflex and humoral mechanisms regulating the activity of the secretory cells, 2) the significance of functional weakening of the cerebral cortex in the development of secretory disorders of the stomach, and 3) involvement of parasympathetic and sympathetic innervation in the impairment of gastric secretion. The individual problems can be combined into three main fields of research:

(1) Work of the gastric glands in the complex reflex and neurochemical phases of secretion during radiation sickness;

(2) Significance of the functional state of the higher divisions of the central nervous system in secretory disorders during radiation sickness;

(3) Involvement of autonomic innervation in disorders of gastric secretion following radiation lesions.

FUNCTION OF THE GASTRIC GLANDS IN THE COMPLEX REFLEX
AND NEUROCHEMICAL PHASES OF SECRETION DURING
RADIATION SICKNESS

Data available on the function of the gastric glands in the complex reflex and neurochemical phases of secretion are highly important in analyzing the mechanism of secretory impairment following radiation lesions.

Experimenting on three dogs with a Pavlov pouch of the greater curvature, M. F. Nesterin (1956, 1957, 1960) made individual measurements of the volume of secretion for the first hour after feeding, which largely reflects the function of the gastric cells during the complex reflex phase, and for the subsequent hours, which reflect the function of the cells during the neurochemical phase. This analysis, not very precise, to be sure, was made in the two-week period that followed total-body X-irradiation of the animals with doses of 200 to 400 r.

The results of these experiments showed that after eating meat, the total volume of juice secreted by the animals during the next five hours was much greater in all three dogs than in the controls. After eating bread, the volume of juice secreted was much greater in one animal, unchanged in another, and somewhat less in the third (Table 21).

The volume of juice secreted according to the phases of the secretory process was as follows: after eating meat it was much higher during the neurochemical phase; after eating bread it was higher in the neurochemical but lower in the complex reflex phase.

Two things stand out amidst these data. First, the uneven impairment of glandular activity in both phases—intensification during

Table 21

Changes in the function of the gastric glands during the first and
second phases of secretion of dogs after irradiation.

(Reported by M. F. Nesterin.)

Experimental conditions	Meat			Bread		
	Amount of gastric juice (ml)					
	First phase	Second phase	5-hour total	First phase	Second phase	5-hour total
Before irradiation... ₀	24.5 23.0 37.0	36.7 33.5 51.0	61.2 56.5 88.0	18.0 17.5 17.5	19.3 24.5 22.5	37.3 42.0 40.0
After irradiation...	28.0 33.0 30.0	106.0 82.0 86.0	134.0 115.0 116.0	24.5 11.0 4.0	66.0 32.0 26.0	90.5 43.0 30.0

the neurochemical phase and moderate activity, sometimes even
weakening of activity, during the complex reflex phase. Second, the
uneven change in response of the secretory cells to different kinds
of food—very strong after meat, mild after bread.

I. G. Chursin traced the development of gastric secretory disorders during mild, moderate, and severe radiation sickness after
total-body X-irradiation of dogs with doses of 250 to 350 r. He
observed secretion from a Pavlov pouch for six hours after ingestion of meat. The volume of juice secreted during the first three
hours was arbitrarily used as a criterion of glandular activity during
the complex reflex phase, while the juice secreted during the next
three hours was used as a criterion of glandular activity during the
neurochemical phase.

The experiments demonstrated that during the latent period of
mild radiation sickness, the total volume of juice scarcely changed
during the six hours of observation. It increased 10 to 12% over
the original level only at the height of the disease. Within 1-1/2
months after irradiation, gastric secretion returned to normal
(Table 22).

Tracing the course of changes in secretion by individual phases,
we see that starting with the second day after irradiation, the function
of the glands decreases during the complex reflex phase while it
increases during the neurochemical phase. Consequently, there are

Table 22

Changes in the activity of the gastric glands of the greater curvature during the complex reflex and neurochemical phases of secretion following the dog Medved's eating 200 g of meat after being irradiated with 250 r (mild radiation sickness).

(Reported by I. G. Chursin.)

Phase of secretion	Amount of secretion (ml)			
	Before irradiation	After irradiation		
		2nd day	20th day	54th day
Complex reflex.	52.7	46.7	47.9	53.1
Neurochemical	16.1	23.9	33.1	16.3
Total for period of secretion.	68.8	70.6	81.0	69.4

phasic changes in the rate of secretion, although at the onset of the sickness the work of the glands, judging by the total volume of juice, is practically normal. At the climax of the sickness, the total volume of juice for the entire period of digestion rises perceptibly due entirely to the increased activity of the cells during the second phase of secretion.

The functional picture of secretory disorders in moderate sickness is the same as in mild sickness, i.e., secretion increases. The function of the glands by individual phases, however, is peculiar in that cell activity increases both in the neurochemical phase, as with the mild form of sickness, and in the complex reflex phase (Table 23).

The duration of secretory disorders varies with the severity of the sickness. They last longer in cases of moderate severity than in mild cases. It is noteworthy that normalization of secretion during the complex reflex phase sets in later than normal secretion during the neurochemical phase.

In cases of severe sickness, secretory disorders differ markedly from those in mild and moderately severe cases. The volume of juice secreted during the period of digestion increases a little only when the sickness is latent. It decreases at the height of the pathological condition, becoming very small on the days preceding the animal's death (15 to 20 days after irradiation). Analysis of secretion by phases shows that the decrease in the total volume of juice is caused mainly by the lowered activity of the glands during the complex reflex phase (Table 24).

The examples mentioned above suggest a definite relationship between the character of secretory disorders and the severity of the radiation sickness. The hyperfunctional state of the glands is evidently typical of the initial stages of radiation disease of the stomach and of comparatively mild, shallow radiation injury. The hypofunctional state more frequently reflects a severe course of the sickness and serious involvement of the secretory apparatus of the stomach; it is also common with chronic radiation sickness. There are intermediate forms between these two extremes which are characterized by frequent or rare (depending on the injury) exchange of one form for another. This accounts for the wavelike course of the secretory disorders that is so often observed both as radiation sickness develops and during the recovery period.

The degree to which the above-mentioned forms may differ varies both with the depth of functional and morphological changes in the secretory glands proper and with the extent of impairment of the neurohumoral mechanisms that regulate its activity. This relationship between secretory disorders and severity of the pathological condition, however, is not always present. According to G. A. Revnivykh (1959), who statistically processed the results of experiments on 11 dogs with a Pavlov pouch, hypersecretion is found with first, second, and third degree chronic radiation sickness, the

Table 23

Changes in the activity of the gastric glands of the greater curvature during the complex reflex and neurochemical phases of secretion following the dog Chernyĭ's eating 200 g of meat after total-body X-irradiation with a dose of 350 r (moderate radiation sickness).

(Reported by I. G. Chursin.)

Phase of secretion	Amount of secretion (ml)				
	Before irradiation	After irradiation			
		5th day	19th day	48th day	96th day
Complex reflex	17. 5	32. 8	21. 7	21. 2	19. 1
Neurochemical	7. 9	11. 1	12. 5	6. 5	7. 7
Total for period of secretion	25. 4	43. 9	34. 2	27. 7	26. 8

Table 24

Changes in the activity of the gastric glands during the complex reflex and neurochemical phases of secretion following the dog Seryĭ's eating 200 g of meat after being irradiated with 350 r (severe radiation sickness).

(Reported by I. G. Chursin.)

Phase of secretion	Amount of secretion (ml)			
	Before irradiation	After irradiation		
		4th day	10th day	15th day
Complex reflex.	35. 4	35. 3	26. 8	19. 6
Neurochemical.	15. 4	19. 4	14. 9	15. 8
Total for period of secretion	50. 8	54. 7	41. 7	35. 4

increase in secretion being directly related to the severity of the sickness and extent of glandular innervation; with third degree sickness and maximum denervation of the stomach, hypersecretion is unusually pronounced. Revnivykh emphasizes that one of the main results of his investigation is the finding that secretion becomes intensified during all the stages of radiation sickness. Yet the literature and our own observations on many dogs clearly indicate that there is no such common pattern of radiation impairment of the gastric glands; Revnivykh's statement reflects merely a special case.

Both hypersecretion and hyposecretion must be regarded as characteristic of radiation injury to the stomach. Depending on a variety of conditions, chiefly the severity of the sickness, they may appear either in pure or mixed form. Incidentally, the actual results of Revnivykh's experiments contradict his categorical statement.One of his experimental dogs developed the hyposecretory rather than the hypersecretory type of gastric disorder during acute radiation sickness, while two other dogs had a decrease in production of hydrochloric acid instead of an increase. Moreover, it is evident from the tables and figures in his report that on some days there was a decrease in gastric glandular activity against a background of postirradiation hypersecretion, which was responsible for the wavelike nature of the secretory disturbances. Hypersecretion sometimes gave way to hyposecretion before the animal died.

As for the dynamics of the secretory process by phases, it turns out that the activity of the cells in the complex reflex and neuro-chemical phases may at times change in one direction—by increasing or decreasing—and at other times in different directions, e.g., by increasing in the complex reflex phase and decreasing in the neuro-chemical phase. The last reaction frequently occurs when the course of the sickness is severe.

Although the changes in glandular activity in the first phase may be attributed to disruption of the complex reflex regulatory mecha-nism, the nature of the secretory changes in the second phase is not quite clear. It is hardly correct to assume that the changes in this phase are due solely to impairment of the complex reflex mechanism, for the function of the glands at this time is stimulated chiefly by the hormones of the pylorus (gastrin, ventriculin, etc.), the hormones of the mucosa of the duodenum and small intestine (enterogastrone, gastric secretin), stimulants of gastric juice mucus, and products of food digestion. Consequently, the changes in glandular activity in the second phase of secretion are primarily due, we may suppose, to impairment of the regulatory mechanism. This problem, however, requires further experimental study. In addition, one must consider the fact that the excitability of the secretory cells to stimuli changes after radiation injury. For example, local irradiation of the mucosa of a Heidenhain pouch markedly inhibits gastric secretion stimulated by histamine (Simon, 1949).

The toxicity theory of the pathogenesis of radiation sickness would suggest the involvement of toxins (e.g., the histamine-like sub-stances) which are known to be the most vigorous stimulants of gastric secretion. If this were the case, however, the secretory reaction of the glands would have to be as pronounced after eating meat as after eating bread, which is not the case, as demonstrated by the aforementioned experiments by Nesterin. Moreover, the histamine theory of radiation injury has found no confirmation in the research of recent years.

On the basis of the foregoing considerations, we must assume that increased secretion in the second phase is caused not by the action of toxic substances, but by changes in excitability of the secretory cells by natural chemical stimulants of secretion. This explains the increase in secretion after the ingestion of such foods as meat, which contains a great deal more of the natural gland stimu-lants (extractives, products of proteolysis, etc.) than bread does.

Visceral influences from the stomach and intestine may also play some part in the process because the function of the receptors changes markedly and in different ways following radiation injury.

The experimental evidence to date suggests, then, that the gastric disorders arising from ionizing radiations are largely caused by impairment of the neurohumoral mechanisms regulating the activity of the secretory cells.

SIGNIFICANCE OF THE FUNCTIONAL STATE OF THE HIGHER
DIVISIONS OF THE CENTRAL NERVOUS SYSTEM IN SECRETORY
DISORDERS OF THE STOMACH DURING RADIATION SICKNESS

In analyzing the significance of the functional state of the higher
divisions of the central nervous system in the mechanism governing
secretory disorders of the stomach during radiation sickness, it is
necessary to have fairly accurate information on disturbances of
the complex reflex mechanism of excitation of the secretory cells.
This information is now available as a result of experiments with
sham feeding.

Experimenting on gastroesophagotomized dogs, Case and Boldyreff (1928) were the first to discover that gastric activity following
sham feeding remains unaltered for two months after irradiation
of the abdomen. A. M. Vorob'ev, E. M. Krasina, and I. G. Lesnoi
(1939) repeated these experiments, showing that gastric activity
following sham feeding increases during the first 10 to 12 days after
a single exposure to doses of 600 to 1200 r.

O. V. Solodkina (1958) performed sham feeding experiments on
two dogs with chronic gastric fistulas and two Pavlov pouches, one
on the lesser curvature, the other on the greater curvature. Unlike
the earlier investigators, she fed the animals in such a way that after
they ate, bits of meat came out through the open fistula while the
volume of secretion from the two pouches and greater stomach was
recorded simultaneously. After irradiating the animals with 500 r,
she observed serious disturbances of gastric activity in the complex
reflex phase. They were characterized, depending on the stage of
the sickness, either by complete inhibition of secretion or by marked
intensification, unequally manifested in the different secretory fields
(Table 25).

During the period of hypersecretion, sham feeding resulted in
the secretion of juice for 3 to 4 hours instead of 1 to 1-1/2 hours,
as was the case before irradiation.

Our colleague N. A. Yaroslavtseva (1957) performed sham feeding experiments on five gastroesophagotomized dogs according to
the classic method of I. P. Pavlov. Her objective was to determine
not only the nature and degree of radiation injury to the complex
reflex mechanism of gastric gland excitation, but also the connection between the various secretory disorders and the type of animal
nervous system together with the functional state of the higher
divisions of the central nervous system.

The experiments were conducted as follows. Sham feeding with
meat was continued for 5 minutes. Juice was collected for 3 hours
and its acidity and digestive activity measured. These experiments
alternated (on different days) with experiments on conditioned
salivary reflexes carried out in a soundproof room. Three animals
were irradiated with 350 r, two with 250 r. The clinical picture

Table 25

Gastric secretion (ml) following simulated feeding of meat to a dog
before and after total-body X-irradiation with 500 r.

(Reported by O. V. Solodkina.)

Period of observation	Lesser curvature		Greater curvature		Greater stomach	
	1st hour	2nd hour	1st hour	2nd hour	1st hour	2nd hour
Before irradiation. .	1.4	1.3	1.5	1.0	53.5	4.8
After irradiation						
8th day	0.0	0.0	0.0	0.0	0.0	0.0
36th day	1.7	1.7	3.5	4.5	78.5	14.0
43rd day	0.9	1.8	1.0	1.6	83.5	27.7

of the sickness was determined from the usual radiopatho-
logical signs.

Total-body irradiation of the dogs was followed by radiation
sickness of varying severity. The two animals irradiated with 350 r
were severely sick and died on the 14th and 20th days, respectively.
There was moderate sickness in the other three animals and they
survived; thus, it was possible to observe the behavior of the gastric
glands when normal secretion was restored. Since these three animals had different types of nervous activity and since their gastric
secretory changes and their conditioned reflexes had similar as
well as dissimilar features, we shall briefly describe the results
for each dog separately.

The dog Chernysh exhibited the strong type of higher nervous
activity with excitability predominating (impulsive type); conditioned
reflexes in this dog decreased sharply after irradiation with a dose
of 350 r. The decrease was particularly marked at the height of
the sickness. Starting with the 23rd day, the reflexes gradually began
to increase and at the end exceeded the original level. There was,
however, a considerable fluctuation in their magnitude. The reflexes became completely normal two months after irradiation.

Against this background of altered higher nervous activity,
the following disturbances in gastric secretion took place. Secretion of juice caused by sham feeding was practically normal during
the latent period of the sickness until the 9th day after irradiation.
Changes appeared only on the 10th day in the form of increased
secretion. The volume and acidity of the juice increased while its

digestive activity diminished. On the 14th day, the increase in secretion reached a maximum of 370 ml as compared with the original level of 240 ml. On different days of experimentation, it later fluctuated between 180 and 370 ml. It gradually returned to its normal level by the second month.

In the dog Belka, which possessed the strong, balanced type of nervous system, conditioned reflexes decreased sharply immediately after irradiation with a dose of 250 r, but they returned to the original level on the second day. They increased on subsequent days and remained on a high level throughout the sickness, fluctuating only slightly from experiment to experiment. Meanwhile, differentiation became disinhibited and "intensity relations" of the reflexes changed. Conditioned activity returned to normal two months after irradiation.

Changes in gastric secretion corresponded in general to the pattern of changes in higher nervous activity. Secretion following the application of food stimulation decreased almost twofold on the second day after irradiation; there was a simultaneous reduction in the magnitudes of the conditioned reflexes. Moreover, the acidity and digestive activity of the juice likewise decreased. Gastric secretion subsequently rose as conditioned activity increased. On the fifth day, the volume of juice secreted in response to sham feeding was 410 ml, or 36% above the original level. The acidity and digestive activity of the juice also increased at this time. Later, moderate hypersecretion was observed, which coincided with a somewhat elevated level of conditioned activity of the cerebral cortex. Secretion and higher nervous activity became normal at the same time.

In the dog Laska, an animal with the weak type of nervous system, there was marked inhibition in the cerebral cortex along with suppressed gastric activity the first day after irradiation with a dose of 250 r. During the next two days, hypersecretion was moderate against a background of normal conditioned activity. Highly pronounced hypersecretion in response to sham feeding was noted at the height of radiation sickness, particularly from the 14th day after irradiation; the volume of juice secreted was 2-1/2 times the normal volume. In addition, conditioned salivary reflexes decreased, remaining on a low level for about a month. Secretion was high during this period and there were marked variations in the volume from one experiment to another, which imparted a distinct wavelike appearance to the changes in the functional state of the glands throughout the sickness (Figure 5). By the end of the second month, the activity of both the cerebral cortex and the gastric glands was completely normal.

This, in outline, is the course of the changes in higher nervous activity and gastric secretion during the complex reflex phase in dogs with different types of nervous systems during radiation sickness. The question arises as to just what the significance of these findings is.

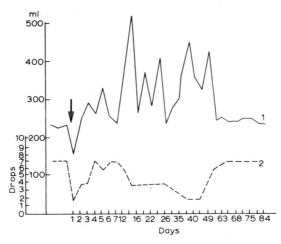

Figure 5. Changes in gastric secretion in response to sham feeding and in conditioned salivary reflexes in the gastroesophagoto-mized dog Laska during acute radiation sickness. (Reported by N. A. Yaroslavtseva.)
1—Gastric secretion. 2—Conditioned salivation. Arrow indicates day of irradiation (250 r).

They suggest, to begin with, that the impairment of gastric secretion following ionizing radiation and the development of radiation sickness is larely the result of injury to the complex reflex regulatory mechanism. This impairment is both quantitative and qualitative with respect to the juice secreted. Moreover, the nature and duration of secretory disorders is related to changes in cerebral cortex activity. In most of the animals, gastric secretion was suppressed while the inhibitory process was intensified in the cerebral cortex, both phenomena occurring during the first few days after irradiation. The picture changed as the sickness progressed, depending on the animal's type of nervous system. Hypersecretion against a background chiefly of pronounced cortical inhibition was noted in the dog with a weak type, whereas in the dog with a strong, balanced type it appeared with cortical excitation predominating. The same thing was observed in the impulsive dog except that the correlation took place in the second period of the sickness; the hyperfunctional gastric disorders, however, developed against a background of cortical inhibition.

Therefore, the nature and duration of gastric disorders during radiation sickness is related, first, to the typological characteristics of the nervous system and, second, to the functional state of the higher divisions of the central nervous system at different stages of the sickness. We are inclined to ascribe the marked suppression of gastric secretion during the first few days after irradiation to the influence of cortical inhibition on the subcortical autonomic centers (Belka, Laska); we would ascribe the development of hypersecretion in the course of the sickness, in some cases, to the action of cortical excitation on the subcortical centers from the inhibited cerebral cortex (Laska).

In experiments on the dogs Bol'shaya and Druzhok during very severe radiation sickness, Yaroslavtseva observed a decrease in the positive conditioned reflexes, pronounced successive inhibition attesting to inertia of the inhibitory process, and the appearance of hypnotic phases in the activity of the cortical cells. The gastric glands showed gradually decreasing activity and the development of "spontaneous" secretion. The day before the dogs died, they suffered total inhibition of artificial conditioned reflexes to all stimuli together with suppression of gastric gland activity. Apparently, hypofunctional gastric disorders in severe radiation sickness are caused in part by the action of cortical inhibition on the subcortex and medulla oblongata.

It seems to us that this relationship between gastric activity and the functional state of the higher divisions of the central nervous system is clearly shown in Figure 6, where hypofunction during the first month of radiation sickness was seemingly caused by the action of cortical inhibition on the subcortical centers of the brain, while hyperfunction was possibly caused by positive induction of the subcortical centers from the inhibited cerebral cortex.

If the nature and duration of gastric secretory disorders following irradiation is caused largely by injury to the complex reflex mechanism regulating the activity of the secretory cells and is definitely related to the functional state of the higher divisions of the nerve centers, it is a fair assumption that irradiation of animals whose nerve centers have first been weakened functionally should have an even stronger effect on gastric secretion.

Our co-workers I. G. Chursin, N. A. Yaroslavtseva, A. D. Golovskiĭ, and A. A. Fadeeva performed numerous experiments on dogs to test this assumption. Gastric secretion was studied in dogs with a developed system of conditioned salivary reflexes. The cerebral cortex was functionally weakened by the combined application of a very strong sound stimulus, by successive and uninterrupted application of positive and inhibitory conditioned stimuli, and by occasionally irritating the skin with an electric current during eating, thus producing the conflict of a defense reflex with a food reflex. This complex of stimulations was usually applied four or five days in a row. The experiments showed that under these conditions the course of the radiation sickness was more severe and the impairment of autonomic functions, including gastric secretion, more extensive and prolonged than when the animals were exposed

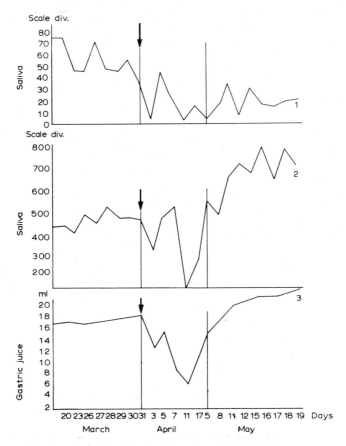

Figure 6. Changes in the correlation between magnitudes of conditioned and unconditioned salivary reflexes and secretion of gastric juice in a dog during acute radiation sickness. (Reported by A. A. Fadeeva, I. T. Kurtsin, and A. D. Golovskiĭ.)
1—Conditioned reflexes. 2—Unconditioned reflexes. 3—Gastric secretion. Arrows indicate days of irradiation.

to the same dose of ionizing radiation and at the same rate but when their cerebrocortical activity was normal.

Particularly instructive in this respect were the so-called cross experiments when radiation sickness was induced twice in the same animal. In one group of dogs, it was induced first against the background of a normal cerebral cortex, and then, after recovery and normalization of corticovisceral relations, against the background of experimental neurosis. In another group it was induced first against the background of neurosis; then, in cases of recovery, the animals were once more exposed to ionizing radiation after normalization of higher nervous activity and restoration of visceral functions, including those of the stomach. The intervals between exposures were from 3–4 to 5–7 months. I. G. Chursin's data (1958) on dogs with a Pavlov pouch are illustrative (Table 26).

It is evident from Table 26 that hyperfunction in dogs after functional traumatization of the cerebral cortex and irradiation was more pronounced throughout the sickness (averaging 50.1 to 72.5 ml of juice per experiment) and more prolonged than in dogs exposed to radiation against the background of a normal cerebral cortex (averaging 33.0 to 38.1 ml of juice per experiment). Moreover, in the traumatized dogs, hypersecretion on certain days of experimentation was so heavy (154.9 to 164.9 ml) as to exceed by far the maximum volumes secreted by the normal dogs (54.8 to 58.8 ml), not to mention those in the original experiments (26.0 to 26.6 ml). This unusual response of the gastric glands to food stimulation is the result of profound injury to the complex reflex mechanism regulating the activity of the secretory cells.

Thus, in radiation sickness caused by irradiation against the background of neurosis, disorders of gastric secretion are more profound than in radiation sickness caused by irradiation against the background of a normal state of the higher divisions of the central nervous system.

INVOLVEMENT OF AUTONOMIC INNERVATION IN DISORDERS OF GASTRIC SECRETION FOLLOWING RADIATION LESIONS

Impairment of the complex reflex mechanism of regulation is not, of course, the only factor responsible for disorders of gastric secretion following radiation lesions. The condition of autonomic innervation of the stomach is very important in this respect. Some information on the problem is offered by A. V. Solov'ev and O. V. Solodkina (1957) who experimented on dogs with two small stomach pouches, one in the lesser and one in the greater curvature; both were cut out in such a way as to retain their vagus nerve branches. They discovered that secretory changes after total-body irradiation of the animals with doses of 400 to 500 r were similar.

Table 26

Juice secreted from a Pavlov pouch in dogs after eating 200 g of meat following irradiation against a background of normal and pathological conditions of the cerebral cortex.

(Reported by I. G. Chursin.)

Experimental conditions	Before irradiation	Volume secreted (ml) during 6 hours								Mean data
		Days after irradiation								
		2	11–12	19	28	33	45	50	58	
Dog No. 1										
1. Irradiation	25.3	39.6	26.2	41.2	40.3	37.4	27.8	25.1	26.6	33.0
2. Conflict + irradiation....	26.6	50.2	46.9	67.3	47.1	42.3	50.1	52.8	54.0	50.1
Dog No. 2										
1. Conflict + irradiation...	25.7–15.1	29.4	20.5	164.9	34.2	114.8	27.9	33.6	154.9	72.5
2. Irradiation.........	26.0	43.9	40.3	58.8	54.8	27.7	26.7	27.1	26.1	38.2

This fact testifies to the involvement of the vagus nerves in disorders of gastric secretion.

They further discovered in experiments on other dogs, also with two Pavlov pouches, one of which retained the vagus nerve branches while the other retained its sympathetic innervation, that the activity of the "vagal" stomach is inhibited after irradiation whereas the activity of the "sympathetic" stomach is intensified. This suggests involvement of sympathetic innervation also in radiation lesions of gastric secretion and the existence of complex functional relations between the parasympathetic and sympathetic innervations of the stomach.

The experiments of Solov'ev and Solodkina thus concretely confirmed the fact previously noted by a number of investigators (Schneider and Dürre, 1948; Ivy, McCarthy, and Orndorf, 1924; Case and Boldyreff, 1928; A. V. Kantin, 1938)—viz., that the autonomic nervous system is involved in radiation lesions of the gastric glands. In addition, their findings make it possible to link the dissociation of various aspects of gastric secretion (formation of juice, hydrochloric acid, enzymes) that constantly arise in radiation pathology with disruption of the synergistic influences of parasympathetic and sympathetic innervation on the body. This may also explain the disharmony that develops in the activity of cells in the different fields of the stomach during secretion.

Solov'ev and Solodkina's analysis of secretion by phases (1957) showed that the inhibition of glandular activity in the lesser curvature, which occurs the first days after irradiation, develops only in the complex reflex phase, whereas the activity of the glands in this curvature during the second phase is either normal or slightly elevated (Figure 7).

On the other hand, glandular activity of the greater curvature is abnormally high during the first and second phases of secretion. Since the pouch of the lesser curvature is innervated largely by the vagus nerves while the pouch of the greater curvature is innervated by sympathetic nerves (the pouches were cut out according to Solov'ev's method), the above-mentioned effect may be ascribed to decreased parasympathetic tone and increased sympathetic tone.

Solov'ev and Solodkina's research, then, has revealed one of the mechanisms responsible for the differences in reaction of the gastric secretory cells to food stimulation during radiation sickness, as reflected in disruption of the normal functional relations between the parasympathetic and sympathetic innervations of the gastric glands.

G. A. Revnivykh's experiments with dimedrol [Benadryl] (1959) also testify to involvement of the autonomic nervous system in radiation impairment of gastric secretion. The author found that this ganglion blocking agent causes more pronounced inhibition of

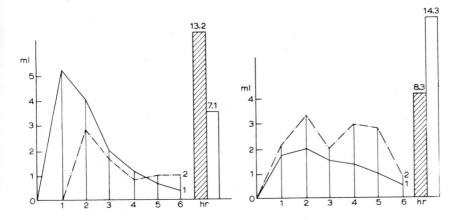

Figure 7. Changes in secretion in the isolated pouches of the lesser and greater curvatures in a dog after eating 100 g of meat during radiation sickness. (Reported by A. V. Solov'ev and O. V. Solodkina.)
a - Secretion of a lesser curvature pouch. b - Secretion of a greater curvature pouch. 1 - Secretion before irradiation. 2 - Secretion after irradiation. Columns show total juice secreted (ml) during the six hours of the experiment: crosshatched columns, before irradiation; blank columns, after irradiation.

secretion in irradiated dogs with a Pavlov pouch than in nonirradiated dogs (Table 27).

Our understanding of disorders of gastric secretion following radiation lesions is enhanced by Solov'ev and Solodkina's findings on changes in the acidity of gastric juice. They observed that in the first phase of inhibition the juice was half as acid, on the average, as it was normally. Changes in the second phase of secretion showed an inverse relationship, i.e., acidity increased when the original value was low but decreased when the original value was high. This is the physiological explanation of a phenomenon which has been repeatedly noted by clinicians when analyzing the gastric secretion of patients suffering from the effects of ionizing radiation. The nature of this phenomenon is apparently related to some extent to the parabiotic state of the neuroglandular apparatus of the stomach.

It is also worth noting that at the height of the sickness there is sometimes a dissociation between the volume of secretion and the degree of juice acidity. It seems that irradiation does not injure the chief, parietal, and other cells equally. We also encountered

Table 27

Effect of dimetrol [Benadryl] on gastric secretion in irradiated and nonirradiated dogs
(Reported by G. A. Revnivykh.)

Hours of the experiment	Volume of gastric juice (ml)							
	Dog No. 142, nonirradiated		Dog No. 163, nonirradiated		Dog No. 12, irradiated		Dog No. 116, irradiated	
	Experiment without dimedrol	Experiment with dimedrol	Experiment without dimedrol	Experiment with dimedrol	Experiment without dimedrol	Experiment with dimedrol	Experiment without dimedrol	Experiment with dimedrol
1st · · · · · ·	4.5	0.4	3.8	0.1	11.3	0.3	2.7	1.3
2nd · · · · · ·	5.5	1.5	2.6	1.6	8.9	1.0	2.9	1.8
3rd · · · · · ·	4.6	2.3	3.0	1.8	5.9	2.0	3.1	2.0
4th · · · · · ·	2.4	8.9	3.2	4.3	3.5	2.8	2.5	0.8
5th · · · · · ·	2.6	4.6	2.4	3.1	2.4	2.8	3.3	1.7
Total for experiment	19.6	17.7	15.0	10.9	32.0	8.9	14.5	7.6

the same phenomenon in patients with ulcers or gastritis and in dogs with experimental neuroses (I. T. Kurtsin, 1952, 1954). We assumed the possibility of differential injury to the innervation of the secretory and motor elements of the stomach and to the innervation of the individual cells secreting water and salt, acid, pepsin, and mucus. The research of Solov'ev, Solodkina, Chursin, and Revnivykh on radiation lesions of the stomach have confirmed this view.

In summary, impairment of gastric secretion during radiation sickness is caused largely by radiation injury to the neurohumoral mechanisms regulating gastric secretion. Disruption of the complex reflex mechanism of secretory cell excitation and impairment of the functional state of the higher divisions of the central nervous system are highly important factors. Radiation injury changes the functional relations of the cerebral cortex with the subcortical autonomic centers. This disrupts the synergistic influence of the parasympathetic and sympathetic innervations in the secretory cells, thereby involving this section of the nervous system in the mechanism of radiation injury to the process of secretion. Injury to the hormonal mechanisms regulating gastric secretion along with injury to the reflex mechanism is also possible. Besides the disruption of hormonal influences from the hypophysis, adrenals, etc. on secretion, an important part is apparently played by impaired hormone production in the gastrointestinal mucosa (gastrin, enterogastrone, etc.) and by changes in the reactivity of the secretory cells themselves to the action of hormones and other stimulants. The latter may be caused to some extent by morphologic changes in the gastric cells following the direct and indirect (through the nervous system and blood) action of ionizing radiation.

CHAPTER 3

Pancreatic Secretion

While we have fairly abundant experimental and clinical material on functional disorders of the stomach following radiation lesions, the same cannot be said of radiation lesions of the pancreas.

CLINICAL AND EXPERIMENTAL OBSERVATIONS

Clinical observations are contained only in the work of N. N. Rynkova (1956) and P. M. Kireev (1957), who noted pancreatic hypofunction in man during chronic radiation sickness, and in the work of A. L. Morozov, É. A. Drogichira, M. A. Kazakevich, N. I. Ivanov, and S. F. Belova (1957), who noted increased amylase in the duodenal contents during this disease.

Experimental physiology has provided us with very little information on the problem. S. V. Gol'dberg (1904) in experiments in vitro discovered that enzymes in pancreatic juice are highly resistant to the action of ionizing radiation. These findings were confirmed by Fenton and Dickson (1954), who were unable to detect any effect exerted by total-body irradiation of mice with 500 r on the synthesis of amylase in the pancreas. The morphological studies of L. M. Gorovits (1906) and J. Tullis (1954) indicate that the gland exhibits extremely low sensitivity to the action of X-rays.

On the other hand, there are some published reports suggesting that the pancreas is highly sensitive to ionizing radiation. Henri and Mayer (1904) observed the total inactivation of dissolved trypsin when kinase was added and radium rays were used at a temperature of 25°C for 42 hours. Dale (1940, 1942) discovered that X-rays inactivated carboxypeptidase. McDonald and Moore (1955) observed the inactivation of dilute solutions of crystalline trypsin after irradiation. It is interesting to note that inactivation of dry crystalline trypsin requires a dose of radiation 170 times greater than that required for the same enzyme in solution (Bier and Nord, 1952). Inactivation of crystalline trypsin occurs both at the time of irradiation and afterwards (McDonald, 1954). An investigation of the amylolytic properties of extracts obtained from irradiated and nonirradiated fragments of the dog pancreas led the earlier French physiologists Lépine and Bould (1904) to conclude that X-rays promote amylase formation in the gland cells. In studying the production of enzymes in cells of the pancreas perfused with nutrient fluid, A. Ya. Bogaevskiĭ and B. Gol'dshtein (1928) found that small doses of X-rays increase, while large doses decrease, the enzyme content of the perfusate.

The experiments of Rauch and Stenstrom (1952) are interesting. They described changes in the pancreatic activity of dogs with a Pavlov fistula of the duct, after X-irradiation of the abdomen with doses of 365 to 530 r. These observations, however, lasted only about two weeks. The authors found no evidence of radiation sickness, yet pancreatic function was altered after irradiation. There was a temporary decrease in secretion, with subsequent elevation above the original level. At the same time, the activity of amylase, lipase, and trypsin in the juice decreased; the decreased activity disappeared after a few days, except that of the proteolytic enzyme, which remained low until the 10th day.

Thus, most investigators of radiation injury to the pancreas have concentrated on changes in the enzymatic properties of the juice itself, ignoring the dynamics of the secretory process, and have performed their experiments primarily in vitro or on glands supplied with artificial nutrient fluid. They have not taken account of the fact that the most valid data can be obtained only by studying the function of the gland in the intact organism while preserving the neurohumoral connections of the gland not only with the digestive organs but also with other physiological systems, especially the central nervous system, which exerts a constant influence on glandular activity. The data of L. M. Gorovits and J. Tullis cited above must be appraised just as critically because functional disorders of an organ are not always accompanied by perceptible changes in its structure. According to N. A. Kraevskiĭ (1955, 1957), gross changes in the gland are sometimes scarcely perceptible during acute radiation sickness, whereas the microscope reveals destructive changes in the epithelium, including focal necroses. Furthermore, information is now available on structural modifications of the pancreas caused by ionizing radiation. For example, N. N. Kurshakova (1957) observed changes in nucleic acid metabolism arising in the pancreatic tissue of animals the very first day after irradiation—a decrease in the amount of desoxyribonucleic acid together with an increase in the amount of ribonucleic acid. A. V. Kozlova (1957) reported the results of the autopsy performed on the radio operator of the "Lucky Dragon" 207 days after he was exposed at Bikinĭ atoll. Thickenings, small foci of fat necrosis with slight lymphocytic infiltration, cloudy swelling, and some other indications of degeneration were found in the pancreas.

Accordingly, the fact that several investigators have failed to observe significant structural changes in the gland, even after substantial doses of radiation, does not mean that the function of the gland was not somewhat impaired. It is also well to remember that glandular function in an intact organism may change as a result of disruption of the neurohumoral regulatory mechanisms.

Rauch and Stenstrom chose the correct method, but the brevity of their observations and the limited number of indicators of secretion make it impossible to draw, even schematically, the picture of radiation injury of the pancreas.

Hence we found the data of our co-worker A. E. Karpenko (1957, 1960) especially interesting and important. Karpenko studied external secretion of the pancreas in six dogs suffering from acute radiation sickness induced by a dose of 250 r of X-rays. These dogs had chronic fistulas of the main pancreatic duct; in addition, two animals had permanent fistulas of the parotid gland, which made it possible to establish conditioned acid-defense reflexes and thus to study simultaneously disorders of pancreatic secretion and of higher nervous activity. It was also important that systematic experiments were begun only after the animals had completely adapted to the chronic loss of juice, as revealed by a number of signs: steady weight, the presence of pronounced food excitability, the absence of degenerative processes in the skin (alopecia, ulcers), adequate glandular response to food stimuli, and normal higher nervous activity, body temperature, and peripheral blood composition.

The course of pancreatic secretion after ingestion of 100 g of meat was studied. The reaction of the gland to the drinking of 600 ml of milk was also determined periodically. The volume of juice was measured at hourly intervals for 6 hours, sometimes every 10 minutes during the first hour of secretion. The concentration of the principal enzymes was investigated in the hourly batches of juice: amylase (by the Wohlgemuth method), free and total lipase (by the Brondy-Rozhkova method), and trypsin (by the Sorensen method); in addition, juice alkalinity was determined in three dogs.

Total-body irradiation of all six dogs was followed by prolonged impairment of external secretion of the pancreas and by changes in the digestive properties of the juice. The most characteristic feature of the secretory disorders was an extremely unsteady level of secretion elicited by the same food stimulus. The range of the volume secreted during 6 hours of observation, insignificant before irradiation, multiplied many times after radiation, the intensity varying with the severity of the sickness. The impairment lasted 1-1/2 to 2 months in two dogs, 3 to 4 months in two others (Figure 8).

Two dogs died after irradiation, one after 17, the other after 21 days, but the undulating character of secretion persisted right up until they died.

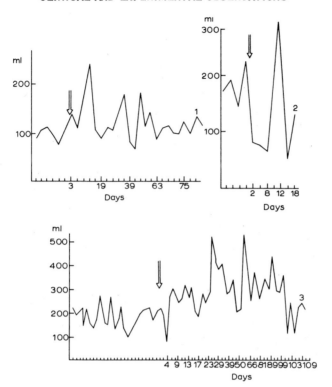

Figure 8. Changes in pancreatic secretion in dogs with acute radiation sickness of varying severity. (Reported by A. E. Karpenko.) 1—The dog Ural, mild sickness. 2—The dog Ryzhyĭ, very severe sickness ending in death. 3—The dog Volk, severe sickness ending in recovery. Arrow indicates day of irradiation (250 r).

The animals developed "spontaneous" secretion at the height of the sickness. It was unsteady and was more pronounced in some dogs than in others. It persisted in the animals with severe sickness until they died. The type of juice secretion curve was altered, acquiring an inert or serrated character, thereby reflecting disruption of the secretory process. The latent period of secretion lengthened and there was a slow increase in the rate. The maximum one-hour secretion shifted from the first or second hour to later hours (Figure 9) while the period of secretion increased from 5-6 hours to 7-9 hours or more.

These characteristics of pancreatic disorders during radiation sickness suggest impairment of secretion in both the complex reflex and neurochemical phases, chiefly in the former. The most noteworthy of the qualitative changes is a dissociation in the activity of various enzymes of juice secreted in response to the same food stimulus. There is a definite parallelism in the dynamics of enzyme secretion when the organism is normal, but during radiation sickness this parallelism is considerably impaired throughout the entire secretory process. It was also established that the activity of different enzymes of the juice secreted during an experiment changes in different directions. A decrease in activity predominates in dogs with mild radiation injury.

There is still another interesting feature. Whereas in the normal animal the enzyme activity of the juice is inversely proportional to the rate of secretion, during radiation sickness, approximately three or four weeks after irradiation, against a background of abundant secretion of juice and low enzyme content there is a sharp increase in the activity of one enzyme. For example, in the dogs Volk and Chert, in the presence of low amylase and trypsin content, the activity of free lipase increased to five, seven, and even ten times the normal level. In the dog Ryzhii, amylase and lipase activity rose sharply against a background of decreased trypsin activity. This phenomenon, Karpenko notes, appears during severe radiation sickness.

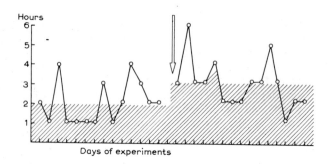

Figure 9. Changes in maximum pancreatic secretion in the course of digestion in the dog Ural during acute radiation sickness. (Reported by A. E. Karpenko.)
Circles on the curve show hour of maximum secretion in individual experiments; shaded level indicates mean hour of maximum secretion during 15 experiments before and after irradiation (arrow).

An important quantitative and qualitative change in pancreatic secretion is the persistent disruption of normal "intensity relations" in the secretion of juice and enzymes induced by different kinds of food. While sick, all the dogs secreted more juice after drinking milk than after eating meat; the activity of the enzymes changed accordingly (Table 28).

Table 28

Quantitative and qualitative changes in pancreatic secretion in the dog Ural during radiation sickness.

(Reported by A. E. Karpenko.)

Food stimulus	Amount of juice during an experiment (ml)	Amylase (in arbitrary units)	Lipase (ml of 0.1 N NaOH solution)		Trypsin (ml of 0.2 N HCl solution	Mean titratable alkalinity (ml of 0.1 N HCl solution)	Mean viscosity (sec)
			Free	Total			
Before irradiation							
Meat	63	1250	0.40	1.50	1.6	1.44	69.5
Milk	54	1130	1.95	2.77	2.2	1.29	75.0
After irradiation							
Meat	105	810	0.52	1.94	2.6	1.45	71.5
Milk	111	170	0.59	1.45	3.1	1.78	70.5
Meat	89	150	0.67	1.67	2.2	1.57	70.5

The author termed these changes "phasic phenomena" in the external secretion of the pancreas. They persist a long time. For example, they lasted about a month in one dog and three to four months in two other animals. They are apparently due to a parabiotic state of the brain centers and possibly of the neurosecretory apparatus of the gland itself. Some of Karpenko's data have recently been corroborated by several other investigators. For example, N. F. Shlyakhtova (1960), studying periodic secretion in seven dogs with duodenal fistulas, found cyclic changes in the activity of lipase, trypsin, and, in particular, amylase in the intestinal contents after total-body irradiation with doses ranging from 200 to 650 r; there was also marked inhibition of pancreatic secretion during severe radiation sickness, especially in the terminal stage.

E. A. Gudkova (1958, 1960) discovered that total-body irradiation of dogs with doses of 400 to 600 r produces hypo- and hyperfunctional pancreatic disorders which arise immediately after exposure and remain throughout the period of acute radiation sickness. Unfortunately, the author did not trace the changes in enzyme activity of the pancreatic juice, a knowledge of which is important in evaluating the activity of the pancreas. On the other hand, she presents interesting material on changes in pancreatic secretion after total-body irradiation and local irradiation of the region of the pancreas, which makes it possible to draw conclusions on the mechanism of pancreatic secretory disorders following radiation injury. She found that shielding the region of the gland during total-body irradiation of three dogs did not prevent the occurrence of secretory disorders which more or less resembled those in dogs totally irradiated without a shield. Changes in pancreatic function in both cases were marked by inhibition of secretion after irradiation, development of hypersecretion in the latent period of radiation sickness, and a second wave of inhibited secretion in the period of clinical signs of the disease. This inhibition was particularly marked when the sickness was severe.

The same inhibition was observed in all three dogs after local irradiation of the region of the pancreas. It was strongest when the dose rate was increased from 10 r/min to 62 r/min, although the total dose in all cases remained the same (600 r).

Thus, Gudkova's observations suggest, first, the possibility of a direct action of ionizing radiation on the neurosecretory apparatus of the pancreas, which leads to a decrease in secretion; and, second, the possibility of an indirect influence on the gland through injury to the neurohumoral mechanisms for the regulation of its activity whereby, in addition to inhibition, the hypersecretory form of disorders may arise, if the course of the sickness is not severe.

To sum up the experimental evidence cited above, the changes in external pancreatic secretion arising from ionizing radiation are caused mainly by disruption of the neurohumoral mechanism regulating the activity of the pancreas and, in part, by radiation injury to the gland itself.

The impairment of pancreatic secretion may also be related to the impairment of gastric secretion, specifically, the production of hydrochloric acid, which plays a very important part in the hormonal mechanism of excitation of the pancreatic secretory cells. This problem, however, has not been sufficiently studied with reference to radiation lesions of the gastrointestinal tract. Some pertinent data will be presented below.

An analysis of Karpenko's findings show that secretory disorders varied with the severity of the disease and were manifested in two forms: hypersecretion and hyposecretion. The latter occurred when the sickness was severe and ended fatally. In dogs with mild sickness, hypersecretion was, however, insignificant. It was more pronounced in very sick but surviving dogs.

The following results were obtained in experiments on two dogs with previously formed conditioned reflexes and a background of pancreatic secretion established in response to the eating of meat. Ryzhik developed severe radiation sickness after being irradiated and died 21 days later. Higher nervous activity was characterized immediately after irradiation by a decrease in positive conditioned reflexes which began to progress rapidly on the fifth day, after a one-day increase in the reflexes, achieving maximum intensity between the 15th and 20th days. Against the background of inhibition developing in the cerebral cortex, the activity of the nerve cells was marked by equalizing and paradoxical phases.

Comparing the dynamics of changes in conditioned activity with the dynamics of changes in pancreatic secretion, Karpenko discovered that development and deepening of inhibition in the cerebral cortex was paralleled by the development of pronounced pancreatic hyposecretion, probably because of the action of cortical inhibition on the nerve centers of the subcortex. However, this correlation did not continue throughout the sickness. At the first manifestation of clinical signs of radiation sickness, hypersecretion appeared and persisted for several days against a background of deepening cortical inhibition. The temporary increase in secretion was apparently caused by positive induction of the subcortical autonomic centers that regulate pancreatic activity.

Radiation sickness followed a mild course in the dog Ural, and the relationship between changes in higher nervous activity and pancreatic secretion was different. All the positive conditioned reflexes increased sharply immediately after irradiation while differentiation was disinhibited, indicating intensification of cortical excitation. Subsequently, as the disease progressed, the cerebral cortex maintained a high functional level. Higher nervous activity became normal when the animal recovered. Changes in external secretion of the pancreas paralleled those in the functional condition of the cerebral cortex. By and large, cortical function remained high throughout the sickness. This elevation was not stable, however, and on some days it dropped, thus imparting a cyclic character to the secretory disorders which coincided in time with the same cyclic changes in conditioned activity.

In most cases, however, the periods of intensified excitation in the cortex coincided with periods of decreased pancreatic activity and vice versa. Therefore, these experiments demonstrated the existence of inductive relations between the cerebral cortex and the subcortical autonomic centers, influencing the intensity of the secretory process. It is also possible that the difference in secretory effects in both dogs, and, in general, in the course and outcome of the disease, is partly attributable to the animals' nervous systems, because Ryzhik had the weak inhibitory type while Ural had the strong type with excitation predominating.

PANCREATIC SECRETION DURING RADIATION SICKNESS COMPLICATED BY NEUROSIS

Experiments on dogs have demonstrated a definite relationship between pancreatic secretion disorders and the functional state of the higher divisions of the central nervous system. A. E. Karpenko performed two "cross" experiments in which two dogs were irradiated twice, once when the central nervous system was normal and again when it was pathological. The functional state of the nervous system was impaired by frequent clashing of the food and defense reflexes.

The dog Volk was first irradiated with its central nervous system functioning normally; then after it had recovered and its physiological functions (blood constituents, body weight, temperature, etc.), including pancreatic secretion, had become normal, its nervous system was impaired and several weeks later it was irradiated again.

The reverse order was followed in the case of the dog Brom; the first irradiation was done against the background of a pathological nervous system, the second against the background of a normal nervous system.

The dose of X-rays was the same (250 r) in all the "cross" experiments. The results showed that irradiation of Volk (with nervous system normal) induced mild radiation sickness. The pancreatic disorders were hypersecretory. On the other hand, irradiation of the animal with its nervous system in a pathological condition induced severe radiation sickness that ended in death. Pancreatic secretion was low throughout the sickness (Figure 10).

Impairment of pancreatic secretion in the dog Brom, after initial irradiation against the background of a traumatized nervous system, was more pronounced and lasting than that caused by irradiation against the background of a nervous system functioning normally (Figure 11). Therefore, this series of experiments confirmed the existence of a definite relationship between the nature, duration, and extent of pancreatic secretory disorders during radiation sickness and the functional state of the central nervous system.

In this connection we should like to cite some general findings of A. E. Karpenko on two groups of dogs, one of which was irradiated with normal central nervous systems, the other with pathological

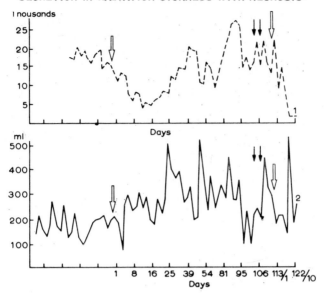

Figure 10. Changes in pancreatic secretion and leukocyte count in the dog Volk irradiated first with a normal nervous system, then with the cerebral cortex in a pathological condition.
(Reported by A. E. Karpenko.)
1—Leukocytes per mm³ of blood. 2—Secretion of pancreatic juice. Arrows: white shows day of irradiation (250 r), black shows day of disruption of nervous activity.

central nervous systems. Both groups received the same dose of X-rays (250 r), and both suffered from mild as well as severe radiation sickness. Two in the first group of five animals died as compared with three in the second group of four animals.

A comparison of the clinical signs of the course of the sickness in dogs of both groups shows that in animals irradiated against the background of a functionally weakened cerebral cortex, the mean leukocyte count was lower and the period of leukopenia was longer in the surviving dogs than in the animals irradiated with their nervous systems in a normal condition. The hemorrhagic syndrome appeared much sooner in the irradiated neurotic dogs (on the third day) than in the other dogs (on the ninth day), and they had a greater loss of weight, more pronounced tachycardia, adynamia, and dystrophy.

Irradiation of dogs with traumatized nervous systems also caused substantial changes in the enzymatic function of the pancreas.

The pancreatic enzymes of these dogs had the same characteristics that were noted after the irradiation of nontraumatized dogs, but they were more marked. For example, there was a more frequent decrease in the proteolytic activity of trypsin, which, according to several investigators, is the most resistant of all the pancreatic enzymes to ionizing radiation.

During the acute period of radiation sickness, amylase activity in all four dogs of the second group was 42 to 74% below normal, an important phenomenon because it occurred with unusual regularity.

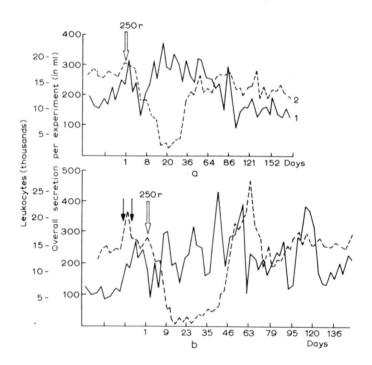

Figure 11. Changes in pancreatic secretion and leukocyte count in the dog Brom irradiated first with a
pathological nervous system, then with the cerebral
cortex normal. (Reported by A. E. Karpenko.)
1—Secretion of pancreatic juice. 2—Leukocytes
per mm³ of blood. a—Irradiation with cerebral
cortex normal. b—Irradiation against the background of neurosis. Other symbols the same as
in Figure 10.

Analysis of the secretory disorders by phases showed that 1) the irradiated neurotic dogs manifested more frequent inertness of secretion than the irradiated normal animals, 2) that they manifested two maxima of juice secretion, one at the end of the complex reflex phase and the other in the middle of the neurochemical phase, and 3) that they developed secretion disturbances several days sooner than the irradiated normal dogs.

"Spontaneous" secretion appeared in both groups of irradiated animals, and it sometimes equalled in volume and quality the juice secreted in response to food stimuli (Table 29).

Table 29

Comparison of the rate of secretion and composition of pancreatic juice in dogs during acute radiation disease.

(Reported by A. E. Karpenko.)

Name of dog	Nature of secretion	Volume of juice (ml) for 30 min.	Amylase (in arbitrary units)	Lipase (ml of 0.1 N NaOH solution		Trypsin (ml of 0.2 N HCl solution)	Viscosity (sec)
				Free	Total		
Brom	"Spontaneous"	10	1600	0.05	0.60	1.7	67.5
	Food	24	800	0.15	0.55	3.3	69.5
Chert	"Spontaneous"	7	200	2.35	2.85	1.4	—
	Food	8	1600	1.00	1.80	1.5	66.5
Bulat	"Spontaneous"	6	400	1.25	3.05	2.0	—
	Food	38	800	0.95	2.40	2.3	76.0

The appearance of secretion at times other than during digestion, along with strong digestive properties of the juice secreted, is indicative of serious disruption of the neurohumoral mechanism regulating pancreatic activity. This glandular condition may result in exhaustion of the secretory apparatus and disturbance of the acid–base balance, which the pancreas helps to maintain at a normal level.

In conclusion, we wish to call attention to a fact of considerable importance in appraising the various functional disorders of the pancreas during radiation sickness. Of the four experimental dogs irradiated after traumatization of their nervous systems, three died in 15 to 21 days with signs of decreased pancreatic capacity, while one animal survived with increased capacity during the sickness (Table 30).

Table 30

Effect of functional weakening of cortical activity and subsequent total-body irradiation on the level of pancreatic secretion in dogs.

(Reported by A. E. Karpenko.)

Observation conditions	Increase (+) or decrease (−) in secretion with respect to the original level taken as 100%			
	Brom	Bulat	Ural	Volk
Original level of secretion	100	100	100	100
Level of secretion after clash of reflexes	+27	+15	−26	−12
Level of secretion after irradiation against a background of neurosis	+28	−19	−20	−28

Note. Bulat, Ural, and Volk died between 15 and 21 days after irradiation.

Hypofunctional secretory disorders closely resemble the disorders observed in the dogs Ryzhiĭ and Chert of the first group, who died during the acute period of radiation sickness.

Thus, if radiation sickness does not end fatally, the secretory capacity of the pancreas is quite high; otherwise it is very low. This relationship is obviously attributable to the severity of the disease. It will be noted that decreased function of the gland during severe sickness is paralleled by decreased function of the cerebral cortex, whereas increased function of the gland during mild sickness is paralleled by increased function of the cerebral cortex (Table 31).

Table 31

Correlation between mean levels of positive conditioned reflexes and pancreatic secretion in dogs with mild and severe forms of radiation sickness.

(Reported by A. E. Karpenko.)

Form of the disease	Before the disease		During the sickness			
			Conditioned reflexes		Pancreatic secretion	
	Conditioned reflexes (saliva in scale divisions)	Pancreatic secretion (ml)	(Saliva in scale divisions)	Change (%)	Volume of juice (ml)	Change (%)
Mild	86	120	115	+34	133	+10
Severe	90	194	52	-42	122	-37
Severe	147	70	96	-35	56	-20

We are therefore justified in regarding the above-mentioned types of pancreatic disorders as being caused by differences in the condition of the defense-adaptation mechanisms of the higher divisions of the central nervous system.

To summarize, under the influence of ionizing radiation, external pancreatic secretion undergoes acute and prolonged impairment. This is reflected in hypofunction, hyperfunction, or a combination of both; dissimilar secretory reactions to the same food stimulus and cyclic fluctuations in the level of secretion; a changed relationship between the volume and quality of secretion elicited by different kinds of food; distortion of the secretion curve type; development of inert secretion; lengthening of the latent period of secretion; changes in correlation of enzyme activity in response to the same food stimulus; disruption of the relative parallelism in the discharge of enzymes (phenomenon of dissociation); and the development of "spontaneous" secretion.

The degree of impairment of pancreatic secretion varies with the severity of radiation sickness. If the clinical course of the sickness becomes aggravated, profound secretory disorders set in, most of them hypofunctional. These secretory disorders are to a certain extent determined by the disorders of higher nervous activity which arise before pancreatic function is impaired.

Quantitative and qualitative changes in pancreatic secretion are more pronounced in radiation sickness caused by irradiation against the background of neurosis with functional weakening of the cerebral cortex than they are in radiation sickness caused by irradiation against the background of a central nervous system functioning normally. It is possible that the hypofunctional pancreatic disorders during acute radiation sickness reflect extreme exhaustion of the regulatory and defense-adaptive mechanisms. For this reason, they have the least favorable prognosis.

CHAPTER 4

The Bile Forming and Bile Secreting Functions of the Liver

Three aspects of radiation injury of the liver have been and are being investigated: (1) the significance of morphological and biochemical changes in liver tissue in the general pathogenesis of radiation sickness; (2) the role of radiation injury of the liver in metabolic disorders; (3) the nature of disorders of external secretion of the liver under the influence of ionizing radiation. Of these, the third is most relevant to our subject. Data on the other two, however, are of some interest because they reflect radiation injury to liver tissue and help to elucidate the effect of radiation on bile formation and secretion.

Many investigators have wondered about the specific role of radiation injury in the development of radiation sickness, with particular reference to the following phenomena: (a) less injury following shielding of the liver region during total-body external irradiation, (b) the protective properties of certain chemical fractions in liver tissue, (c) the formation of toxic, incompletely oxidized fatty acids as a result of chain reactions in the liver after irradiation, and (d) the presence in the liver of extensive mesenchymal and lymphoid tissue with high sensitivity to ionizing radiation.

M. F. Belovintseva and E. N. Speranskaya (1958) recently obtained some information on the significance of the functional condition of the liver in the development of radiation sickness. After altering the condition of the liver of white mice by ligating the pancreaticoduodenal vein and then irradiating the animals with doses of 500 and 800 r, the authors observed that the mice died before the control animals did.

Functional weakening of the dog liver was achieved by transplanting the pancreaticoduodenal vein (which transports most hormones to the liver) from the wall of the portal vein to the wall of the inferior vena cava. Double doses of 300 r each caused considerable impairment of the sugar-regulating and detoxifying functions of the liver as compared with the controls. This was determined from the blood-sugar curves after sugar loading and intravenous injection of glucose and insulin, as well as from the formation of sulfuric ether compounds before and after hydroquinone loading. Total-body irradiation with a single dose of 600 r induced radiation sickness in dogs with weakened liver function and killed them on the fourth day; the control animals, however, suffered only minor impairment of the sugar-regulating and synthesizing functions of the liver.

Other investigators using histochemical methods have discovered a lower concentration of liver glycogen after irradiation, increased sudanophilic fat, and changes in the nucleoprotein concentration. Impaired lipid metabolism and changes in liver cholesterol after ionizing radiation have been observed by E. M. Belyaev, V. D. Blokhin, S. S. Vasileĭskiĭ, N. N. Demin, L. I. Il'ina, A. S. Kaĭnova, K. V. Smirnov, L. T. Tutochkin, T. A. Fedorova, and V. A. Shaternikov (1959). D. E. Grodzenskiĭ and K. A. Tret'yakova (1959) noted an acceleration of cholesterol synthesis from acetic acid, an increase in the inclusion of radioactive carbon (C^{14}) into liver fatty acids, and a change in the fatty acid content in liver tissue.

V. P. Fedotov (1959) observed impairment of the sugar regulating function of the liver in both acute and subacute radiation sickness caused by radioactive polonium. This impairment was reflected in a decreased capacity of the liver to retain and metabolize blood sugar. According to G. Kh. Bunatyan and G. T. Alunts (1954), injecting rabbits with radioactive phosphorus (20 to 30 μc of P^{32} per kg body weight) decreases liver glycogen five to tenfold, sometimes fifteen to twentyfold.

Other investigators have noted a correlation between functional impairment of the liver and changes in protein and carbohydrate metabolism following irradiation of animals. Irradiated persons have been found to have lowered liver function as shown by galactose, lactic acid, and bilirubin tests. E. A. Denisova (1957) discovered that persons who had had contact with ionizing radiation suffered changes in hepatic protein synthesis fairly early.

P. M. Belyaev (1959) observed prolonged changes in nucleic acid metabolism in rat liver after single total-body irradiation with the gamma rays of radioactive cobalt. V. G. Vladimirov (1960) noted a decrease in liver desoxyribonucleic acid in white rats within 24 hours of total-body irradiation with a dose of 600 r of Co^{60} gamma rays. According to R. S. Krivchenkova (1960), injecting rats with 0.1 mc/kg of radioactive polonium (Po^{210}) increases succinic dehydrogenase activity, especially in the terminal stage of radiation sickness.

I. K. Zyuzin, O. S. Vergilesova, I. A. Korovina, and I. A. Shishakova (1960) observed an increase in the liver content of trace elements (copper, iron, and cobalt in particular) in rabbits after single total-body exposure to 1250 to 1500 r of gamma rays on an EGO-2 cobalt apparatus at a dose rate of 470 r/min.

The foregoing data on biochemical changes arising in the liver after ionizing radiation and resulting in impaired metabolic processes both in the liver proper and elsewhere in the body suggest that radiation injury is necessarily associated with serious impairment of the bile forming and bile secreting functions of the liver.

BILE FORMATION

There has been comparatively little research on the cholepoietic function of the liver following exposure to ionizing radiation. Reports dealing with changes in the chemical composition of liver tissue include those by Rother (1927) and, more recently, by N. E. Ponomarenko (1957) on changes in the content of cholesterol, lipid phosphorus, and total fat in the liver of dogs after total-body irradiation with a single dose of 500 r. Within 48 hours of exposure, the cholesterol level falls 50% temporarily, rising on the third day and remaining at this level for a few days. On the seventh day, however, it again falls, this time 70 to 80%. It rises once more on the 14th day and achieves a high level by the 21st day.

This undulant pattern of changes in liver cholesterol occurs even after irradiation with a dose of 1000 r. Soon after irradiation, the level falls 30 to 40%, then rises within 24 to 72 hours to a level 25 to 30% above the original level. The lipid phosphorus content also increases during the period from 30 minutes to 7 days after irradiation. This is also true of total fat content, which starts to increase 5 minutes after irradiation, the original amount tripling in 24 hours. An elevated total fat level (an increase of 20 to 60%) remained throughout the 21-day period of investigation.

Ponomarenko's findings on the undulant character of cholesterol changes and the periodic, abrupt decreases of cholesterol in liver tissue attest to the profound disruption of cholepoiesis. They agree with the data of other authors who have studied changes in bile composition in animals suffering from radiation sickness.

Our colleague V. L. Popkov (1957, 1960), analyzing changes in the concentration of cholates (by Irvin's method) and bilirubin (by Jendrasic's method) in dogs after total-body external irradiation with a dose of 250 r, discovered that the concentration of these substances in the bile increases soon after exposure, decreases markedly at the height of radiation sickness, and again rises to, and sometimes exceeds, the original level during the period of recovery (Table 32).

According to K. S. Martirosov (1957, 1960), who exposed dogs with gallbladder fistulas to doses of 200 to 650 r, bilirubin increases in the bile on the very day of irradiation and remains on a high level during the next two months. If the sickness is mild, the bilirubin level is high only during the first few days after irradiation.

Table 32

Changes in bile composition in dogs during acute radiation sickness.

(Reported by V. L. Popkov.)

Name of dog	Before irradiation		The first few days after irradiation		At the height of the sickness		During recovery	
	Bilirubin (mg%)	Cholates (mg%)	Bilirubin (mg%)	Cholates (mg%)	Bilirubin (mg%)	Cholates (mg%)	Bilirubin (mg%)	Cholates (mg%)
Seryĭ	147.5	1163.4	271.2	3225.0	58.5	1029.0	195.0	2355.7
Ryzhiĭ	80.4	856.2	—	—	34.2	311.8	—	—
Kosoĭ	155.6	3730.0	501.0	5484.0	108.0	3853.0	231.0	3853.0
Kosoĭ (second irradiation)	224.0	4313.0	341.0	8244.0	140.0	2311.0	225.7	2996.6
Almaz	91.5	1170.9	170.0	2051.2	70.0	160.0	94.5	2017.7
Almaz (second irradiation)	94.5	2017.7	238.9	2435.9	95.0	1920.9	122.7	1103.8

A stimulating effect has been observed by other authors, e.g., Barbaczy (1925). They have also noted inhibition of cholepoiesis under the influence of ionizing radiation (Smyth and Whipple, 1924). The dose and irradiation conditions, of course, are also significant factors in this respect. It has been established that local irradiation of the liver with small doses increases bile secretion and that large doses decrease it (Takeda and Jouen, 1926).

In the experiments of R. S. Zhur and V. A. Sonkina (1960) on seven dogs with chronic gallbladder fistulas, total-body irradiation with a dose of 250 r had no affect on the level of bile secretion the first two or three days, thereafter, however, it began to fluctuate up and down in an undulating fashion but without ever exceeding the original level.

The same unstable, undulant pattern was exhibited by "spontaneous" bile secretion in dogs exposed to radioactive polonium. L. L. Fedorovskiĭ (1960) injected eight dogs with chronic gallbladder fistulas with a single subcutaneous dose of radioactive polonium (0.03 to 0.06 mc/kg body weight) and observed during the first few days thereafter that the volume of bile secreted fluctuated around the upper normal limit but decreased sharply during the terminal period. The bile composition (bilirubin, bile acids) was equally unstable.

E. P. Gvozdikovskaya (1937), irradiating the hepatic region of dogs with 50 to 300 erythema doses, concluded that radiation injury inhibits cholepoiesis, the degree of inhibition varying with the size of the dose. Some data on liver excretion disorders are presented in the work of Yu. N. Uspenskiĭ (1957, 1960), who experimented on three dogs with chronic gall bladder fistulas using Schiff's method. Radiation sickness was induced by a total dose of 350 to 400 r. All three dogs died at the height of the disease, one on the 15th day, another on the 19th day, and the third on the 20th day after irradiation. The secretory disorders were associated with the severe course of the sickness. The experiments showed that the amount of B bile decreased markedly after irradiation. There was also a considerable decrease in bile secretion during the three hours in which secretion was observed (Table 33).

It will be noted that during severe radiation sickness liver secretion does not have the undulant character which is almost invariably associated with mild radiation injury and which also reflects the changes in bile composition.

BILE SECRETION

Besides changes in bile formation, ionizing radiation causes significant impairment of bile evacuation into the intestine. In experiments on dogs with chronic fistulas of the common bile duct

Table 33

Cholepoietic function of the liver in dogs during severe radiation sickness.

(Reported by Yu.N. Uspenskiĭ.)

No. of dog and irradiation dose	Volume of bile (ml)					Remarks
	Before irradiation		After irradiation			
	B bile	C bile	B bile	C bile		
Dog No. 13 (irradiation dose - 400 r)	13.0-21.0	6.5-7.2	3.5-4.2	3.6-4.5		1st week
			2.0-2.5	3.0-0.5		2nd week
Dog No. 14 (irradiation dose - 350 r)	17.5-26.0	8.0-18.0	2.8-5.0	2.8-5.0		1st week
			4.3-2.5	1.3-2.5		2nd week
			2.0-6.0	3.5-3.0		3rd week
Dog No. 15 (irradiation dose - 400 r)	14.0-23.0	15.0-20.0	5.5-13.0	3.8-7.0		1st week
			4.7-7.0	0.9-4.3		2nd week
			4.5-6.5	2.0-2.5		3rd week

and fistulas of the gallbladder, E. P. Gvozdikovskaya (1957) discovered that local irradiation of the liver in amounts ranging from 50 to 300 erythema doses inhibits bile secretion. This is reflected in prolongation of the latent period of bile discharge into the intestine after eating, in decreased volume of bile secreted per experiment, and in changes in the type of bile secretion curve. According to Gvozdikovskaya, however, irradiation has a more deleterious effect on the bile-forming function of the liver than on the bile-secreting function.

The most thorough study of the problem was made by V. L. Popkov (1957, 1960), who experimented on eight dogs with chronic fistulas of the common bile duct operated on according to S. M. Gorshkova's method. Six dogs were investigated at the same time for bile discharge into the intestine after eating 200 g of meat and for higher nervous activity by conditioned salivary reflexes. Bile secretion alone was investigated in two dogs. The analysis of bile secreted by the liver after the eating of meat took into account the latent period of bile discharge into the intestine, the volume of bile secreted per hour, and the total volume of bile for the 4 hours that each experiment lasted. Peripheral blood determinations were made of the leukocyte and erythrocyte counts, hemoglobin content, and erythrocyte sedimentation rate. The general condition of the animals was appraised from behavior, pulse, weight, and body temperature. After a general examination, the dogs were irradiated with 250 r, six animals once and two animals three times at intervals of several months.

A variety of impaired functions was noted after total-body irradiation of the animals. The dog Ryzhiĭ immediately exhibited changes in higher nervous activity, as shown by an increase in the positive conditioned reflexes per experiment from 278 to 390 scale divisions (about 40% above normal), by the appearance of equalizing and paradoxical hypnotic phases in the cortical cells, and by disinhibition of differentiation. The increase in conditioned activity was followed by a period of inhibited conditioned activity during which the number of positive reflexes per experiment dropped from 390 to 90 scale divisions; also during this period, the latent period of the reflexes increased, and successive inhibition was intensified after application of a differential stimulus.

The animal had leukopenia and anemia; the leukocyte count dropped from 19,620 to $1900/mm^3$, i.e., by almost 90%, and the erythrocyte count dropped from 4.48 million to 3.48 million/mm^3, i.e., by almost 25%. The hemoglobin content decreased 10% (from 12.4 g% to 11 g%).

Bile evacuation into the intestine became weakened between the 11th and 20th days after irradiation. During this time the total volume of bile for 4 hours of observation averaged 52.3 ml, as compared with an average of 90 ml when normal. The volume of bile secreted in response to food stimulation decreased about 40%. There was also a change in the bile secretion curve. Maximum bile discharge occurred during the first hour after eating, but it shifted to later hours at the height of the sickness. After the 21st day, secretion gradually approached the original level. Normalization of bile secretion at the original level and of all other functions occurred three to four weeks after irradiation.

In the dog Kosoĭ secretion became impaired as early as the first day after irradiation; this was reflected in a decreased volume of bile secreted in response to food stimuli (by 29% of the original level). This persisted for 10 days; then such secretion began to fluctuate against a background of lowered secretory function. Normally, the total volume of bile was 57.5 ml, but at this time it was 51.0 ml, a reduction of 10%. The type of bile evacuation curve changed similarly. On the second day after irradiation, maximum bile discharge shifted from the first hour to later hours after eating (Figure 12).

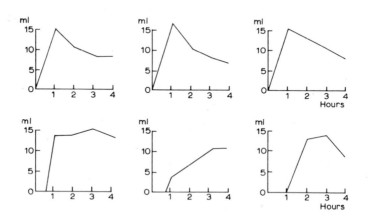

Figure 12. Changes in the rate of bile discharge into the intestine in the dog Kosoĭ during acute radiation sickness. (Reported by V. L. Popkov.)
Top row, before irradiation; bottom row, after irradiation with 250 r on the 2nd, 3rd, and 11th days (from left to right).

Bile secretion began to return to normal on the 14th day, and there was complete restoration about 1-1/2 months after irradiation. At this time the peripheral blood composition also became normal; it had changed after irradiation as follows: the leukocyte count dropped from 7600 to 1700/mm^3 (by 75%), the erythrocyte count from 6.46 to 4 million/mm^3 (by 38%), and hemoglobin content from 12.2 to 10.3 g% (by 15%).

After normalization of the above functions, the dog was again irradiated with the same dose, 250 r. The leukocyte count now dropped from 4500 to 1400/mm^3 (by 69%), the erythrocyte count decreased by 24%, and the hemoglobin concentration by 9%.

The impairment of bile secretion was comparable to that observed in the first case. The total volume of bile secreted in response to food decreased the first day after irradiation from 51 to 23 ml. The next three days it ceased altogether, but then began to fluctuate between increases and decreases. The hourly curve of bile discharge into the intestine changed from the 10th day on, but gradually started to return to normal on the 21st day, becoming fully restored by the 40th day after irradiation. By this time the functions of the other organs had likewise become normal.

In the dog Seryĭ, changes in higher nervous activity exhibited a phasic quality as early as the first day after irradiation, the mean magnitude of positive conditioned reflexes per experiment increasing by 20%. It decreased somewhat with the onset of acute radiation sickness but remained 8% above the original magnitude. The amplitude of these wavelike variations in conditioned reflexes during the sickness was 4-1/2 times that of the original experiments. During the period of recovery, cortical cell function increased, as reflected in a 37% increase in the positive conditioned reflexes per experiment over their magnitude before the sickness.

During the acute period of the sickness, the leukocyte count dropped from 18,600 to 4500/mm^3 (by 70%), the erythrocyte count from 5.82 million to 4.49 million/mm^3 (by 33%), and the hemoglobin concentration from 10.8 to 9.8 g% (by 11%).

The total volume of bile secreted after the ingestion of meat changed little during the acute period of the sickness; it dropped below the original level by an average of only 5%. It then became stable and remained so throughout the sickness, dropping on certain days to very low figures (Figure 13).

Meanwhile, there was also a change in the curve of hourly bile secretion, which became sluggish, the maximum bile evacuation shifting from the first hour after eating to later hours of the experiment. The latent period of bile secretion increased from 15 to 20 minutes, while in certain experiments it lasted an hour or more.

The dog Almaz was irradiated twice, each time with its nervous system normal. The initial irradiation was followed by an increase in the volume of juice secreted per experiment from 71 to 58 ml, i.e., by an average of 18%. Moreover, the type of evacuation curve changed in 40% of the cases. These phenomena were noted during acute radiation sickness. The leukocyte count dropped from 11,970 to 2300/mm^3 (by 81%), the erythrocyte count from 5.8 million to

4.4 million/mm^3 (by 24%), and the hemoglobin concentration from 12 to 10.5 g%, (by 12.5%).

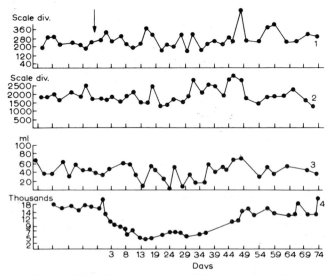

Figure 13. Changes in conditioned (1) and unconditioned (2) salivary reflexes, total volume of bile
per experiment (3), and leukocyte count per mm^3
of blood (4) in the dog Seryĭ during acute radiation
sickness. (Reported by V. L. Popkov.)
Arrow indicates day of irradiation.

The changes in bile secretion after the second irradiation were similar to those noted above but were less pronounced. The latent period of secretion lengthened from 21 to 29 minutes, whereas it had remained virtually unchanged after the first irradiation. The leukocyte count dropped to 1400/mm^3, the erythrocyte count to 4.18 million/mm^3, and the hemoglobin concentration to 8 g%.

These figures show that disruption of bile evacuation into the intestine during digestion, which occurs in cyclic fashion at different stages of the sickness, sometimes elevates and at other times lowers the level of bile secretion in response to the same food stimulus. There is a definite connection between the different types of secretory disorders (hyperfunctional and hypofunctional) and the functional state of the central nervous system in that intensification of cortical excitation frequently coincides with increased bile secretion into the intestine; and, conversely, a decrease in bile secretion frequently coincides with an intensification of cortical inhibition.

ROLE OF THE GALLBLADDER IN THE MECHANISM OF IMPAIRMENT OF BILE SECRETION

The undulant character of radiation-induced changes in bile secretion may be due either to interference with the rhythm of cholepoiesis in the liver or to disruption of coordination in the bile-secreting apparatus. In all likelihood both factors are involved. It will be noted that these changes in bile secretion are by no means uniquely characteristic of radiation injury to the liver and its cholepoietic apparatus. They also occur during radiation sickness in the activity of the other digestive organs and, in general, of those organs innervated by the autonomic nervous system. Consequently, the origin of disorders with an undulant course may apparently be partly attributed to impaired synergism in the parasympathetic and sympathetic innervations. As far as the bile secreting function of the liver is concerned, disruption of the reflex regulatory mechanism affects primarily the reciprocal nerve influences on the muscles of the gallbladder and the common bile duct.

Under normal conditions, bile is discharged into the intestine after intense contraction of the muscles of the gallbladder walls and relaxation of the muscles of the sphincter of Oddi and the terminal part of the common bile duct. The bladder is filled at times other than during digestion after spastic contraction of the sphincter of Oddi and terminal part of the common bile duct and relaxation of the muscles of the gallbladder. This complex process of secretion and storage of bile in the liver and bile ducts is regulated largely by reflexes. Radiation apparently injures the reflex mechanism that regulates the above-mentioned portions of the bile secreting system. This problem, however, has not as yet been investigated experimentally. There are available only some data on changes in motility of the gallbladder in dogs during acute radiation sickness. For example, we observed two dogs with chronic gallbladder fistulas in which contraction of gallbladder muscle was recorded by S. M. Gorshkova's direct water delivery method before and after three egg yolks or 600 ml of milk were ingested (I. T. Kurtsin and A. G. Korobkina, 1960). Radiation sickness was induced by total-body irradiation of the animals with a dose of 250 r.

In presenting the results of these experiments, we do not intend to discuss the clinical picture of the radiation sickness because it was scarcely distinguishable from that observed in the experiments already described. We should simply like to note that one of the dogs developed serious sickness and died 22 days after being irradiated; the other had mild sickness. We also do not think it worthwhile to go into detail on the day-to-day dynamics of the disruption of gallbladder contractility. Instead we shall comment only on the most important and characteristic features.

The dog gallbladder is known to exhibit continuous, rhythmic contractions of slight amplitude at the rate of 5 to 7 per minute when the animal's stomach is empty. Tonic contraction of the bladder muscles begins a few minutes after eating (reflex increase in tone) and continues for 5 to 20 minutes. The bladder then relaxes for 5 to 20 minutes; this is followed by a prolonged increase in bladder tone lasting for 2 to 2-1/2 hours. The rhythmic contractions are almost imperceptible; the recording curve shows flattened waves corresponding to the spastic bladder contractions. When digestion is completed, bladder tone decreases to the original level while the rhythmic contractions become intensified, regaining their former amplitude and frequency. In addition to the rhythmic and spastic contractions, there may also be peristaltic contractions characterized by wide and undulant fluctuations in bladder tone.

That is why we believe the following features adequately characterize the nature of gallbladder dysfunction during radiation sickness: (1) contractions of the smooth muscle of the gallbladder on an empty stomach, (2) reflex increase in bladder tone upon eating food, (3) bladder activity at the height of digestion, and (4) contractility of the bladder at the end of digestion.

The "hunger" contractions of the gallbladder are somewhat weak throughout radiation sickness (Figure 14). Bladder tone decreases at the same time.

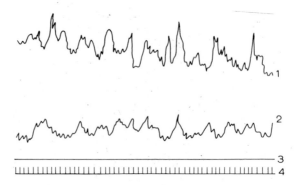

Figure 14. Changes in "hunger" contractions of the dog gallbladder during acute sickness. (Reported by I. T. Kurtsin and A. G. Korobkina.)
1—Bladder contractions before irradiation. 2—Bladder contractions during sickness. 3—Stimulation marker. 4—time marker, 5-sec intervals.

After eating, the reflex increase in bladder tone begins either sooner or later than usual. During the first two days after irradiation, the time preceding the increase in tone is shortened; but by the end of the latent period of the sickness, the time is virtually identical to that in the control experiments. At the height of the sickness, the time it takes for a reflex increase in tone to develop may be sharply reduced, sometimes requiring several seconds, at other times several minutes. The reflex increase in tone the first few days after irradiation may be almost imperceptible. The same phenomenon also occurs for a few days at the height of the sickness; on other days during this phase, however, it is scarcely distinguishable from that in the control experiments, if one disregards the marked shortening or lengthening of the latent period of its development (Figure 15).

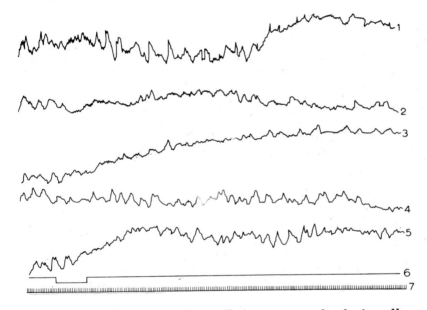

Figure 15. Changes in the reflex increase of a dog's gallbladder tone during acute radiation sickness. (Reported by I. T. Kurtsin and A. G. Korobkina.)
1—Gallbladder contractions before irradiation. 2—On the 2nd day. 3—On the 9th day. 4—On the 13th day. 5—On the 17th day after total-body external irradiation (250 r). 6—Stimulation marker (eating of 3 egg yolks). 7—Time marker, 5-sec intervals.

The magnitude of tonic gallbladder contraction after eating becomes abnormally low during the first two days after radiation trauma, on certain days during the climax of the sickness, and on the days preceding the animal's death. It is sometimes normal or above normal, especially at the end of the period of digestion.

This inadequate bladder reaction to food is often quite pronounced during actual tonic contraction when bladder tone decreases in some cases but increases in others (Table 34).

Table 34

Changes in the functional condition of a dog's gallbladder during acute radiation sickness.

(Reported by I. T. Kurtsin and A. G. Korobkina.)

Before eating	After eating 3 egg yolks				
	Latent period of reflex change in tone (min and sec)	Magnitude of tonic contraction (mm H_2O)		Duration of tonic contraction (hrs and min)	Amplitude of rhythmic contractions (mm H_2O)
		At the start of digestion	At the end of digestion		
Before sickness					
180-200	6.20-6.40	220-240	170-180	2.20-2.30	25-35
During sickness					
160-190	0.30-37.0	175-225	160-225	1.20-3.30	5-50

This condition of bladder tone exists during the first few days after irradiation and persists when clinical signs of the sickness become pronounced.

There is also a difference in the nature of bladder contractions at the height of digestion. At this time rhythmic contractions are either absent or very pronounced; peristaltic contractions sometimes arise, probably a result of weak bladder tone at this time (Figure 16).

Bladder tone decreases at the end of digestion as it does under normal conditions. Rhythmic contractions are frequently combined with strong peristaltic contractions, which normally does not happen. Such contractions occur the first few days after irradiation and on some days at the climax of radiation sickness, especially when the animal is about to die (Figure 17).

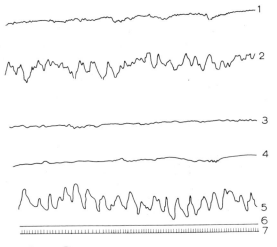

Figure 16. Changes in gallbladder contractions at the height of digestion in a
dog during acute radiation sickness.
(Reported by I. T. Kurtsin and A. G.
Korobkina.)
1—Bladder contractions before irradiation.   2—On the 2nd day.   3—
On the 5th day. 4—On the 9th day.
5—On the 17th day after irradiation.
6—Stimulation m a r k e r.   7—Time
marker, 5-sec intervals.

These changes in gallbladder contractility after radiation injury
closely resemble the functional dyskinesia of the gallbladder associated with a number of other diseases.
    A comparison of impaired gallbladder motility with the discharge
of bile into the intestine clearly reveals that disorders of bile
secretion definitely depend to some extent on disturbances of bladder
motility. For example, shortening or lengthening of the latent period
of bile discharge into the intestine may be due to a hyperkinetic or
hypokinetic reaction, respectively, of the bladder to the ingestion
of food. This may account for the difference in volume of bile
secreted after the same food stimulus, and for the asthenic and
inert types of bile secretion curves noted in V. L. Popkov's experiments. This hypothesis, however, requires direct experimental investigation of bile secretion and gallbladder contractility simultaneously. Then, too, nothing is known of the part played here by
the sphincter of Oddi and the closure mechanism of the common
bile duct generally. There is also a complete lack of information

on changes in the hormonal mechanism regulating bile secretion. It is possible that some role in the origin and development of dyskinetic disturbances of the gallbladder and sphincter of Oddi may be played by cholecystokinin, a hormone known to cause, under normal conditions, contraction of the muscles of the gallbladder and relaxation of the muscles of the common bile duct.

An analysis of bile constituents after radiation injury is very important in elucidating the changes in bile secretion that occur at this time. The available data indicate the existence of considerable fluctuations in, for example, the cholesterol and bilirubin contents of the bile, which might be explained either by a difference in the rate at which they are elaborated by the liver cells or by a difference in the rate of water absorption by the gallbladder mucosa—i.e., a difference in the degree of condensation of bile in the mucosa. Impairment of absorption from the gallbladder due to

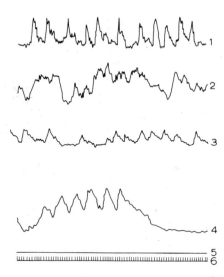

Figure 17. Changes in gallbladder contractions at the end of digestion in a dog during acute radiation sickness. (Reported by I. T. Kurtsin and A. G. Korobkina.) 1—Bladder contractions before irradiation. 2—On the 2nd day. 3—On the 5th day. 4—On the 21st day after irradiation. 5—Stimulation marker. 6—Time marker, 5-sec intervals).

ionizing radiation has not been investigated at all, and the part played by this factor in the dynamics of changes in bile secretion can only be conjectured. However, even if the questions mentioned above were answered, we would still not have a clear idea about the mechanism responsible for impairment of the bile secreting function of the liver. We must study disturbances in the relation between the normally closely connected processes of bile secretion and discharge into the intestine.

At this stage of our knowledge, we can only say that ionizing radiation severely impairs both cholepoiesis in the liver and bile secretion into the intestine, and that impairment of the latter is in large part attributable to changes in gallbladder motility.

BILE FORMATION AND SECRETION DURING RADIATION SICKNESS COMPLICATED BY NEUROSIS

The connection noted between the functional state of the higher divisions of the central nervous system and the character of disorders of bile secretion during radiation sickness, and the normally existing dependence of bile secretion and discharge into the intestine on cortical influences, made it essential to investigate the nature of changes in bile secretion following the combined action of total-body ionizing radiation and trauma to the higher divisions of the central nervous system. This was the problem which V. L. Popkov (1960) set for himself in experiments on six dogs, in three of which stereotypes of conditioned salivary reflexes were formed. After original levels of bile secretion, blood constituents, temperature, body weight, etc. were determined in the dogs with sterotypes of conditioned reflexes, the cortical processes were disrupted by Pavlov's method with simultaneous overstraining of the intensity of the excitatory process. The neurotic animals were then X-irradiated with a dose of 250 r.

Traumatization carried out daily for four days resulted in chronic impairment of higher nervous activity in the dog Belogolovyĭ. The magnitude of the positive conditioned reflexes decreased, hypnotic phases (equalizing, paradoxical, and ultraparadoxical) appeared in the activity of the cortical cells in approximately 50% of the experiments, and successive inhibition was intensified. The mean total of all the positive conditioned reflexes per experiment decreased from 288 to 85 scale divisions. All this indicated functional weakening of the cerebral cortex, with the inhibitory process predominating.

The bile discharge into the intestine also changed. After eating, the total amount of bile secreted increased on the average from 42.1 ml to 52.1 in the first experiments, then to 58.6 ml in the later experiments.

After irradiation, the positive conditioned salivary reflexes decreased further—the mean total fell to 40 scale divisions per experiment. The salivary reaction to certain conditioned stimuli was completely lacking and hypnotic phases became more frequent. At the same time, there was a significant change in bile secretion, which became inhibited, the total amount after eating averaging 39% less than before irradiation, i.e., after traumatization. It averaged 33.3 ml per experiment, instead of the 52.1 to 58.6 ml after traumatization. The volumes secreted on individual days of experimentation varied over a range that amouted to 62% of the original level. The type of bile secretion curve changed and the maximum evacuation shifted from the first hour to subsequent hours. It was characteristic of the acute period of radiation sickness that the leukocyte count in the peripheral blood decreased 97%, the erythrocyte count 13%, and hemoglobin content 10%.

Experiments performed on the dog Chernyĭ showed that after traumatization the mean total of positive conditioned reflexes increased from 130 to 166 scale divisions per experiment, or by 28%. Equalizing and paradoxical phases appeared in the activity of the cortical cells, and differentiation became disinhibited—in some experiments by 30 to 50% of the magnitude of the corresponding positive conditioned reflex. Changes in higher nervous activity were wavelike, in that periods of intensification alternated throughout with periods of weakening of conditioned activity. For example, whereas during the period of intensification the mean total of positive conditioned reflexes increased from 130 to 184 scale divisions, or by 42%, it decreased in the subsequent period from 184 to 79 scale divisions, or by almost 60% of the original level; it then increased again from 79 to 107 scale divisions, or by almost 35%.

These changes in higher nervous activity were paralleled by changes in bile secretion of the liver. During the period of decreased conditioned reflexes, the discharge of bile into the intestine decreased an average of 29%, from 45.9 to 33.0 ml. During the subsequent period of increased reflexes, it rose an average of 46% above the original level. This periodicity was apparently caused by cerebrocortical influences on the subcortical centers—initially, an inhibitory influence, then an excitatory influence.

Three months after the first traumatization, when the functions under study had become normal, another traumatization was induced and the dog was irradiated once more. The result was a sharp decrease in conditioned activity, with cerebrocortical inhibition predominating. Changes in the conditioned reflexes at the height of the sickness proved to be wavelike, increasing on some days, decreasing on others. These day-to-day fluctuations in conditioned salivation were far greater than those observed when the cerebral cortex was normal. The fluctuations in the conditioned reflexes were paralleled by fluctuations in the unconditioned salivary reflexes, although the latter had less amplitude. Bile secretion after eating during the first few days after irradiation decreased 60% on the average (Figure 18). The latent period of discharge into the intestine lengthened, and the time of maximum secretion shifted from the first hour, the normal time, to later hours (Figure 19). Secretory impairment at the height of the sickness was also wavelike. On some days the amount of bile entering the intestine was substantial, on others it was slight. This alternation in response to the same food stimulus continued as long as the animal was sick.

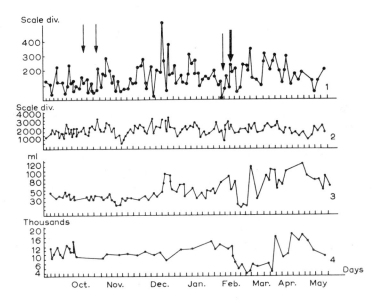

Figure 18. Changes in the magnitude of conditioned (1) and unconditioned (2) reflexes, total volume of bile per experiment (3), and leukocyte count per mm³ of blood (4) in the dog Chernyĭ during acute radiation sickness. (Reported by V. L. Popkov.)
    Thin arrows show   days of traumatization; thick arrow shows day of irradiation (250 r).

The length of the latent period varied inversely with the quantitative changes in bile secretion. When the volume discharged into the intestine increased, the latent period usually was shorter, and vice versa.
    Some fluctuations in the volume of bile secreted after application of the same food stimulus occurred even under normal

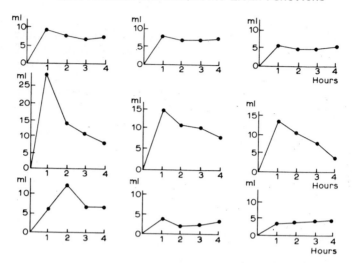

Figure 19. Changes in rate of bile discharge into the
intestine in the dog Chernyĭ after trauma to the central nervous system and irradiation. (Reported
by V. L. Popkov.)
Top row—normal, middle row—after traumatization, bottom row—after irradiation (250 r)
against a background of disturbed central
nervous system function.

conditions, but the fluctuations were not as large as under pathological conditions when the amplitude of fluctuations was six times
the normal amplitude and twice that observed in the period following
traumatization.

The direct cause of the fluctuations in bile secretion was evidently impairment of the nervous reflex mechanism which co-
ordinates gallbladder motility with the activity of the sphincter of
Oddi, which we discussed above.

Fluctuations in bile secretion were matched by fluctuations in
conditioned activity which were twice the normal amplitude. For
example, with a decrease in the conditioned reflexes, the volume
of bile entering the intestine sometimes decreased by 60% of the
normal volume. A moderate decrease in the concentration of bilirubin and liver cholates was noted during the acute phase of the
sickness.

The above-mentioned changes in higher nervous activity and
bile secretion progressed throughout the sickness, which, judging
by the hematological indices, was severe. The leukocyte count
after the combined action of central nervous system trauma and

irradiation fell from 12,600 to 2000 (by 85%); the erythrocyte count fell from 5.58 to 4.54 million (by 20%); and the hemoglobin content fell from 14.7 to 11.0 g% (by 25%).

The magnitude of the conditioned reflexes in the dog Dik normally adhered strictly to the law of intensity relations while differentiation usually varied from 20 to 50% of the magnitude of the associated reflex. The conditioned reflexes decreased after traumatization of the central nervous system, i.e., the work capacity of the cortical cells diminished. The total volume of bile secreted during the 4 hours of an experiment increased an average of 26% at first and then by 33%, as compared with the norm, in the experiments immediately preceding irradiation. The latent period of bile secretion was reduced from 23 to 13 minutes. The bile secretion curve usually showed maximum secretion during the first hour, but in 3 out of 19 experiments maximum secretion occurred the third hour after eating. Irradiation thus caused profound changes in higher nervous activity and in the bile secreting function of the liver. A narcotic phase in cerebrocortical activity was observed soon after traumatization, along with later equalizing, paradoxical, and ultraparadoxical phases. Bile secretion meanwhile was markedly inhibited. The total volume secreted during the 4 hours after eating meat decreased an average of 22% of the norm and by 41% of the level noted after traumatization but before irradiation. The latent period of bile discharge into the intestine rose to 44 minutes. Moreover, secretion after eating food was completely absent for several days (Figure 20).

These changes were accompanied by the familiar signs of acute radiation sickness. The leukocyte count decreased from 10,530 to 600 cells (by 95%); the erythrocyte count fell from 5.42 to 2.87 million (by 47%); and the hemoglobin content fell from 12.0 to 7.6 g% (by 37%).

The central nervous system of the dog Korichnevyĭ was traumatized before irradiation by means of repeated "electric clashing," which was followed by a decrease in the total volume of bile secreted per experiment from 53.6 ml to 42.0, or by 22%; there was also a lengthening of the latent period from 14 to 22 minutes and a change in the bile evacuation curve which reflected a shifting of maximum secretion to later hours after eating. The ensuing irradiation then inhibited bile secretion even more. The total volume of bile decreased 33%, the latent period lengthened to 40 minutes, and the bile evacuation curve changed even more drastically (Figure 21).

These phenomena were accompanied by the familiar signs of acute radiation sickness. The leukocyte count decreased from 13,400 to 800 (by 94%); the erythrocyte count fell from 4.39 to 2.8 million (by 36%); and the hemoglobin content fell from 9.11 to 7.3 g% (by 20%).

The dogs Kosoĭ and Almaz were experimented on under the same conditions. "Electric clashing" in Kosoĭ caused a decrease in the

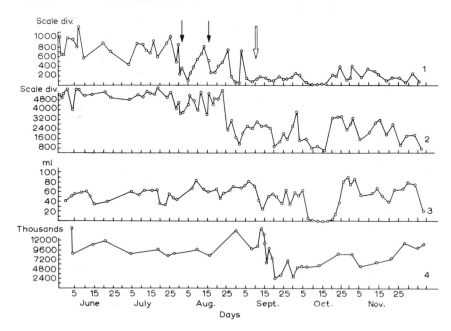

Figure 20. Changes in the magnitudes of conditioned (1) and unconditioned (2) reflexes, total volume of bile secretion per experiment (3), and leukocyte count per mm³ of blood (4) in the dog Dik irradiated after trauma to the central nervous system.
(Reported by V. L. Popkov.)

total volume of bile from 63 ml to 53 per experiment, or by 16%; a lengthening of the latent period from 9 to 30 minutes; and a shifting of maximum bile discharge from the first to the second hour. Irradiation then produced even greater inhibition of the bile secreting function of the liver. The total volume of bile decreased to 43 ml, or 32.1% below the normal level. The latent period lengthened to 37 minutes and maximum bile discharge shifted to the later hours of the experiment.

These disorders developed against a background of acute radiation sickness. The leukocyte count dropped from 7300 to 500 cells (by 87%); the erythrocyte count fell from 6.06 to 4.13 million (by 36%); and the hemoglobin concentration fell from 13.1 g% to 10 g% (by 24%).

After "electric clashing" the dog Almaz had a shortened latent period of bile secretion, a change in the evacuation curve as a result of increased secretion during the second hour, and sharp fluctuations in the total volume of bile secreted after eating (from

complete absence to 100.0 ml for 4 hours). Irradiation then produced even greater impairment of bile secretion, reflected mainly
in a lengthening of the latent period from 25 to 40 minutes, a decrease in the volume of bile secreted per experiment from 58 ml to
40 ml (by 31%), and a shift in the time of maximum secretion to
later hours of digestion. Pronounced signs of acute radiation
sickness were noted. The leukocyte count dropped from 7400 to
800 (by 89.2%); the erythrocyte count fell from 5.49 to 3.53 million
(by 35.7%); and the hemoglobin content dropped from 12.6 to 10 g%
(by 20.7%).

In another series of experiments, observations were made on two
groups of dogs, one of which (four animals) was irradiated with
the cerebral cortex normal, the other (six animals) after trauma to
the central nervous system. The results can be summed up as
follows.

Changes in the nontraumatized dogs during radiation sickness
included a 79% drop in the leukocyte count, a 39% drop in the
erythrocyte count, a 24.5% reduction in hemoglobin content, and a
23% decrease in the volume of bile secreted per experiment.

Changes in the traumatized dogs during radiation sickness included a 92% drop in the leukocyte count, a 31% drop in the

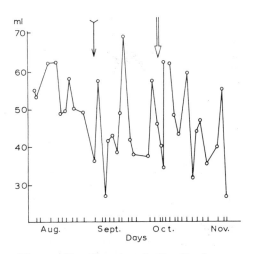

Figure 21. Changes in the discharge
of bile into the intestine of the dog
Korichnevyǐ after "electric clashing" and irradiation with a dose of
250 r. (Reported by V. L. Popkov.)
Black arrow shows day of clash;
white arrow shows day of irradiation.

erythrocyte count, a 23% reduction in hemoglobin content, and a 39.3% decrease in the volume of bile secreted per experiment (Table 35).

Table 35

Relationship between impaired bile secretion in the liver and the functional condition of the higher divisions of the central nervous system in dogs during acute radiation sickness.

(Reported by V. L. Popkov.)

Experimental conditions	Percentage of decrease from original level	
	Leukocyte count per mm^3	Volume of bile (ml) for 4 hours after eating meat
Irradiation with the central nervous system normal (four dogs)	79	23
Irradiation with traumatized central nervous system (six dogs)	92	39.3

A comparison of the figures reveals that radiation sickness followed a more severe course in the dogs with traumatized central nervous systems (the leukocyte count decreased 92% of the original level) than in the nontraumatized dogs (the leukocyte count decreased 79% of the original level). In addition, bile secretion was much more inhibited. This is borne out by a study of other indices of bile secretion. For example, the latent period after irradiation of the dogs with a normal nervous system lengthened from 15 to 20 minutes (Seryĭ), from 11 to 17 minutes (Kosoĭ), by no more than one minute (Ryzhiĭ); there was no change at all in Almaz. In the dogs which were irradiated after traumatization of the central nervous system, however, the latent period lengthened from 23 to 44 minutes (Dik), from 5 to 13 minutes (Chernyĭ), from 11 to 19 minutes (Belogolovyĭ), from 14 to 40 minutes (Korichnevyĭ), and from 21 to 40 minutes (Almaz), i.e., bile retention was more pronounced than in the nontraumatized animals.

A change in the bile evacuation curve after irradiation, reflecting a shifting of maximum secretion from the first to later hours, was observed in all the dogs; but the number of experiments with a distorted curve was much larger in those cases where irradiation followed traumatization of the nervous system. For example, in the dog Ryzhiĭ, which was irradiated without central nervous system trauma, distortion of the bile evacuation curve occurred in only 25% of the experiments; in the dogs Seryĭ, Almaz, and Kosoĭ, this occurred in almost 50% of the experiments. Distortion was much more common, however, in the traumatized animals: in Dik and Korichnevyĭ, curve distortion was observed in 90% of all the experiments; in the dogs Chernyĭ, Belogolovyĭ, Kosoĭ, and Almaz, in approximately 70%.

All these changes took place both during the latent period and during the period of clinically pronounced signs of radiation sickness. They were less frequent, however, during the recovery period. The disturbances disappeared when normalcy was restored, i.e., the changes were functional and reversible. It is worth noting, though, that full restoration of the bile secreting function of the liver set in much later in the traumatized dogs than in the non-traumatized dogs—2 to 2-1/2 months and 1-1/2 months, respectively.

As for changes in the constituents of bile, the normal mean concentration of bilirubin and the cholates differed from animal to animal, with only slight parallelism in changes in concentration. Irradiation usually caused phasic changes, increased concentrations of bilirubin and cholates being noted immediately after irradiation in all the animals. A phase of low concentration followed and was most marked in Seryĭ, Chernyĭ, Dik, and Ryzhiĭ, less so in Almaz and Kosoĭ, perhaps because even before the latter were irradiated, fluctuations in bilirubin and cholate concentrations were quite sharp.

The experimental findings described above testify to the major role played by the higher divisions of the central nervous system in the development of functional liver disorders caused by radiation lesions.

Impairment of the bile forming and bile secreting functions of the liver is more severe and prolonged in radiation sickness resulting from irradiation against a background of disturbed central nervous system function than in radiation sickness resulting from irradiation against a background of normal higher nervous activity.

CHAPTER 5

Intestinal Secretion

The earliest observations on radiation injury of the intestine showed that this part of the digestive system is highly sensitive to ionizing radiation (Wetterer, 1908). Some investigators (Warren and Whipple, 1922; De Coursey, 1953) compare it to lymphatic tissue, which is one of the most radiosensitive of all tissues. It is no accident that the clinical pictures of radiation sickness include an "acute intestinal form" (Quastler, Lanzl, Keller, and Osborn, 1951). This form is now recognized by many investigators as a result of data accumulated on impairment of the secretory, absorptive, and motor functions of the intestine and on morphological changes after radiation injury.

INTESTINAL SECRETION FOLLOWING EXTERNAL AND INTERNAL IRRADIATION

A detailed description of the impairment of intestinal function following ionizing radiation was made possible by chronic experiments on dogs with intestinal loops isolated by the Thiry, Thiry-Vella, and Babkin methods. The first to present pertinent data was Yu. N. Uspenskiĭ (1956, 1957, 1958, 1960), who induced radiation sickness in four dogs with Thiry fistulas by X-irradiating them with doses of 350, 400, and 660 r centered on the abdominal cavity. Two of the four irradiated dogs died, one on the 16th day, the other at the end of the sixth week. The other two survived, but took a long time to recover from exhaustion. The changes that occurred in intestinal juice secretion during the sickness are shown in Table 36.

It is evident from Table 36 that there was an increase in secretion of the small intestine during the first few days after irradiation, which then gave way to hyposecretion during the height of the sickness. Increased secretion was noted by the fourth week when it sometimes exceeded the original level. As the author notes, increased secretion was accompanied by an increase in the amylolytic

Table 36

Secretion of intestinal juice during 3 hours of mechanical irritation of the intestinal mucosa of dogs before and after irradiation of the abdomen with a dose of 660 r.

(Reported by Yu. N. Uspenskiĭ.)

Days and weeks	Volume of juice (ml)			
	Dog No. 2	Dog No. 9	Dog No. 11	Dog No. 12
Before irradiation	5.2–6.5	3.5–6.0	8.0–15.0	6.5–8.0
2nd day after irradiation	9.2	6.5	20.0	2.2
4th " "	3.5	6.8	22.0	13.2
6th " "	8.0	5.0	19.7	15.0
8th " "	10.2	3.0	10.9	4.8
10th " "	4.5	2.4	6.3	2.5
13th " "	2.1	3.3	6.0	0.8
18th " "	0.0	2.5	15.2	Died
21st " "	0.9	4.8	18.5	—
4th week	3.0–10.0	4.0–7.5	8.2–16.5	—
5th "	3.5–8.5	4.0–10.5	7.5–16.2	—
6th "	8.0–14.0	4.2–8.5	12.0–23.0	—
9th "	Died	3.8–10.0	22.5–28.5	—

activity of the juice from 256-512 to 1024-2048 Wohlgemuth units. "Spontaneous" secretion, which never occurred before irradiation, was observed in some experiments, amounting to 0.5 to 2.0 ml of juice per hour. Mechanical irritation of the intestine, at first produced inhibition, then excitation of secretion (Table 37).

Table 37

Secretion of intestinal juice after mechanical irritation of the intestinal mucosa in dogs on the 6th and 8th days after irradiation of the abdomen with a dose of 660 r.

(Reported by Yu. N. Uspenskiĭ.)

Volume of juice per		Remarks	Volume of juice per		Remarks
15 min	1 hour		15 min	1 hour	
On the 4th day			On the 8th day		
0.0 0.2 0.0 0.0	0.2	Start of mechanical irritation	0.5 0.6 0.8 0.5	1.9	Start of mechanical irritation
1.2 3.2 2.0 1.8	8.2	Amylase - 1024 units	0.0 0.2 1.5 0.4	2.1	
1.7 0.3 0.3 2.3	4.6		0.9 2.0 2.1 0.7	5.7	Amylase - 1024 units
3.8 1.0 0.6 1.5	6.9	Mechanical irritation halted	0.1 0.3 1.3 0.8	2.5	Mechanical irritation halted
0.0 0.0 0.0			0.0 0.0 0.0 0.0	0.0	
Total per experiment 19.9			Total per experiment 12.2		

In experiments on dogs with both a Pavlov pouch and a small intestine fistula, Yu. N. Uspenskiĭ (1957, 1958) observed marked inhibition of gastric secretion the first few days after irradiation of the abdomen and increased secretion of intestinal juice; he ascribed this to an inhibition of the intramural innervation of the intestine resulting from increased inhibitory influence from the higher divisions of the central nervous system.

K. V. Smirnov (1956) studied intestinal secretion during radiation sickness in dogs kept on different diets. First, Thiry fistulas were produced in the animals. Then normal levels of enterokinase, alkaline phosphatase, lipase, and the polypeptidases were determined in a homogenate of intestinal juice. After total-body irradiation with a dose of 400 r, marked changes were observed in the secretory and enzyme-forming functions of the intestine, and they had the same wavelike character as the changes noted in Uspenskiĭ's experiments with local irradiation.

M. F. Nesterin (1956, 1957, 1960) studied changes in the periodic secretion of intestinal juice in nine dogs with Thiry fistulas irradiated with doses of 200, 400, and 600 r. He made determinations of the volume of juice secreted during 5 hours and its content of enterokinase, phosphatase, sucrase (invertase), lipase, and peptidase. The author discovered that the volume of secretion varied with the radiation dose. In dogs irradiated with 200 r, he could find no changes in periodic secretion, but the total volume secreted during all the hours of observation was abnormally high. For example, whereas before irradiation it was 2.4 to 5.6 ml, the first day thereafter it rose to 7.4 ml and then to 7.9 ml on the eight day. At the same time, there was an increase in both the solid and liquid constituents of the juice. The enterokinase content on the first day after irradiation rose from 1470 to 3870 units per g of solid matter to 6390 units. It remained high for 20 days, fluctuating between 5500 and 10,950 units. On the 22nd day it dropped to the level of the original experiments, but soon rose again to 9735 to 11,770 units and remained at this level for three days. The enterokinase content of the juice became normal on the 60th day after irradiation.

Changes were also noted in the alkaline phosphatase content. Before irradiation it fluctuated between 26,460 and 47,260 units per g of solid matter. On the third day after irradiation, it rose to 72,560 units and for the next seven days fluctuated between 63,600 and 109,500 units. A slight drop between the 27th and 36th days was followed by a new rise to 53,900 to 78,000 units. As in the case of enterokinase, the original level was restored on the 60th day after irradiation.

According to the author, there were no changes in the content of lipase, peptidase, and sucrase after irradiation.

Increased amounts of enterokinase and phosphatase were noted in the feces after irradiation; this increase was not paralleled by changes in the enzyme content of the secretion, however, which indicates impaired inactivation of these enzymes in the large intestine.

Thus, while 200 r doses produced no clinically pronounced signs of radiation sickness in dogs, they did cause distinct and prolonged changes in the secretory and enzyme-forming functions of the small intestine.

Dogs irradiated with 400 r developed clinically pronounced radiation sickness with vomiting, leukopenia, erythropenia, decreased food excitability, adynamia, loss of weight, and severe impairment of intestinal secretion. Periodic secretion disappeared and was replaced by a continuous secretion frequently admixed with blood. The volume of juice and its enzyme content changed from the very first day after irradiation, when they increased and then decreased. This cyclic quantitative and qualitative changes in the secretion continued for nine months. For example, the enterokinase per g of solid matter fluctuated between 4650 and 7950 units. During the first 11 days after irradiation it rose to 12,650 units. It dropped between the 16th and 25th days to 510 units, rising again on the 30th and 32nd days to 13,600 to 18,240 units and fluctuating thereafter between 750 and 2460 units.

Even more striking changes were observed after the dogs were irradiated with 600 r. These took place against a background of severe radiation injury. We need say little more than that all the animals died 10 to 18 days later, during which time the activity of the intestinal glands, unlike that during the preceding experiments, remained very low (Table 38).

The degree of sensitivity of the different parts of the alimentary canal to ionizing radiation is a matter of some interest. According to the literature, intestinal epithelium is highly sensitive. Using functional criteria, M. F. Nesterin (1957, 1960) compared the vulnerability of the gastric and intestinal glands and discovered after irradiating dogs with the same dose (400 r) that disorders of intestinal secretion were much more pronounced than those in gastric secretion—quantitatively, qualitatively, and in the length of time they persisted. For example, at certain stages in the sickness, the amount of enzymes in intestinal juice (enterokinase and phosphatase) decreased markedly despite the absence of any changes in the digestive activity of pepsin. After irradiation, the intestinal juice was frequently found to contain blood, which was not the case with gastric juice. Gastric secretion became normal on the 83rd day, whereas restoration of duodenal juice took place on the 164th day and that of the central portion of the small intestine on the 198th day.

All these facts indicate that the intestine is more sensitive and vulnerable to ionizing radiation than the stomach. The vulnerability of the enzyme-forming function of the small intestine is worth

Table 38

Changes in the enzyme content of intestinal juice in dogs during acute radiation sickness.

(Reported by M. F. Nesterin.)

Enzymes	Before irradiation	After irradiation with a dose of 600 r on the			
		2nd day	3rd day	5th day	6th day
Dog No. 10					
Enterokinase	5 490–87 60	5 540	3 800	3 680	2 480
Phosphatase	36 900–57 700	21 840	14 000	11 000	18 600
Dog No. 8					
Sucrase (invertase)	615–990	95	285	180 12th day	350 16th day

stressing, because changes here, according to Nesterin and other investigators, vary with the degree of radiation injury. They are very persistent, remaining long after the clinical symptoms of radiation sickness have disappeared.

Our colleague A. V. Popov (1957, 1960) presented detailed information on the changes that he observed in intestinal secretion during radiation sickness in seven dogs with Thiry-Babkin fistulas. Popov was interested not only in the dynamics of the quantitative and qualitative changes in intestinal juice after total-body external irradiation, but also in the relationship between the nature of these changes and the functional condition of the higher divisions of the central nervous system. He therefore investigated simultaneously intestinal secretion in response to mechanical irritation of the intestinal mucosa, enzymatic activity of the juice (amylolytic, in Wohlgemuth units; proteolytic, in Sorensen units; and lipolytic, in Bondy-Rozhkova units), and higer nervous activity (by I. P. Pavlov's method). At the same time, he observed changes in the peripheral blood (the leukocyte and erythrocyte counts and the hemoglobin content), erythrocyte sedimentation rate, and some systemic indicators (temperature, pulse, and weight). The animals were irradiated with 250 r.

Popov's data will be set forth later, but we should like to present here, by way of illustration, some findings from the experiments on

Trezor, a dog with a strong, balanced type of nervous system. Before irradiation, the mean magnitude of the positive conditioned reflexes per experiment fluctuated between 10 and 11 drops of saliva, the length of the latent period between 2 and 3 seconds. The magnitude of the unconditioned reflexes upon oral administration of a 0.125% solution of hydrochloric acid was 28 to 30 drops per minute.

Intestinal secretion after 3 hours of mechanical irritation was 28 to 30 ml of juice, the amylolytic activity of which averaged 4 units; the proteolytic activity was equivalent to 3.5 ml of 0.2 N NaOH and the lipolytic activity to 0.3 ml of 0.01 N NaOH.

The leukocyte count in the peripheral blood fluctuated from day to day between 6500 and 7000/mm^3, the erythrocyte count from 4 to 4.5 million, and the erythrocyte sedimentation rate from 6 to 8 mm per hour.

After irradiation, the animal developed a mild form of radiation sickness at the height of which, higher nervous activity was inhibited and the magnitude of the conditioned reflexes per experiment decreased by 18% from the original level; the latent period of the reflexes lengthened somewhat, and differentiation was disinhibited. The leukocyte count the first few days after irradiation and on the 10th day of the sickness dropped to 1000/mm^3. The original level was restored only on the 45th day when it reached 6200/mm^3.

Intestinal secretion rose the first four days, remained low the next few days, then rose again on the ninth day to a high level where it remained almost 1-1/2 months. It exceeded the original level by an average of 30 to 40%. In several experiments the volume of juice was almost double the normal volume (Figure 22).

At the height of the sickness the juice contained blood. Amylolytic activity was high throughout, rising from 4 to 8 to 16 units; proteolytic activity was also high, about 20 to 23% above the original level; lipolytic activity was low, especially when the signs of the sickness were most pronounced, being two to four times below normal (Figure 23).

It is evident in this experiment that impaired intestinal secretion during radiation sickness developed simultaneously with disorders of higher nervous activity, intestinal hypersecretion paralleling hypofunction of the cerebral cortex.

Cyclic secretory disorders in which secretory impairment is dependent on the dose and rate of ionizing radiation, the appearance of "spontaneous" secretion, the dissociation in enzyme formation, and related phenomena occurring after external irradiation are also observed after internal irradiation.

S. R. Perepelkin (1957, 1960) studied changes in intestinal secretion in two dogs (Trezor and Al'ma) with Thiry fistulas after oral administration of 0.4 to 1.235 mc/kg of polonium. The clinical picture of the ensuing sickness was described above in the discussion

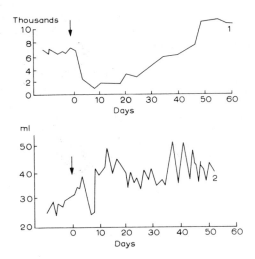

Figure 22. Changes in intestinal secretion and leukocyte count in the dog Trezor during acute radiation sickness. (Reported by A. V. Popov.) 1—Leukocyte count per mm³ of blood. 2—Volume of juice secreted per experiment (ml). Arrow shows day of irradiation (250 r).

of radiation lesions of the stomach. Changes in intestinal secretion were slight.

The dog Trezor, poisoned with 0.4 mc/kg of polonium, developed a hyposecretion which was insignificant the first 15 days but was quite marked thereafter.

The dog Al'ma, poisoned with 1.235 mc/kg of polonium, developed hypersecretion during the first nine days, after which secretion diminished very sharply and remained diminished until the animal died (Table 39).

Functional disorders of the intestinal glands occur in wavelike fashion during radiation sickness caused by administering the products of uranium fission. This was demonstrated by Perepelkin who observed four dogs with chronic Thiry fistulas. The sickness was induced by injecting 1 or 5 mc/kg of the radioactive substance. The sickness was acute in Krasivyĭ and Dozor, the former dying on the 20th day, the latter on the 26th day. Shustryĭ and Lokhmatyĭ developed chronic radiation sickness; observations on changes in intestinal secretion in these animals lasted from 511 to 563 days.

Clinically, acute radiation sickness was characterized by temporary leukocytosis followed by pronounced leukopenia, decreased food excitability, uncontrollable vomiting, hemorrhages in the visible mucosa, general sluggishness, and diarrhea.

In Krasivyǐ, who received a large dose (5 mc/kg), impaired intestinal secretion was characterized by a sharp decrease in the volume of juice; in Dozor, who received a small dose (1 mc/kg), there was a sharp increase in the volume of juice which subsequently gave way to an equally sharp decrease (Table 40).

Chronic radiation sickness had the same symptoms, but in less pronounced form. Changes in intestinal secretion set in as early as the first day after administration of the radioactive substance

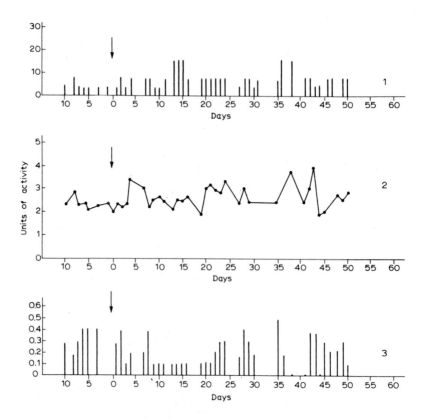

Figure 23. Changes in the intestinal juice enzymatic activity in the dog Trezor during acute radiation sickness. (Reported by A. V. Popov.)

1—Amylolytic,   2—Proteolytic,   3—Lipolytic activity of intestinal juice. Arrow indicates day of irradiation (250 r).

Table 39

Changes in intestinal secretion in dogs poisoned with polonium.

(Reported by S. R. Perepelkin.)

Name of dog	Volume of juice (ml) secreted from an isolated portion of the small intestine during the 6 hours of the experiment after eating 200 g of meat.											
	Before administering polonium	Days after administering polonium										
		1	2	3	5	7	9	13	18	23	28	49
Trezor	25.3-36.5	44.6	28.2	22.8	29.2	23.9	28.8	34.3	13.5	11.8	20.9	16.8
Al'ma	26.5-20.7	45.2	29.0	31.7	43.6	42.7	40.7	2.5	Dog died on the 14th day			

(1 mc/kg); these changes were characterized in the dog Lokhmatyĭ, for example, by a prolonged decrease in secretory volume and in Shustryĭ by periods of hyposecretion alternating with periods of hypersecretion (Table 41).

We see, therefore, that the problem of radiation injury of the intestinal glands is far from solved. At the present time we have data only on secretory volume changes after the application of certain stimuli and on secretory composition (chiefly in enzymes

Table 40

Changes in intestinal secretion in dogs during radiation sickness caused by oral administration of uranium nuclear fission products.

(Reported by S. R. Perepelkin.)

Name of dog	Volume of juice (ml) secreted from an isolated portion of the small intestine during the 6 hours of the experiment after eating 200 g of meat.										
	Before administration of uranium	Days after administration of uranium									
		1	3	6	8	10	13	15	17	20	21
Krasivyĭ	25.8-23.7	25.0	8.7	12.6	8.0	9.3	16.0	16.9	Dog died on the 20th day		
Dozor	20.0-17.3	15.0	14.6	15.9	13.1	15.8	16.8	20.9	14.0	13.7	23.9

Table 41

Changes in intestinal secretion in dogs during chronic radiation sickness caused by oral administration of the uranium nuclear fission products.

(Reported by S. R. Perepelkin.)

Name of dog	Volume of juice (ml) secreted from an isolated portion of the small intestine during the 6 hours of the experiment after eating 200 g of meat.											
	Before administration of uranium	Days after administration of uranium										
		1	6	15	22	64	161	232	295	514	521	560
Shustryĭ	17.3-15.3	16.2	7.6	18.1	12.8	26.6	11.5	23.2	16.7	24.0	24.9	20.4
Lokhmatyĭ	38.3-39.2	36.6	27.9	35.2	28.5	22.5	32.0	20.6	19.3	25.0	—	—

concentration) following total-body external and internal irradiation and external irradiation of the abdomen with different doses. The material reveals, however, that severe radiation injury of the intestinal secretory cells immediately follows irradiation, regardless of the conditions under which it may be applied. When the sickness is mild, there is increased secretion; when the sickness is severe, there is a marked decrease. Increased secretion is frequently the initial non-specific sign of a secretory disorder in radiation sickness, while decreased secretion is the later sign, coinciding with the development of more characteristic and clinically pronounced signs of radiation sickness. With recovery, secretion returns to the normal level and sometimes exceeds it.

The cyclic character of secretory volume changes is paralleled by variations in the digestive activity of the juice, the enzymatic activity of which may rise, then fall, then rise again. These changes in digestive activity of the juice are not identical for the different enzymes. For example, when the concentration of some enzymes decreases, that of the others increases. This dissociation in enzyme secretion and the consequent fluctuation in the digestive capacity of the intestinal juice with respect to different foods (proteins, fats, and carbohydrates) possibly reflect 1) the extent of radiation injury to the intestinal secretory apparatus and its neurohumoral regulatory mechanism and 2) the loss of certain protective-compensatory mechanisms resulting from impaired digestion in the alimentary canal and from impaired metabolic processes in general.

The development of this reaction during radiation sickness can also be seen when one studies gastric and intestinal juice secretion simultaneously. When secretion is suppressed in the stomach, it increases in the intestine. However, it is not always possible to detect this type of reaction. Massive doses of ionizing radiation are usually followed by profound changes in both secretion and the neurohumoral regulatory mechanism. The most characteristic features are sharply decreased secretion after eating meat, continuous secretion when the animal is hungry, the development of multiple hemorrhages in the intestinal walls which impair the normal blood supply, and degeneration of tissues, especially the innervation of the intestinal wall. All these ultimately result in marked impairment of digestion in the intestine.

Simultaneous analysis of the intestinal glands and higher nervous activity during radiation sickness reveals a definite relationship between the type of intestinal disorders observed and the state of excitation or inhibition in the cerebral cortex and subcortical autonomic centers. This indicates that disorders of intestinal secretion are caused directly by injury to the glands, nerves, and blood vessels of the intestine and by impaired neurohumoral control of intestinal secretion, particularly with respect to higher cortical influences.

INTESTINAL SECRETION DURING RADIATION SICKNESS COMPLICATED BY NERVOUS DISORDERS

The significance of the higher divisions of the central nervous system in disorders of intestinal secretion during radiation sickness was demonstrated in experiments on dogs with induced nervous disorders. These experiments were performed in several variations, the most interesting being: (1) experiments on two groups of dogs, one of which was irradiated with their central nervous systems normal, the other with traumatized nervous systems; (2) experiments on dogs irradiated twice, once with the cerebral cortex normal, then with the cerebral cortex pathologically traumatized. In the latter case, the experimental nervous disorders were induced in one subgroup of animals before the first irradiation and in the other subgroup before the second irradiation, the interval between the first and second irradiations being 2-1/2 to 5 months. The nervous disorders were produced by using a very strong sound stimulus four days, thereby overstraining the excitatory process, and by collision of the excitatory and inhibitory processes through continuous and successive application of positive and inhibitory conditioned stimuli. In dogs with a strong type of nervous system, the nervous disorders were produced by a combination of the above-mentioned methods. "Electric clashing" was used on two dogs. The nervous disorder was induced in four dogs before the second irradiation, in three dogs before the first irradiation.

This approach made it possible to study changes in body responses to repeated irradiation. Moreover, in three dogs collision between excitation and inhibition and overstraining of the former were carried out several times during the course of radiation sickness. The irradiation dose and conditions were the same in different variations of the experiment. The results of A. V. Popov's research on seven dogs (1958, 1960) were as follows.

Before Seryĭ was irradiated, juice secretion after 3 hours of mechanical irritation averaged 19 to 20 ml; amylolytic activity of the juice in most cases was 16 units, the proteolytic activity 3.0 to 3.5 ml of 0.2 N NaOH, and the lipolytic activity zero. After irradiation with the central nervous system normal, secretion beginning with the fifth day increased by 23%. A marked increase was noted one month after irradiation when it rose 75% on certain days. Blood was occasionally found in the juice. Amylolytic activity did not change; proteolytic activity decreased an average of 20%, but on some days as much as 50%; lipolytic activity rose to 0.6 ml of 0.01 N NaOH. The digestive activity of the juice became normal at the same time as secretion, approximately 55 days after irradiation.

The same dose (250 r) was used for the second irradiation after a nervous disorder had been induced, and this produced severe radiation sickness with mucosal hemorrhages and blood in the intestinal juice. The leukocyte count in the peripheral blood dropped to $1200/mm^3$. Secretion remained inhibited for 30 days; it decreased sharply after the 13th day, and in some experiments it was 60% below the volume secreted in the original experiments. On the 31st day it rose considerably, exceeding the original level by 25 to 30%. The disorders disappeared 85 days after irradiation. Beginning with the 15th day and continuing for 55 days, amylolytic activity was low (8 units). Proteolytic activity ranged from 2.3 to 3.2 ml, compared with the normal 3.0 ml, and beginning with the 20th day remained low, sometimes 40 to 50% below the original level. Lipolytic activity was higher for 52 days after irradiation, on some days amounting to 1.3 ml of 0.01 N NaOH. The disorders lasted 85 days.

After recovery, Seryĭ was again irradiated, this time in combination with prolonged traumatization of higher nervous activity. Secretion dropped 48% of the original volume. Blood appeared in the juice as early as the second day after irradiation. Amylolytic activity of the juice decreased fourfold; proteolytic activity doubled at first, then decreased by about 20% of the original volume; lipolytic activity increased at first to 0.4 ml, then dwindled to zero. The dog died on the 17th day after irradiation. The nervous system was traumatized several days before irradiation and on the 2nd, 5th, 9th, 12th, and 16th days after irradiation. Pronounced generalized hemorrhages were observed at autopsy. The small intestine was filled with masses of blood, and the mucosa was flaccid and saturated with blood.

On the day following irradiation of the dog Dobryĭ, which was irradiated with normal brain centers, intestinal secretion rose from 28 to 33 ml, and then for 98 days it remained 39% below the original level, on some days 60% below. The juice contained blood. Amylolytic activity between the 2nd and 74th days was two to four times higher than normal. Proteolytic activity remained high throughout the sickness, 133% above normal, and on some days even higher. Lipolytic activity was also very high, 1.6 times above normal between the 16th and 86th days of the sickness, and in some experiments 4 to 5 times above normal (Figure 24). The disorders lasted 102 days.

Twenty-three days after restoration of the dog's normal functions, a nervous disorder was induced after which the animal was

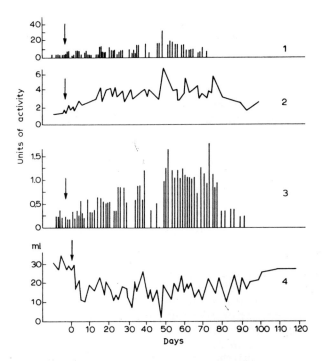

Figure 24. Changes in the secretion and enzymatic activity of the intestinal juice of the dog Dobryĭ during acute radiation sickness. (Reported by A. V. Popov.) 4—Intestinal secretion. Other symbols the same as in Figure 23.

again irradiated with a dose of 250 r. The resulting radiation sickness was very severe, and the animal died 41 days after irradiation.

Intestinal secretion, which decreased after impairment of higher
nervous activity, rose 14% on the third day after irradiation and
remained high until the 31st day of the sickness, on some days
reaching 60% above normal. Secretion diminished sharply several
days before the animal died. From the 13th day after irradiation
until death, blood was constantly present in the juice. Amylolytic
activity sometimes rose and sometimes fell during the first six
days. Proteolytic activity dropped on the third day after irradiation
and remained 36% below normal for 28 days, on some days
dropping to 60% below normal; it rose almost to the original level
however, shortly before death. Lipolytic activity was generally 50%
below normal between the 13th and 36th days (Figure 25).

Thus, impairment of intestinal secretion during radiation sickness following functional weakening of the cerebral cortex was more
profound in Seryĭ and Dobryĭ than when they were irradiated with
the same dose and under the same conditions but with normal higher
nervous activity.

The results were similar in the other dogs under comparable
experimental conditions.

In the experiments on the second group of dogs, the first irradiation followed an experimentally induced nervous disorder, the
second came after the animals had recovered, i.e., when all the
functions under study were normal.

After traumatization of Belyĭ's higher nervous activity, intestinal secretion decreased 25% or more. The subsequent irradiation,
however, caused sharp fluctuations in secretion. In some experiments the volume of juice was 12 to 15% below normal, in other
experiments it was above normal. Starting with the 8th day after
irradiation, however, the glands remained inhibited and the volume
of juice secreted was 40% below normal (Figure 26).

The digestive activity of the juice was also low. Amylolytic
activity decreased from 16 to 4-8 units; lipolytic acitivity decreased
an average of 60% but sometimes as much as 100%; proteolytic
activity fluctuated between high and low values and sometimes
exceeded the original level by 25 to 40%.

Three months after recovery, the animal was irradiated again.
As early as the second day thereafter, secretion decreased sharply
from 18 to 9 ml; however, starting the third day it became normal
and remained so until the 15th day, after which the volume fluctuated
between normal and 50 to 80% above normal until the 47th day (Figure 27).

Amylolytic activity of the juice from Belyĭ remained normal;
proteolytic activity rose 28% only on the 25th day and remained at
this level until the 55th day; lipolytic activity remained high from
the first to the 27th days. Impairment of higher nervous activity,

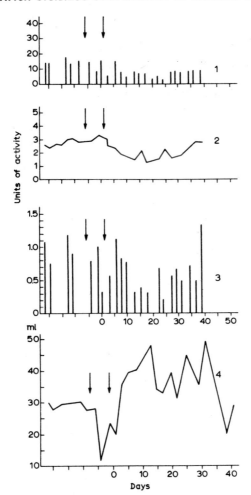

Figure 25. Changes in the secretion and enzymatic activity of intestinal juice in the dog Dobryĭ
during acute radiation sickness complicated by a
traumatized nervous system. (Reported by A. V.
Popov.)
Symbols the same as in Figure 24. Arrow on the
left indicates clashing; on the right, irradiation.

intestinal secretion, blood constituents, and other functions lasted
60 days.
    After recovery, the dog was irradiated a third time with a dose
of 250 r. This time the radiation sickness that followed prolonged

traumatization of the nervous system was severe and ended fatally
on the 18th day.

Changes in higher nervous activity were profound. There was
marked inhibition of the cortical cells; the magnitude of the positive
conditioned reflexes approached zero; hypnotic phases occurred;
and unconditioned salivation decreased.

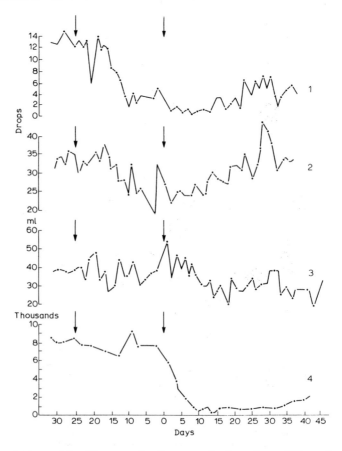

Figure 26. Changes in the magnitudes of conditioned
(1) and unconditioned (2) salivary reflexes, total intestinal juice (3), and leukocyte count per mm^3 of
blood (4) in the dog Belyĭ during acute radiation
sickness caused by irradiation against a background
of nervous system trauma. (Reported by A. V.
Popov.)
Arrow on the left indicates clashing; on the right,
irradiation.

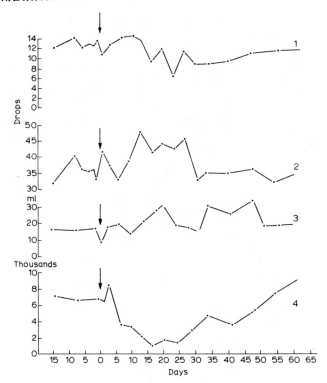

Figure 27. Changes in the magnitudes of the conditioned (1) and unconditioned (2) salivary reflexes, total intestinal juice (3), and leuko-cyte count per mm³ of blood in the dog Belyĭ during acute radiation sickness caused by irradiation with the central nervous system normal. (Reported by A. V. Popov.)
Arrow indicates day of irradiation.

On the second day after irradiation, the leukocyte count dropped from 12,000 to 4500/mm³. The erythrocyte count dropped from 6 to 3.7 million. General weakness developed, body temperature rose to 40.1°C, and there was a loss of weight.

The volume of juice began to increase from the very beginning and by the 13th day was double the original volume. It decreased the day before the animal died (Figure 28).

The amylolytic activity of the juice decreased immediately after irradiation from 16 to 8 units, remaining at this level thereafter; proteolytic activity increased about 25% the first six days and then dropped 50 to 55%, remaining at this level until the animal died; lipolytic activity was markedly suppressed. Blood was constantly present in the juice.

The original level of intestinal secretion in Bars fluctuated between 25 and 27 ml during 3 hours of observation. Amylolytic activity was 8 units, proteolytic activity was 2.9 to 3.0 ml, and lipolytic activity was 0.2 to 0.3 ml. As the nervous disorder became more manifest, the volume of juice dropped to 12 to 15 ml, proteolytic activity rose to 4.0 to 4.5 ml, and lipolytic activity

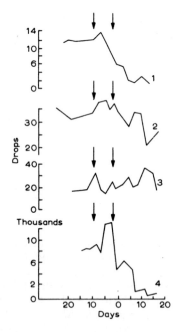

Figure 28. Changes in magnitudes of the conditioned (1) and unconditioned (2) reflexes, total intestinal juice (3), and leukocyte count per mm³ of blood (4) in the dog Belyi during acute radiation sickness caused by irradiation after chronic traumatization of the cerebral cortex. (Reported by A. V. Popov.) Arrow on the left shows beginning of traumatization of the cerebral cortex; on the right, day of irradiation (250 r).

increased to 2.2 to 2.3 ml; amylolytic activity remained unchanged. The next irradiation caused a further decrease in secretion for 36 days, the volume being 44% and sometimes 70 to 75% below normal (Figure 29).

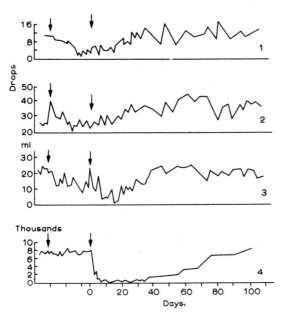

Figure 29. Changes in magnitudes of the conditioned (1) and unconditioned (2) re- flexes, total intestinal juice (3), and leuko- cyte count per mm³ of blood (4) in the dog Bars during acute radiation sickness caused by irradiation against a back- ground of an induced nervous disorder.
(Reported by A. V. Popov.)
Arrow on the left indicates clashing; on the right, irradiation.

Secretion was high from the 37th to 65th days. It returned to the original level only on the 75th day after irradiation. Amylolytic activity rose (16-32 units); proteolytic activity was generally 60% above normal for 35 days, while lipolytic activity was two to three times normal for 95 days (Figure 30).

Impairment of the enzyme-forming function of the intestine and of other functions lasted 107 days.

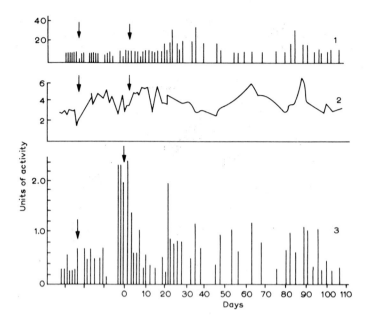

Figure 30. Changes in the enzymatic activity of
intestinal juice in the dog Bars during acute radiation sickness caused by radiation against a background of impaired nervous activity. (Reported
by A. V. Popov.)
Arrow on the left indicates clashing; on the right,
irradiation.

After recovery and normalization of all the functions under study,
the animal was again irradiated. This time the radiation sickness
was comparatively mild. The leukocyte count dropped to $100/mm^3$.
Secretion changed only for 10 days, dropping on some days 40 to
50% and rising a little on other days; the average increase in
glandular capacity during the sickness was 8% above normal
(Figure 31).

The amylolytic activity of the juice did not change, but proteolytic activity dropped from 3.0-3.2 to 2.3-2.0 ml between the 8th and
20th days; lipolytic activity rose from 0.3-0.4 to 0.9-1.2 ml but
only between the 31st and 48th days (Figure 32).

The disorders lasted 62 days.

In the original experiments on the dog Mudryĭ, the volume of
intestinal juice secreted after mechanical irritation was 2.0 to 2.5 ml
for 3 hours. Proteolytic activity fluctuated between 3.2 and 3.6 ml.
The leukocyte count was 8000 to $9000/mm^3$, the erythrocyte count
6 to 6.5 million.

The dog was then subjected to "electric clashing" which caused delayed reactions in the animal, decreased food excitability, and changes in intestinal function. In this condition the dog was exposed to total-body irradiation with a dose of 250 r, resulting in severe radiation sickness. At the height of the sickness, the dog lost about 4 kg in weight, food excitability decreased even more than after "electric clashing", adynamia developed, and a bloody fluid was discharged from the mouth and nose. By the 17th day of the sickness, the leukocyte count had dropped to 1500/mm^3, and by the 24th day to 1000/mm^3; the erythrocyte count had dropped to 890,000/mm^3.

Intestinal secretion increased sharply from the first days after irradiation and remained high throughout the sickness, exceeding the original level by 90 to 100%; in some experiments the volume of juice was five times what it was before irradiation. At the height of the sickness, the proteolytic activity of the juice dropped an average of 78%; in some experiments it amounted to 1.2 ml. The dog responded to special treatment and all the functions under study became normal.

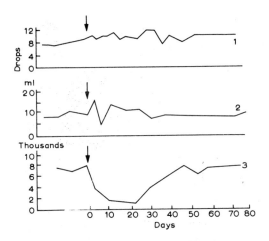

Figure 31. Changes in magnitudes of the conditioned reflexes (1), total intestinal juice (2), and leukocyte count per mm^3 of blood (3) in the dog Bars during acute radiation sickness caused by irradiation with the central nervous system normal. (Reported by A. V. Popov.)
Arrow indicates irradiation.

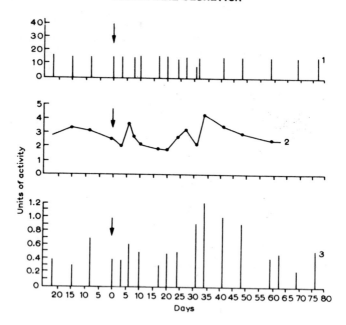

Figure 32. Changes in the enzymatic activity of intestinal juice in the dog Bars during acute irradiation sickness caused by irradiation with the central nervous system normal. (Reported by A. V. Popov.) Arrow indicates irradiation.

Thus, total–body external radiation with a dose of 250 r caused mild radiation sickness in all the experimental animals. The leukocyte count in the peripheral blood dropped from 7000–8000 to 2500–1000/mm³. The disease reached its peak between the 15th and 21st days. During this time, body temperature rose to 39.0 to 39.5°C, adynamia developed, and bleeding appeared in the mucosa of the isolated portion of the intestine. Changes in higher nervous activity set in immediately after irradiation; these were characterized by a decrease in the positive conditioned reflexes lasting one to two days, a lengthening of their latent period, and occasionally by impairment of differentiation. Later on, after some normalization of higher nervous activity, a period of fairly pronounced and persistent changes in the conditioned reflexes set in which coincided with the height of the sickness. These changes included a general decrease in the tone of the cerebral cortex, the appearance of hypnotic phases, disinhibition of differentiation, and a lengthening of the latent period of the reflexes. Changes in the unconditioned salivary reflexes paralleled those in the conditioned reflexes.

At the height of the sickness, the former were generally low. Higher nervous activity became normal between 33 and 48 days after irradiation, or an average of 41 days.

Intestinal secretion became impaired between the 2nd and 9th days after irradiation and remained so throughout the sickness. In two dogs it appeared as persistent hypersecretion, in two others as persistent hyposecretion. It was generally slight in two dogs with a strong type of nervous system. Certain experiments, however, exhibited sharp fluctuations. Changes in the enzymatic activity of intestinal juice during radiation sickness were characterized as follows. Amylolytic activity was high in three dogs and unchanged in three others; lipolytic activity was high in four dogs, low in one, and virtually unchanged in another (Table 42).

Table 42

Changes in intestinal secretion and enzymatic activity in dogs during acute radiation sickness.

(Reported by A. V. Popov.)

Name of dog	Secretion of juice (ml)	Enzymatic activity of the juice		
		Amylolytic	Prote- olytic (as %)	Lipolytic
Dzhul'bars	−45	+45%	−21	+60%
Trezor	+40	+ 2 times	+23	− 2 to 4 times
Belyĭ	+6	Unchanged	+28	+ 3 times
Seryĭ	+23	" "	−20	Unchanged
Bars	+8	" "	−20	+ 3 times
Dobryĭ	−39	+ 2 to 4 times	+133	+160%

Note: + = increase in secretion and digestive activity of the juice in relation to the original level, - = decrease.

Impairment of intestinal secretion and enzyme formation was more profound and longer lasting in the dogs with a weak type of nervous system. For example, in Dobryĭ, Mudryĭ, and Seryĭ, impaired secretion was observed until the 99th day, but only until the 66th day in the dogs with a strong type of nervous system,

Table 43

Changes in intestinal secretion and enzymatic activity during acute
radiation sickness in dogs with experimentally induced nervous
disorders.

(Reported by A. V. Popov.)

Name of dog	Secretion of juice (ml)	Emzymatic activity of the juice		
		Amylolytic	Prote- olytic (as %)	Lipolytic
Dzhul'bars	−70	+50%	−58	+ 4–5 times
Belyĭ	−40	−40%	+25	−60%
Bars	−44	+ 2 times	+60	+ 3 times
Seryĭ	−37.5	−50%	−31.7	+ 6 times
Dobryĭ	+14	− 2 to 4 times	−36	−50%
Mudryĭ	+100	Not determined	−78	Not determined

Note: + = increase in secretion and digestive activity of the
juice in relation to the original level, - = decrease.

Dzhul'bars and Trezor. In two dogs with a strong type of nervous
system, Belyĭ and Bars, postirradiation impairment of secretion
was insignificant.

These figures indicate that the typological characteristics of the
nervous system have some significance in the development of
radiation sickness. They indicate, further, that with a weak type
of higher nervous activity impairment of intestinal function is both
deeper and more lasting than with a strong type.

In all cases intestinal function became impaired after higher
nervous activity was disturbed, and it returned to normal after the
normal activity of the cerebral cortex was restored.

Radiation sickness was more severe when irradiation followed
an experimentally induced nervous disorder; one dog died as a result. Changes in higher nervous activity in these cases were more
prolonged and profound. The magnitude of the positive conditioned
reflexes frequently dropped to zero, the latent period of the reflexes
was considerably lengthened, differentiation became disinhibited,
and in most of the experiments the cortical cells were found to be
in equalizing, paradoxical hypnotic states. These changes were

particularly marked at the height of the sickness. Higher nervous activity became normal 63 days after irradiation, on the average. Leukopenia set in very quickly; the leukocyte count in the peripheral blood dropped to 300/mm³. Impaired intestinal secretion was manifested by hyposecretion in four dogs and by hypersecretion in two dogs (Table 43).

The digestive activity of the juice was changed throughout the sickness.

A comparison of the results of these two series of experiments clearly shows that a nervous disorder considerably lowers the body's resistance to the effects of ionizing radiation. This is shown primarily by a more severe general course of radiation sickness and by deeper impairment of higher nervous activity and intestinal secretion than that observed after irradiation of healthy animals. For example, the duration of all functional disorders under study after irradiation against a background of experimentally induced nervous disorders was 55 to 128% longer than after irradiation of healthy animals; the duration of secretory disorders was 55% longer. This is vividly revealed by the experiments involving prolonged traumatization of higher nervous activity. Radiation sickness was very severe in two of three dogs under observation, although the radiation dose, as in all the other experiments, was 250 r. These dogs died with symptoms of marked impairment of higher nervous activity, hematopoiesis, and intestinal secretion.

The experimental evidence clearly indicates that during radiation sickness caused by irradiation against a background of nervous disorders, intestinal secretory impairment is deeper and more prolonged than during radiation sickness caused by irradiation with the higher divisions of the central nervous system normal.

CHAPTER 6

Intestinal Absorption after External
and Internal Irradiation

Impairment of absorption in the small intestine is one of the more important changes that occur in the digestive system during radiation sickness. It has been demonstrated that impairment may be caused either by total-body or local irradiation (Buchwald, 1931; P. N. Kislev, 1940; Barron, Wolkowitz, Müntz, 1947; Lourau and Lartique, 1951; Goodman, Lewis, and Schuck, 1952; Detrick, Upham, Highby, Debley, and Haley, 1955; S. R. Perepelkin, 1955, 1957, 1960; N. M. Okulov, 1956; V. A. Shaternikov, 1956).

Experiments on rats have shown that radiation sickness caused by irradiation with a dose of 600 r slows up the passage of amino acids from the intestine into tissues, both of amino acids administered orally in the form of hydrolysates and of amino acids formed during the digestion of protein (T. A. Fedorova, 1957). This is indicated, first, by the slow rate of inclusion of radioactive methionine into tissue protein after oral administration of free amino acid or a preparation of the radioactive protein, and, secondly, by the amount of radioactivity in the stomach and intestinal contents under the same conditions (Table 44).

Goodman, Lewis, and Schuck (1952) noted a two-phase change in absorption; first, inhibition of absorption, followed by increased absorption. They are inclined to ascribe the first phase to spastic contraction of the pylorus and impaired evacuation instead of direct injury to the absorption apparatus of the intestine. Some other investigators (Mead, Decker, and Bennet, 1951; Bennet, Chastain, Decker, and Mead, 1951) also believe that impaired gastrointestinal evacuation and peristalsis are significantly involved in these changes in intestinal absorption.

Our colleague E. V. Pashkovskiĭ (1957, 1959, 1960) experimented on eight dogs with chronic Thiry-Babkin fistulas. Each animal had two isolated segments of intestine, one possessing intact nerve connections with the central nervous system, the other segment being denervated. Absorption was studied by introducing a 2% glucose solution and water into the isolated segments for 10 minutes. The concentration difference between the glucose solution introduced and that withdrawn was used to determine the amount of glucose absorbed. The glucose concentration was determined with a polarimeter and monochromator (Schmidt and Ench) using a constant wave length of 14.74 Å; the light source was accurate to 0.01 Å, which corresponded to 3.0 mg per ml of solution. The amount of water absorbed was determined from the difference between the amount entering and the amount leaving the isolated segment after 10 minutes. The secretion of intestinal juice was determined by L. P. Pan'kova's method.

Table 44

Radioactivity of the contents of the gastrointestinal tract (counts/minute per 0.5 ml of emulsion) in non irradiated and irradiated rats (on the 7th day after irradiation) 24 hours after oral administration of radioactive protein.

(Reported by T. D. Fedorova.)

Organs of the gastrointestinal tract	Nonirradiated rat	Irradiated rat
Stomach	30	1130
Small intestine	444	163
Large intestine	200	55
Amount left 24 hours after introducing radioactive protein into the gastrointestinal tract as a % of total radioactivity	15%	30%

Control experiments performed prior to irradiation showed that glucose was absorbed more rapidly than water and that it fluctuated between high and low values from day to day. The fluctuations for both the glucose and the water, however, were in the same direction and were limited to 14 to 18% of the glucose and to 15 to 30% of the water. Similar correlations were noted in the denervated segment of intestine, but with a variation range of 39 to 74% for glucose and 25 to 75% for water.

Radiation sickness was induced by total-body irradiation with 250 r, which produced all the signs of acute sickness. At the height of the sickness, the leukocyte count in the peripheral blood dropped to 1100-2000/mm^3. In several animals body temperature rose to 40°. Adynamia, lowered food excitability, and changes in higher nervous activity were also observed.

Changes in intestinal absorption were periodic and showed an increased range of fluctuations in absorption on certain days. The results of the experiments on the dog Smena will serve as an example.

Before irradiation, absorption in the innervated segment ranged from 57 to 75% of the glucose introduced, the range of fluctuations reaching 18% on certain days. After irradiation, the range of fluctuations increased 2-1/2 times, while the actual absorption of glucose ranged from 45 to 90%. A definite periodicity in absorption changes was observed during the course of the sickness. For example, between the 1st and 9th days after irradiation, the rate of absorption decreased to 45-68%, while the range of fluctuations rose to 23%. Between the 10th and 14th days the fluctuation range increased still further to 90-95%, where it remained until the 75th day when the original range of fluctuation returned.

A comparison of the mean values of absorption for six experimental days during different phases of the sickness (absorption before irradiation in the innervated and denervated segments being taken as 100%) reveals the following. During the latent period of the sickness, an average of 80% was absorbed in the innervated segment and 116% in the denervated segment; at the height of the sickness, 116% was absorbed in the innervated segment and 109% in the denervated segment. During the recovery period 108% was absorbed in the innervated segment, 128% in the denervated segment; after full recovery, absorption in the innervated segment was stabilized at 86%, in the denervated segment at 109% (Figure 33). In addition, after irradiation, fluctuations in absorption in the intact portion of the intestine between individual days of experimentation were less marked, especially at the height of the sickness.

In the other dogs, absorption in the innervated segment changed the same way as in Smena. It decreased during the latent period of the sickness, rose at the climax, and fluctuated during the recovery period.

Absorption in the denervated segment differed from dog to dog. In some, it decreased during the latent period; in others, it rose. At the climax it was generally high. Also worth noting is the fact that changes in glucose absorption in the denervated segment did not coincide with changes in water absorption. Indeed, at times the two processes were directly opposite, e.g., as water absorption increased, glucose absorption decreased. This dissociation was observed in individual dogs up to the 20th to 23rd days of the sickness. Absorption in the denervated segment ultimately set in later than in the innervated segment. In one dog, for example, normalization of the process occurred 16 days later, in another animal 18 days later, and in a third animal 37 days later.

The foregoing indicates that radiation sickness impairs the absorption of food in the small intestine. Such impairment, varying

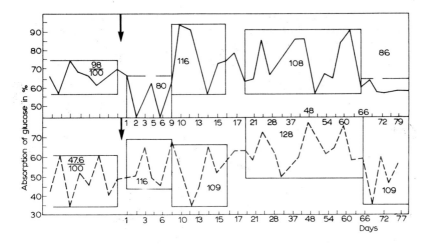

Figure 33. Changes in glucose absorption in innervated and denervated segments of the small intestine of the dog Smena during acute radiation sickness. (Reported by E. V. Pashkovskiĭ.) Curves show absorption of glucose in the innervated (upper) and denervated (lower) segments; figures indicate mean rate of absorption for a fixed number of days; rectangles (from right to left) are period before irradiation, latent period of the sickness, period of clinically pronounced signs of the sickness, period of recovery, period of complete normalcy; arrow shows day of irradiation.

as it does with the severity of the sickness and with individual characteristics, is quite cyclical or wavelike in its development. Early in the sickness, the absorptive capacity is inhibited; at the height of the sickness, it greatly exceeds the normal capacity.

The fact that absorption changes are of shorter duration in the innervated than in the denervated segment of the intestine points up the defensive or adaptational role of the central innervation mechanisms in absorption disturbances during radiation sickness. We frequently called attention to this phenomenon when discussing radiation injury of the stomach, liver, salivary glands, and pancreas.

In this connection, data on the correlation of functional changes in the brain centers and intestinal absorption during radiation sickness are of interest. Z. V. Pashkovskiĭ focussed on this problem during his observations on five dogs with an established system of conditioned food reflexes. The relationship between the nature and degree of impaired intestinal absorption and the nature and degree of impaired higher nervous activity was determined. In the dog Pirat, for example, irradiation was followed by increased absorption and a progressive decrease in the functional capacity of the cortical cells with a predominance of cortical inhibition, which was particularly pronounced at the height of the sickness (Figure 34).

The typological characteristics of higher nervous activity are also of some significance. Pashkovskiĭ discovered a definite connection between absorption and type of nervous system when the animal was normal (Table 45).

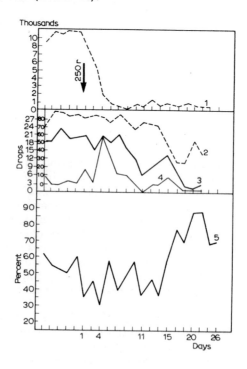

Figure 34. Changes in higher nervous activity and absorption in the small intestine of the dog Pirat during acute radiation sickness. (Reported by E. V. Pashkovskiĭ.) 1—Leukocyte count per mm³ of blood. 2—Magnitude of unconditioned reflexes. 3—Magnitude of conditioned positive reflexes. 4—Magnitude of the differentiation reflex. 5—Amount of a 2% glucose solution absorbed in the intestine. Arrow shows day of irradiation with 250 r.

Table 45

Relationship between changes in intestinal absorption and
type of higher nervous activity in normal dogs.

(Reported by E. V. Pashkovskiĭ.)

Type of nervous system	Name of dog	Mean magnitude of conditioned reflex (drops of saliva)	Mean magnitude of unconditioned reflex (drops of saliva)	Range of fluctuations in amount absorbed (%)	Mean rate of absorption (%)	Limits of glucose absorption (%)
Weak	Dzhul'bars . . .	5.7	47	12	33.9	25-37
	Volchok	8.5	50	20	39.0	32-52
Strong	Dzhon	15.1	73	14	62.6	54-68
	Pirat	12.6	71	18	58.7	50-68
	Lipa	11.8	78.5	11	42.6	38-49

The author concluded from these findings that the rate of
absorption is related to some extent to the intensity of excitation,
while changes in intestinal absorption depend on the correlation of
excitation and inhibition in the cerebral cortex.

It is, of course, not always a simple matter to discover this
relationship. Yet the available observations suggest the existence
of a definite connection between changes in intestinal absorption and
the dynamics and interaction of the nervous processes in the brain.

INTESTINAL ABSORPTION DURING RADIATION SICKNESS
COMPLICATED BY NERVOUS DISORDERS

The relationship between changes in intestinal absorption and
the functional condition of the higher brain centers mentioned above
was clearly brought out in experiments on dogs irradiated after an
experimental nervous disorder had been induced.

Using I. P. Pavlov's method, E. V. Pashkovskiĭ (1959, 1960)
induced a nervous disorder in five dogs which had mild radiation
sickness, from which they completely recovered, judging by the
usual signs—blood, temperature, body weight, pulse, respiration,

higher nervous activity, intestinal absorption, food excitability, and behavior. He then irradiated them again with the same dose used the first time. Thus, the changes observed after the first irradiation served as a control for this series of experiments. As before, the main criteria of changes in absorption were: (a) increases in the range of fluctuations in the rate of absorption, (b) the duration and degree of subsequent inhibition of absorption, (c) the time that perceptible changes in absorption began, and (d) changes in the nature, depth, and duration of disorders of higher nervous activity.

It was proved experimentally that radiation sickness in dogs with nervous disorders is more severe than in normal dogs. Four of the five animals exposed died. Absorption changes were greater and more persistent after irradiation (Figure 35), and the range of fluctuations in the rate of absorption was much wider. For example, after the initial irradiation it was 2.9 times above normal in Dzhon, 1.9 times in Dzhul'bars, 2.5 times in Smena, and 4.2 times in Tuzik; after the second irradiation following the induced nervous disorder, however, it was 3.2, 2.8, 2.6, and 6.2 greater in the same dogs, respectively. At the same time, the period of inhibited absorption was shortened: it ranged from 9 to 12 days after the first irradiation but from 3 to 7 days after the second irradiation. Impaired absorption paralleled the course of the sickness and appeared much sooner than after the first irradiation. Then, too, the nature of absorption itself became distorted. For example, a sharp decrease in the rate of absorption was observed in Tuzik and Smena. Volchok, who died on the 12th day of radiation sickness, showed signs of extremely severe disorders: a marked increase in the range of fluctuations in absorption rate (4.3 times) and an absorption curve not at all like that of the other animals. The curve had a pronounced wavelike character, and the rate of absorption increased abruptly.

After sharp and prolonged functional weakening of the cerebral cortex, intestinal absorption fluctuated substantially on some days, but it was generally high (Figure 36).

The following conclusions may be drawn from the foregoing data: (a) there is an increase in the range of fluctuations in absorption rate if the animal is irradiated with a nervous disorder; (b) the period of inhibited absorption is shortened; (c) pronounced impairment of absorption develops early. Changes in higher nervous activity are also more substantial, as revealed by the sharp fluctuations in the mean magnitudes of the positive conditioned reflexes on certain days of the sickness, as well as by more severe and enduring qualitative changes in conditioned activity—for example, the appearance of hypnotic phases, successive inhibition, quick exhaustibility of the cortical cells, etc. It has been demonstrated that the most profound disturbances in higher nervous activity coincided with the most significant changes in intestinal absorption. As was observed after irradiation with the central nervous system normal, these

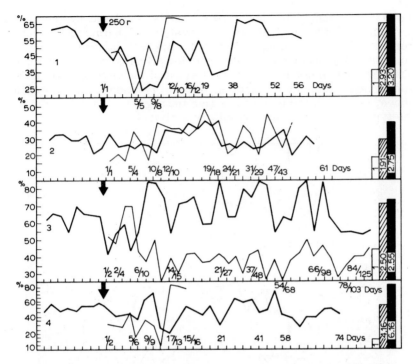

Figure 35. Glucose absorption by the innervated segment of the small intestine in the dogs Dzhon (1), Dzhul'bars (2), Smena (3), and Tuzik (4) during radiation sickness caused by total-body irradiation with a dose of 250 r followed by irradiation with the same dose after functional weakening of the cerebral cortex. (Reported by E. V. Pashkovskiĭ.) Curves reflect glucose absorption after single exposure (thick) and exposure after the induced nervous disorder (thin). Figures: numerator indicates days after single exposure; denominator indicates days after exposure following induced nervous disorder. Arrows indicate day of irradiation. Columns show range of fluctuations in absorption rate before irradiation (white), after irradiation (cross hatched), and after irradiation following induced nervous disorder (black); the figures included therein indicate the rate of increase in range of fluctuations.

latter experiments also indicate a definite relationship between conditioned activity and intestinal absorption, as shown by the fact that a decrease or increase in conditioned activity is paralleled by an increase or decrease in intestinal absorption, respectively. If

we assume that intestinal absorption is regulated by the higher
divisions of the central nervous system, including the cerebral
cortex (see the findings of K. M. Bykov's laboratory), we can
correlate the changes observed in intestinal absorption with the
changes that arise in the interrelations of the cerebral cortex and
subcortical autonomic centers. These relations, as pointed out
above, vary with the type of positive and negative induction and with
the type of excitatory and inhibitory activity.

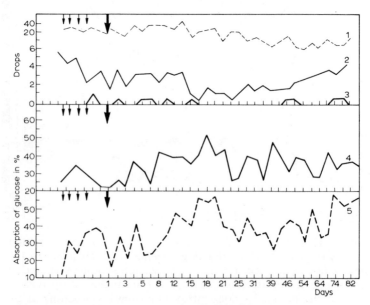

Figure 36. Changes in higher nervous activity and absorption in the innervated and denervated segments of the
small intestine in the dog Dzhul'bars during acute radiation sickness caused by irradiation after an experimental
nervous disorder was induced. (Reported by E. V.
Pashkovskiĭ.)
1—Magnitude of unconditioned reflexes. 2—Magnitude
of conditioned reflexes. 3—Magnitude of differentiation reflex. 4—Amount of a 2% glucose solution absorbed in the innervated segment. The four arrows on
the left show days of interference; arrow on the right
(thick) shows day of irradiation.

Figure 37 shows the changes in conditioned activity and
intestinal glucose absorption in dogs irradiated twice, once with
the cerebral cortex normal and a second time after it had been
pathologically traumatized. By comparing the absorption changes

occurring from the time of irradiation until a few days thereafter, it is easy, in some cases, to see a relationship between the rate of intestinal absorption and conditioned activity of the cerebral cortex.

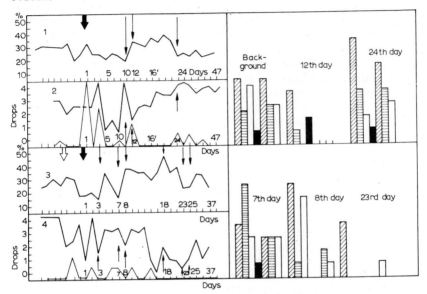

Figure 37. Changes in higher nervous activity and glucose absorption in the small intestine in the dog Zhul'bars irradiated both with the cerebral cortex normal and pathologically traumatized. (Reported by E. V. Pashkovskiĭ.)
On the left: curves of changes in conditioned activity (2 and 4) and glucose absorption in the intestine (1 and 3). On the right: magnitudes of conditioned reflexes—black columns show differential conditioned reflexes; others—positive conditioned reflexes to bell, light, metronome 120, bell, light, metronome 120, on certain experimental days, shown by numbers, before and after irradiation (250 r). Curves 1 and 2—irradiation with cerebral cortex normal, 3 and 4—in pathological condition. Black arrows indicate irradiation, white arrow indicates collision. The long arrows point to the relationship between rate of absorption and the functional condition of the higher divisions of the central nervous system with respect to induction and the spread of excitation and inhibition.

For example, in experiments involving irradiation with the nervous system normal there was a decrease in conditioned activity between the 5th and 10th days that was paralleled by decreased intestinal absorption, due perhaps to the action of cerebrocortical inhibition on the subcortical centers. There was a marked change in the cortical cells between the 10th and 12th days. Their activity increased, as did the magnitude of the conditioned reflexes and the rate of intestinal absorption. This turning point in the functional condition of the cerebral cortex tending toward heightened tone and activity of the cortical cells became more and more apparent on succeeding days as the rate of intestinal absorption rose proportionally. At this time absorption was presumably affected by the influence of cerebrocortical excitation on the subcortical centers. A new pattern developed on the 24th day after irradiation: after the appearance of heightened cerebrocortical tone and normal conditioned activity, absorption decreased and stabilized at an abnormally low rate. This may have been the result of negative induction of the subcortical centers by the cerebral cortex.

A similar relationship obtained in the experiments involving irradiation with the brain in a pathological condition. This is very clearly shown in Figure 37 on the days designated with arrows.

For example, after functional weakening of the cerebral cortex, when the adaptational and defensive mechanisms of the nervous system are low, radiation sickness is more severe and impairment of intestinal absorption is more profound and prolonged.

In discussing the mechanism by which functional disorders of any organ arise, one must keep in mind both the general neurohumoral regulatory mechanisms and the special mechanisms responsible for the specific activity of that organ. This applies in particular to absorption in the small intestine where such processes as diffusion and osmosis play important parts (Verzar, 1936).

Published reports (Ashwelle and Hickman, 1952; Van Bekkum and others, 1954) indicate that oxidative phosphorylation, which is involved in the absorption of certain substances, undergoes changes as a result of radiation injury. In experiments on seven dogs with Thiry fistulas, V. A. Shaternikov (1957) studied the absorption of glycocoll solutions, first with the animals in normal condition, then after they had been irradiated with a dose of 400 r. He determined the rate of absorption as follows. He introduced 25 ml of certain concentrations of glycocoll (0.5 M or 0.33 M) into an isolated segment of the intestine, withdrew the contents 30 minutes later, and determined the amino acid nitrogen by the Van Slyke method. The difference between the amount of glycocoll introduced and that found in the fluid withdrawn indicated the rate of absorption. This was determined twice a day at hourly intervals.

The rate of glycocoll absorption before irradiation usually fluctuated within ± 10% and was somewhat lower in the second 30-minute experiment than in the first. Adding 100 mg of Na_2HPO_4 and 50 mg of adenosinetriphosphate (ATP), the substances involved in oxidative phosphorylation, to the glycocoll solution, which was introduced into the intestine in the second experiment, accelerated the absorption of glycocoll. The animals were irradiated with an X-ray machine containing three tubes but no shield under the following conditions: voltage 180 kv, current 20 ma, focal distance 90 cm, filter 0.5 mm copper and 1.0 mm aluminum, dose rate 16.9 r/min. Four of the seven dogs died on the 14th and 18th days after irradiation.

Experiments performed on the irradiated animals showed that the rate of absorption fluctuates, sometimes increasing, sometimes decreasing. It was abnormally low in the second experiment; the addition of inorganic phosphorus and ATP to the glycocoll solution accelerated the rate, but not to the preirradiation level (Table 46).

Table 46

Rate of absorption of a glycocoll solution in a segment of dog intestine, isolated by Thiry's method, before and after irradiation with a dose of 400 r.

(Reported by V. A. Shaternikov.)

Conditions of the experiment	Amount of glycocoll absorbed		
	in the first experiment	in the second experiment	
		without Na_2HPO_4	with Na_2HPO_4
Before irradiation ...	100	85	152
After irradiation:			
1st day	120	—	94
2nd "	113	88	—
3rd "	64	—	130
4th "	62	48	—
5th "	90	—	138
7th "	72	54	—
8th "	103	—	113
10th "	108	74	—
11th "	118	—	121
13th "	154	83	—
14th "	49	—	94

The results imply that there was impaired phosphorylation in the intestinal wall after radiation injury. This is borne out by other experiments by Shaternikov involving the addition of α-dinitrophenol to glycocoll. Under normal conditions this compound inhibits the absorption of a hypertonic solution of glycocoll by an average of 79% and inhibits the concomitant discharge of acid-soluble phosphorus from the intestinal wall into the intestinal cavity by an average of 41%. Consequently, by determining the content of acid-soluble phosphorus, using the Fiske and Subbarow method, and by testing the effect of α-dinitrophenol (an inhibitor of oxidative phosphorylation) on the absorption of glycocoll and the discharge of acid-soluble phosphorus simultaneously, the author was able to determine the rate of oxidative phosphorylation in the intestinal wall both under normal conditions and after irradiation. Shaternikov discovered in these experiments that the discharge of acid-soluble phosphorus into the intestinal lumen decreases considerably after irradiation, this decrease varying directly with the decreased rate of glycocoll absorption (Table 47).

Table 47

Rate of glycocoll absorption and the discharge of acid-soluble phosphorus into the intestinal lumen of a dog before and after X-irradiation.

(Reported by V. A. Shaternikov.)

Conditions of the experiment	Amount of glycocoll absorbed (% of the norm)			Amount of acid-soluble phosphorus discharged (μg)		
	in the first experiment	in the second experiment		in the first experiment	in the second experiment	
		without α-dinitrophenol	with α-dinitrophenol		without α-dinitrophenol	with α-dinitrophenol
Before irradiation	100	82	21	862	742	511
After irradiation:						
1st day	61	2	22	1376	—	456
2nd "	79	74	—	480	422	—
3rd "	94	—	19	824	—	352
4th "	69	50	—	720	396	—
5th "	116	—	18	584	—	236
7th "	120	118	—	728	690	—
9th "	108	—	20	680	—	432
11th "	118	67	—	528	440	—
14th "	160	—	19	680	—	316
16th "	158	123	—	592	440	—
19th "	99	—	2	192	—	Traces
23rd "	57	30	—	260	190	—
25th "	38	—	8	376	—	Traces
33rd "	77	57	—	616	144	—
37th "	82	—	20	560	—	168
39th "	96	75	—	736	520	—
44th "	93	—	19	976	—	328
46th "	109	98	—	992	328	—
52nd "	133	—	18	952	—	252
58th "	128	109	—	824	1120	—
60th "	118	—	18	432	—	520
65th "	121	84	—	520	592	—

Once again, then, ionizing radiation has been demonstrated to exert an inhibiting influence on oxidative phosphorylation in the intestinal wall.

To summarize, ionizing radiation impairs the absorption of food in the small intestine. During the first few days after the radiation trauma, absorption usually decreases, while at the height of the sickness, it increases. The most typical feature of the process is its wavelike course, increasing and decreasing according to the degree of radiation injury to local biochemical and physicochemical processes in the intestinal villi (notably oxidative phosphorylation) and to the neurohumoral mechanisms regulating absorption. Impaired regulation by the higher divisions of the central nervous system is another major factor. The most significant and prolonged changes in intestinal absorption occur after functional weakening of the cerebral cortex and the resulting impairment of the normal cortical and subcortical relations.

Several other factors are undoubtedly also involved in radiation injury to intestinal absorption: namely, impairment of the autonomic and endocrine systems, altered permeability of the blood vessels, and an imbalance of ionic and oncotic pressures, although the role of pressure imbalance has not yet been determined. Also of some significance are intestinal motility disturbances and structural changes in the intestinal mucosa, tunica muscularis, villi, blood and lymph vessels, and intramural nerve plexi.

Chapter 7

Gastrointestinal Excretion

Although gastrointestinal excretion has no direct connection with the activity of the alimentary canal and under normal conditions plays a minor role, nevertheless it becomes quite significant in certain diseases of the excretory organs and in diseases accompanied by destruction or degeneration of cells and tissues. In these diseases the gastric and intestinal mucosa vigorously discharges waste substances, thereby easing the load on the excretory organs. The value of this function during radiation sickness can be judged from the data of our colleague I. G. Chursin, who discovered that at the height of radiation sickness in dogs, the filtration and reabsorption capacity of the kidneys becomes impaired, sometimes to the point where the elimination of urine from the kidneys ceases completely.

After investigating changes in intestinal secretion in irradiated dogs, Yu. N. Uspenskii (1958) advanced the hypothesis that the digestive organs may assume the function of excretion during radiation sickness. However, this is not the only way in which the excretory function of the gastrointestinal tract is important during radiation sickness. Relying on the extensive experimental material of his co-workers, I. P. Razenkov (1948) elucidated a new aspect of digestive activity—the involvement of the gastric glands in intermediate metabolism. In his view, prolonged fasting and certain pathological conditions increase the content of high-molecular-weight protein substances in the blood, which cannot be used in that form by the cells. Hence, they are discharged into the gastrointestinal tract with the secretion of the gastric glands; here, under the influence of enzymes, they are broken down into amino acids which are then absorbed into the blood and are used by the cells and tissues as a structural and energy material.

This aspect of digestive activity, which is closely connected with the body's general metabolic processes and with gastrointestinal excretion and absorption, is particularly important in radiation injury, which causes marked cellular damage and impairs nucleic acid metabolism as well as protein metabolism in general.

That is why an investigation of gastrointestinal excretion following radiation injury is of great theoretical as well as practical value. Unfortunately, researchers are paying too little attention to this activity of the digestive apparatus. We have just one serious study in this field, that by our co-worker S. V. Voĭnov, who investigated changes in the content of urea, creatine, lactic acid, and sugar in the gastric and intestinal juices of dogs with Pavlov pouches and Thiry fistulas before and after irradiation with a dose of 250 r.

Experiments were performed on three dogs. The juices were collected for 3 hours after the ingestion of food. The creatine content of the juice was determined by Folin's method, urea content by Van Slyke's method, sugar content by Hagedorn's method, and lactic acid content by Bessey's method. Radiation sickness was diagnosed on the basis of blood analysis and changes in temperature and body weight.

Results of the experiments showed that the creatine and urea content of the gastric and intestinal juices increased in all the dogs after irradiation. Changes in the gastric sugar and lactic acid content were less pronounced while changes in the sugar content of the intestinal juice were virtually nonexistent. The maximum amounts of urea, creatine, and reducing substances in the gastric juice and of urea, creatine, and lactic acid in the intestinal juice were noted 10 to 17 days after irradiation, precisely the days when the sickness was at its height (Table 48).

Table 48

Changes in gastrointestinal secretion of dogs during radiation sickness.

(Reported by S. V. Voĭnov.)

Juice	Urea (mg%)		Difference (%)	Creatine (mg%)		Difference (%)	Sugar (mg%)		Difference (%)	Lactic acid (mg%)		Difference (%)
	Before irradiation	After irradiation		Before irradiation	After irradiation		Before irradiation	After irradiation		Before irradiation	After irradiation	
Gastric	15.47	30.75	98	0.66	0.93	40.8	13.2	15.6	18	3.81	3.92	2.8
Intestinal	37.09	46.02	24.8	0.77	0.92	20	9.2	9.1	0.2	3.85	4.24	7.8

Thus, radiation sickness greatly increases gastrointestinal excretion, chiefly by increasing the excretion of protein metabolic products.

CHAPTER 8

Gastrointestinal Motility and Evacuation

Such signs as vomiting and diarrhea, which usually arise after radiation injury, testify to impaired gastrointestinal motility. There are fairly numerous reports now available on clinical and experimental investigations of gastrointestinal evacuation and motility following ionizing radiation applied in various ways.

CLINICAL OBSERVATIONS

According to many authors (Brügel, 1916; Bensaude, Solomon, and Oury, 1925; Ya. S. Korneeva, 1928; A. A. Bagdasarov and S. L. Kopel'man, 1929; M. A. Turel', 1934; A. M. Yugenburg, E. N. Mozharova, and R. G. Gurevich, 1935; A. M. Yugenburg, 1935; M. I. Nemenov, 1938; 1940; A. Ya. Popov, 1946; others), roentgenotherapy in stomach diseases tends to normalize gastric motility and evacuation. R. A. Golonzko (1935, M. V. Ol'khovskaya, E. Ya. Bril', and V. V. Zorina (1934), and R. Ya. Gasul' (1935) observed a relaxation of the pyloric musculature and disappearance of spasm in irradiated patients. However, I. S. Amosov and L. F. Sinenko (1958), on the basis of extensive clinical materials, showed that total-body and local radiation injury cause pyloric spasm, paresis of the large intestine, and retention of the gastrointestinal contents. Impaired motility is marked by a certain periodicity that is especially pronounced the first two or three days after irradiation (Z. A. Zedgenidze, 1956, 1957).

Ya. S. Korneeva (1928) observed accelerated evacuation of the stomach in patients following irradiation of the abdominal cavity.

Some recent data have been provided by G. A. Gusterin, N. M. Okulov, S. V. Strutsovskaya, and P. A. Buzini (1957) who treated 74 women suffering from cancer of the cervic uteri with ionizing radiation; intracavitary introduction of radiocobalt and external irradiation from a GUT-400 apparatus were used. Depending on the severity of the disease and the course of treatment, the patients received 15,000 to 22,000 r in the lesser pelvic region. Most of them did not develop radiation sickness; only a drop in the leukocyte count to 40% was noted. During the course of treatment, the others suffered from general weakness, loss of appetite, nausea, occasionally diarrhea, and marked leukopenia. At the same time, most of the patients had varying degrees of impaired gastric and intestinal motility, chiefly of the duodenum and jejunum, marked by dystonia and dyskinesia, frequently hypomotile in character. Evacuation of the stomach contents was arrested. All these disorders were temporary, disappearing after the treatments were concluded.

According to V. N. Zvorykin (1957, 1960), who used graphic recording, gastric motility in persons who have had prolonged contact with ionizing radiation is commonly of the asthenic type (42%) with strong and frequent peristaltic waves and heightened tone following mechanical irritation of the gastric wall; motility subsequently becomes inhibited (Figure 38). Second in frequency is inhibited motility (24%) which is marked by the absence of peristaltic waves throughout the period of mechanical irritation. Eleven per cent of the cases show the excited type of motility with high, deep, and frequent peristaltic waves throughout the investigation (2-1/2 hours). The inert type of motility, found in the same number of cases, is characterized by inhibited gastric motility at the beginning of the investigation and gradual excitation at the end.

The aforementioned pathological types of gastric motility occur in 88% of the cases. The other 12% have normal or near normal motility.

Evacuation was also impaired in the persons examined. It was rapid in 33% of the cases, slow in 43%, and normal in 24%.

Clinical observations, therefore, clearly reveal that persons exposed to total-body or local ionizing radiation exhibit changes in motility and evacuation of the gastrointestinal tract.

EXPERIMENTAL OBSERVATIONS

More detailed investigations of radiation injury to gastrointestinal evacuation and motility have been made in experiments on animals utilizing roentgenographic, kymographic, and colorimetric techniques.

. Using roentgenoscopy, K. A. Grineva (1957) found that total-body irradiation of dogs and guinea pigs with small doses of ionizing radiation (on the order of 12.5 to 25 and 50 r) generally alters motor activity of the gastrointestinal tract, frequently by accelerating gastric evacuation and pushing contrast media through the intestine.

A few days after total-body irradiation of rabbits with a dose of 900 r, G. A. Gusterin, N. M. Okulov, S. V. Strutsovskaya, and

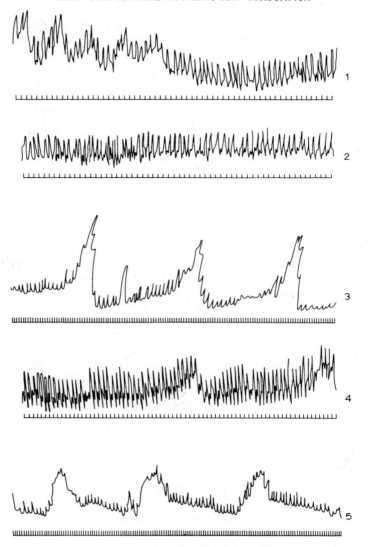

Figure 38. Types of gastric motility in man following prolonged contact with ionizing radiation. (Reported by V. N. Zvorykin.) Gastrograms: asthenic (1), inhibited (2), excited (3), inert (4), and normal (5) types of motility. Below the curves, time in 5-sec intervals.

P. A. Buzini (1957) noted arrested evacuation of the stomach and dystonia and dyskinesia of the small intestine. The contents of the gastrointestinal tract moved more quickly between the fourth and sixth days, which coincided with the initial signs of radiation sickness. Motility and evacuation became normal between the 25th and 30th days after irradiation. Similar but less pronounced phenomena were noted after local irradiation of the abdomen with the same dose. Doses ranging from 100 to 150 r had no marked effect either after local or after total-body irradiation.

N. A. Zhoga (1955) observed the development of radiation sickness causing impairment of the central nervous system and gastrointestinal motility in dogs given radioactive phosphorus at a dose rate of 37.5, 50, and 397 mc lasting 2 to 14 hours. With a fluoroscope he observed substantial changes in gastric and intestinal tone, spasm of the pyloric sphincter, and dyskinesia of the small and large intestines. After a dose of 50 mc, he noted at first temporary acceleration which gave way on the ninth day to marked inhibition of gastrointestinal motility. Intravenous injection of radioactive phosphorus produced changes in intestinal motility sooner than did applications of the beta emitter.

L. R. Protas and A. A. Danilin (1957) observed 70 guinea pigs and 9 rabbits exposed to internal and external irradiation. Internal irradiation was produced by a single subcutaneous injection of radioactive isotopes: phosphorus (P^{32}) in a dose of $7\mu c/g$, strontium (Sr^{89}) in a dose of $7\ \mu c/g$, Sr^{90} in a dose of $21\ \mu c/g$, cesium (Cs^{137}) in doses of 2 to $7\ \mu c/g$, and cobalt (Co^{60}) in doses of 0.1 to $2.5\mu c/g$. Total-body external irradiation was from an RUM-3 apparatus in doses of 350 to 2000 r at the rate of 27.5 r/min and in doses of 400 to 800 r.

All the irradiated animals developed acute or, less commonly, subacute radiation sickness, regardless of the type of ionizing radiation or method used. Seventy-six out of 79 animals died between 2 to 15 days later (66), 3 to 4 weeks later (5), and 1 to 1-1/2 months later (5). Although all but three guinea pigs died, the authors managed to note some peculiarities in the radiation impairment of gastrointestinal motility. They found some differences in the condition of the stomach and intestine at various stages of the sickness which could not be related either to the type of ionizing radiation or to the method of irradiation used. These differences seemed to be related to the dose, for as it was increased, the sickness became aggravated and signs of gastrointestinal involvement became more pronounced. Irradiation was followed in 75% of the cases (59 animals) by heightened gastrointestinal tone and by accelerated movement toward the anus (Table 49).

In 31 of the animals, hypertonia was associated with accelerated peristalsis, pyloric spasm, and slowing of evacuation. In 18, gastric hypertonia proceeded without a change in peristalsis and with normal evacuation. In 10, the rate of evacuation, gastric tone, and peristalsis were unchanged.

Table 49

Characteristics of the digestive tract during acute and subacute
experimental radiation sickness.

(Reported by L. R. Protas and A. A. Danilin.)

Type of emitter	Number of animals				
	Acceleration of peristalsis	Slowing of peristalsis	Dystonia	Unchanged	Total
Co^{60} in gamma apparatus Teleradiation apparatus No. 2					
GUT-400	5	2	1	—	8
X-rays. RUM-3	23	3	1	2	29
Co^{60} subcutaneously	8	1	2	—	11
Cs^{137} sub- cutaneously	6	1	—	—	7
P^{32} subcutaneously	13	2	—	1	16
Sr^{89} subcutaneously	1	—	1	—	2
Sr^{90} subcutaneously	3	1	1	1	6
Total No. of animals	59	10	6	4	79
Percentage	75	13	7	5	100

Significant abnormalities of motility and evacuation were observed in the same animals. Of 59 animals in this group, 18 had hypertonia of the jejunum with increased segmentation of the loops of the ileum; in 23, spastically contracted segments alternated with normal segments in the jejunal and ileal loops; in 18, both intestinal tone and peristalsis remained normal. Movement of the contrast medium through the large intestine was accelerated in all 59 animals, 10 of which also showed cecal hypertonia.

Thus, accelerated evacuation of the intestinal contents, which in some animals was double the normal rate, was determined by intestinal motility. Motility was so great that in time it not only compensated for, but even over-compensated, the delay in evacuation caused by pyloric spasm.

The authors also observed a slowing of peristalsis in 13% of the cases. Of the 10 animals in this group, 5 showed a slowing of evacuation of the contrast medium while the other 5 suffered simultaneous impairment of tone and peristalsis in different parts of the gastrointestinal tract. Marked gastrointestinal atonia was observed in two rabbits and one guinea pig of this group, and as a result, evacuation of the stomach contents into the duodenum took more than a day to complete. In 7% of the cases, there was impairment only of the muscular tone in various parts of the digestive tube (stomach, small intestine, or cecum) with no change in the rate of evacuation through the gastrointestinal tract. In only 5% of the cases were there no pronounced changes in gastrointestinal motility and evacuation during radiation sickness. Unfortunately, the authors failed to analyze the reasons for this phenomenon.

The extent of gastrointestinal motor disorders varied with the phase of the sickness. During the first day or two after irradiation and the initial reactive period, they were quite pronounced. They decreased during the latent period, but increased with the onset of clinically pronounced signs of the sickness. Paresis developed and the rate of evacuation slackened just before the animals died.

The return of normal motility and evacuation was traced in 10 animals on which the authors experimented for quite some time. It started at the end of the third week and ended 30 to 60 days after irradiation (Table 50).

Impairment of gastrointestinal motility and evacuation during acute and subacute radiation sickness, then, is characterized, according to roentgenological data, by increased tone and peristalsis,

Table 50

Beginning and end of return of gastrointestinal motility to normal during radiation sickness.

(Reported by L. R. Protas and A. A. Danilin.)

Beginning of normalization		Normalization completely restored	
Time from start of irradiation (days)	No. of animals	Time from start of irradiation (days)	No. of animals
18–21	3	30–45	3
21–30	4	45–60	1
30–45	3	More than 60 days	1
		Could not be traced	5
Total	10	Total	10

accelerated or (less frequently) retarded motor activity, or weakened gastrointestinal tone and peristalsis. Severe radiation injury is followed by paresis of the gastrointestinal musculature.

N. N. Lebedev and M. A. Sobakin (1957, 1960) made a thorough experimental study of motor disorders of the gastrointestinal tract after radiation injury. Acute and subacute radiation sickness was induced by X-irradiation of the animals; the hardness of the irradiation corresponded to a half-thickness layer of Δ Cu—0.5 mm on a twin RUM-3 apparatus. Gastrointestinal movements were recorded by roentgenological and graphic means.

Emphasis was placed on changes in the periodic motility of the stomach. It turned out that the irradiation dose was the key factor. Doses of 250 to 350 r caused changes to appear soon after irradiation, and these became most pronounced by the sixth to tenth days. They were characterized by longer working and resting periods and by an increased number of contractions during the period of activity. Between the 12th and 15th days, the succession of working and resting periods disappeared, giving way to continuous contractions that lasted 10 or 15 days, and sometimes even longer. The return of normal hunger contractions in the stomach set in after 1-1/2 to 2 months. With doses of 500 to 600 r, changes in the hunger contractions developed the first day after irradiation; the work periods disappeared and there was complete inhibition of movements, a condition that persisted for the rest of the sickness.

Doses of 250 to 300 r accelerated gastric evacuation, especially after milk was drunk. Progressive changes in motility and evacuation followed irradiation with doses of 500 to 600 r. There was vomiting the first day but without perceptible changes in the rhythm and duration of the peristaltic waves; evacuation remained virtually normal. On the succeeding days, however, and, above all, two or three days before the animals died, stomach tone decreased, the peristaltic waves became less frequent, and food was retained in the stomach for many hours, sometimes for days.

A study was made of the motor reaction of the stomach in response to irrigation of its mucosa with 200 ml of a 0.05% solution of copper sulfate, which normally causes fairly distinct stomach contractions. Five days after irradiation with a dose of 350 r, the motor reaction of the stomach to this stimulus was weak and on subsequent days completely disappeared. It was restored only on the 40th day after irradiation. With lethal doses gastric response was distorted on the very first day after irradiation. It was sharply increased on the third day, but became weak on the fifth day and then disappeared altogether.

The available information testifies to the significance of functional changes in the stomach receptors in the pathogenesis of radiation disorders of the gastrointestinal motor apparatus.

K. V. Smirnov (1957, 1958) obtained similar data in chronic experiments on three dogs with Thiry-Vella fistulas. He recorded intestinal movements graphically. Radiation sickness was induced by total-body irradiation with a dose of 400 r. One dog became very sick and died on the 22nd day; the other animals, however, were only mildly sick. Data on changes in intestinal motility during severe radiation sickness are cited below.

Recordings made 50 minutes after irradiation showed a marked decrease in intestinal motility, chiefly through inhibition of peristaltic contractions, along with individual spastic contractions lasting 3 to 4 minutes. Vomiting began at the 170th minute, and intestinal movements ceased at the 208th minute. The same phenomena were observed the next day, although there were frequent spasms during which intestinal tone increased to 28 mm Hg; the force of individual contractions attained 27 mm, although preirradiation tone had not exceeded 6 mm or the force of individual contractions 20 mm. Similar spasms ordinarily ended in retching. Motility was almost normal the next 4 days; it slowed on the 5th day but increased again on the 14th day. During this time the force of individual contractions was 35 mm Hg while tone rose to 14 mm. On the 17th day the latter attained 27 mm and the force of individual contractions 44 mm. This increased intestinal activity lasted until the 22nd day, i.e., until the agonal state, during which time the tone decreased markedly while intestinal movements ceased altogether.

Changes in intestinal motility in the other dogs during mild radiation sickness displayed the same pattern with periods of inhibition and intensification, the latter predominating, usually from the 3rd to 8th days, 14th to 17th days, 21st to 28th days, and 31st to 48th days. Inhibited motility was noted in the dogs between the 55th and 65th days after irradiation.

Our colleague M. S. Seregin (1957, 1960) studied changes in gastric and duodenal peristalsis in six dogs. Gastrointestinal motility was recorded graphically using an inflated balloon in the stomach (300 cm^3 capacity) and in the intestine (10 cm^3 capacity). Recordings were made for three hours on an empty stomach. Radiation sickness was induced by total-body irradiation with doses of 250 to 350 r. Some dogs were irradiated again after recovery with doses of 350 to 700 r. The resulting sickness was mild, moderate, or severe, depending on individual resistance; however, changes in both gastric and duodenal motility were noted in all the experimental animals, and these were greater when the sickness was moderate or severe (Figure 39).

In these cases the changes became manifest soon after irradiation and were characterized by total inhibition of gastric motility and by spells of vomiting. Motility was more or less normal during the latent period, but the abnormalities returned at the height of the sickness. In some dogs inhibition was reflected by a weakening

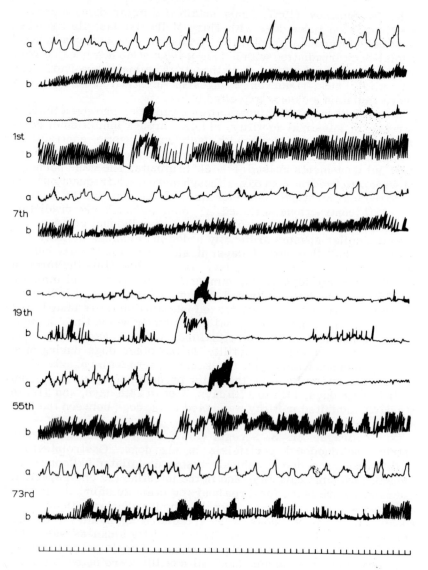

Figure 39. Changes in gastric and duodenal motility in dogs during acute radiation sickness.
(Reported by M. S. Seregin.)
a—Gastrogram. b—Duodenogram. Top curves recorded before irradiation; other curves were recorded on the 1st, 7th, 19th, 55th, and 73rd days after irradiation. Below: time in 5-sec intervals.

or total disappearance of peristaltic contractions, by irregular rhythms, and by changes in the shape of the peristaltic waves. In other dogs it was characterized by decreased amplitude of individual contractions, slowing of the rhythm, and by prolonged gastric resting periods. Not infrequently during mild or moderately severe sickness there was little change in gastric motility; at times it increased somewhat.

Motility of the duodenum during severe sickness was weak in most of the cases, and the same condition was noted occasionally in the stomach. Sometimes intestinal motility increased while gastric motility decreased. Motility in moderately sick dogs was weak, but intense in others. When the sickness was mild, changes in intestinal motility in either direction were insignificant, but increased activity predominated.

Motility became normal in the stomach and duodenum at the same time, two to three months after irradiation. Severe sickness following irradiation with a dose of 700 r and ending in death strongly inhibited gastrointestinal motility.

The experiments of Seregin and other authors show that serious dyskinetic gastrointestinal disorders arise after total-body irradiation with ionizing rays.

Gastrointestinal motility is similarly impaired after local irradiation. Yu. N. Uspenskiĭ (1956, 1957) irradiated the abdomen of four dogs with a dose of 650 r, noting in all cases increased hunger contractions in the stomach. There was a shortening, and even total disappearance, of periods of rest and a marked increase in periods of work.

N. N. Lebedev and M. A. Sobakin (1957, 1960) traced changes in hunger contractions of the stomach after local irradiation of the head, neck, and belly of dogs with doses of 1500 and 4000 r. It turned out that local irradiation of the right ileal region of the belly with 3000 r had the same effect on gastric motility as total-body irradiation with doses of 250 to 600 r. Local irradiation of the head with 4000 r soon accelerated the rate at which periods of work alternated with periods of rest in the stomach, and it was two months before this phenomenon disappeared. Irradiation of the head with 1500 r had no effect on the periodic motor activity of the stomach, but similar irradiation of the abdominal cavity altered the time schedule by five to seven days. It is interesting to note that local but prolonged irradiation of the base of the brain or ileocecal region with radiocobalt (2 mc) had no noticeable influence on hunger contractions in the stomach, even though it killed the animals. Unfortunately, this phenomenon was not adequately analyzed by the authors.

Some data pertaining to radiation impairment of gastrointestinal motility have been obtained by the use of colorimetry. Experimenting on rats, Conard (1951) observed slightly accelerated evacuation through the intestine after irradiation with doses of 100 to 1000 r. These observations, however, were only incidental to other problems in which he was interested. A more detailed study of radiation impairment of evacuation was made by Goodman, Lewis, and Schuck (1952) who traced the movement of Evans blue injected into the stomach of white rats after total-body irradiation with a dose of 450 r. The animals were sacrificed at different periods of time after irradiation and the distance traveled by the dye through the gastrointestinal tract was determined at dissection. They discovered that the rate of evacuation the first day after irradiation was almost half that observed in healthy animals; it reached a maximum after 48 hours and then gradually disappeared. Evacuation of the dye, however, remained abnormal even on the 20th day. The slow progress of Evans blue through the intestine was somewhat less marked. The authors noted that total-body irradiation produced more profound impairment of evacuation than irradiation of the upper or lower half of the body.

Fenton and Dixon (1954) performed similar experiments on mice. Irradiation with a dose of 500 r considerably retarded the evacuation of Congo red from the stomach within 15 minutes. This was more pronounced after 4 hours, but after 24 hours evacuation of the dye from the stomach became normal and remained so until the 7th day, when observation of the animals ended.

The foregoing material indicates that impairment of gastrointestinal evacuation is not always paralleled by impairment of its motor function. Delayed evacuation of gastric contents actually takes place in the presence of both akinesia and hyperkinesia of the gastrointestinal tract. The functional condition of the smooth muscle of the sphincters lying along the tract evidently is considerably involved in the mechanism giving rise to these phenomena. This problem was the object of a special investigation by our co-worker É. K. Kuznetsova (1957, 1960). In chronic experiments on five dogs with permanent fistulas of the stomach, duodenum, ileum, and large intestine, she determined the nature of functional disorders of the pyloric and ileocecal sphincters during radiation sickness caused by total-body irradiation with a dose of 350 r. The rate at which different fluids passed through the pylorus and ileocecal region indicated the functional condition of the sphincter and valve. Accordingly, 200 ml of a 2% solution of sodium bicarbonate (37°) was introduced into the stomach through the fistula. The rate at which the solution passed through the pyloric sphincter was determined from the volume of fluid flowing per minute out of the fistular opening of the duodenum; the fluid residue in the stomach was determined every 15 minutes.

In other experiments the dogs drank milk (37°), and the fluid passing from the stomach into the intestine was collected every 5 minutes for 1-1/2 hours through the duodenal fistula. The volume of fluid remaining in the stomach was measured at the end of the experiment. In addition, the "acid reflex" closing the pyloric sphincter was determined as follows. After obtaining a control rate of evacuation of 400 ml of a 0.5% solution of NaHCO₃ and 200 ml of distilled water from the stomach into the intestine, determinations were made of the rate of evacuation of these fluids after preliminary irrigation of the duodenal mucosa with a 0.5% solution of hydro- chloric acid.

The rate at which the contents passed through the ileocecal value was determined in the same way: 400 ml of a 0.5% solution of sodium bicarbonate was introduced into the small intestine at the point where it joins the ileocecal angle. The volume of fluid emerging from the fistula of the large intestine next to the ileocecal valve was measured every minute.

Irradiation caused mild radiation sickness in two dogs, severe sickness with fatal outcome in two other animals, and moderately severe sickness in the fifth animal.

Within an hour after irradiation, evacuation of the sodium bicarbonate solution from the stomach into the intestine slowed in four of the five dogs; the rate at which the fluid passed through the ileocecal valve was virtually unchanged. As the sickness progressed, a typical sign of impaired motility was the slowing of fluid evacua- tion. This was less evident during the latent period, more so at the climax of the sickness (Figure 40).

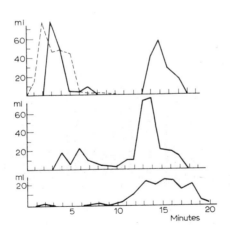

Figure 40. Changes in the evacuation of a solution of sodium bicarbonate from the small intestine into the large intestine of the dog Irtysh during acute radiation sickness. (Reported by É. K.Kuznetsova.)

The extent and duration of the delay varied with the severity of the pathological condition. The maximum delay in evacuation of the 0.5% sodium bicarbonate solution from the stomach was 5 times greater with stage I sickness as compared with the controls, 19 times greater with stage II sickness, and 23 times greater with stage III; evacuation from the small intestine into the large was twice as great with stage I, 3-1/2 times greater with stage II, and 6-1/2 times greater with stage III (Table 51).

The delay in evacuation was particularly marked in the dogs with severe sickness and who died. In some experiments there was total cessation of the flow of fluids from the small into the large intestine, evidently the result of paresis of the intestinal musculature and simultaneous spasm of the ileocecal valve.

Impaired fluid evacuation from the stomach and small intestine was likewise determined. The acid reflex closing the pylorus was impaired, as was the normal relationship between the rates of evacuation of distilled water and sodium bicarbonate solution from the stomach. Before the sickness the sodium bicarbonate solution was evacuated much more quickly than the water, but during the sickness the reverse was true.

Several days before the animals died, fluid evacuation began only 1-1/2 hours after they were introduced into the stomach or small intestine. In the surviving animals sphincter impairment lasted seven or eight months, although there were no clinical signs of radiation sickness (Figure 41).

The results warrant the conclusion that radiation sickness seriously impairs the function of the pyloric sphincter and the

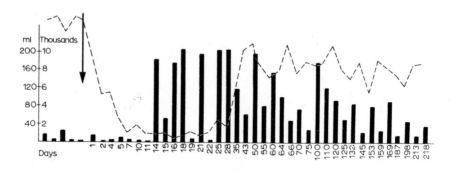

Figure 41. Changes in the evacuation of a sodium bicarbonate solution from the stomach into the duodenum of the dog Pamir during and after acute radiation sickness. (Reported by E. K. Kuznetsova.) Columns show amount of nonevacuated solution in the stomach. Curve shows leukocyte count per mm^3 of blood. Arrow indicates day of irradiation (350 r).

ileocecal valve, the degree of impairment varying with the severity of the sickness. It apparently results from injury to the conditioned reflex mechanism regulating contractility of the smooth muscle of these divisions of the gastrointestinal tract.

Table 51

Changes in the evacuation of a 0.5% solution of sodium bicarbonate from the stomach and small intestine of dogs during radiation sickness.

(Reported by É. K. Kuznetsova.)

Indices of evacuation	Before irradiation	After irradiation (days)							
		1	5	9	16	21	35	55	66
The dog Baĭkal (stage I sickness)									
Stomach									
Latent period (sec)	19	21	70	80	225	Dog died on the 17th day			
Residue of fluid (ml)	5	30	130	75	102				
Intestine									
Latent period (sec)	20	65	11	205	95				
Residue of fluid (ml)	60	58	0	365	395				
The dog Pamir (stage II sickness)									
Stomach									
Latent period (sec)	20	18	48	15	40	50	50	35	14
Residue of fluid (ml)	10	15	10	8	178	190	118	80	42
Intestine									
Latent period (sec)	17	27	17	13	35	40	25	16	21
Residue of fluid (ml)	70	42	52	51	258	116	130	37	46

Table 51 (continued)

Indices of evacuation	Before irradia- tion	After irradiation (days)							
		1	5	9	16	21	35	55	66
The dog Irtysh (stage III sickness)									
Stomach									
Latent period (sec)	31	45	21	10	145	31	26	31	38
Residue of fluid (ml)	15	120	26	100	167	33	20	15	15
Intestine									
Latent period (sec)	21	15	16	17	22	16	15	28	20
Residue of fluid (ml)	68	75	80	73	121	49	62	66	47

Note. 200 ml of a solution of sodium bicarbonate was introduced into the stomach, 400 ml into the small intestine.

Some confirmation of this view comes from the experiments of S. A. Akopyan, E. Arutyunyan, Zh. Govorkyan, and A. Zakharyan (1959), who observed in dogs suffering from radiation sickness impaired evacuation of acid and alkaline fluids from the stomach into the intestine in the presence of epinephrine and acetylcholine. Further confirmation is found in the experiments of G. A. Revnivykh (1959), who noted decreased gastric evacuation during acute radiation sickness, especially at its height.

It has been established with a variety of research techniques that radiation injury impairs gastrointestinal evacuation and motility. If the dose of ionizing radiation is sufficiently large, this effect is observed regardless of whether irradiation is total-body or local. It primarily impairs the periodicity of "hunger" motility of the gastrointestinal tract: the periods of rest shorten while the periods of work lengthen. This is followed by a change in the smooth muscle tone and in the rhythmic and peristaltic contractions; at times these are increased, at other times intestinal paresis sets in. Massive doses of irradiation are followed by the complete disappearance of "hunger" motility and prolonged inhibition of intestinal contractions. These changes in motility are associated with impaired movements of the gastrointestinal contents, which accelerates or slackens, depending on the extent of radiation injury to the digestive apparatus. Changes in the rate of evacuation are sometimes paralleled by changes in gastrointestinal motility. Contributing to the disorganization of gastrointestinal evacuation and motility is the functional condition of the pyloric sphincter and ileocecal valve, which, depending on the degree of radiation injury and the stage of the sickness, may accelerate or retard evacuation of the gastric contents into the duodenum and from the small into the large intestine.

MECHANISM OF RADIATION IMPAIRMENT OF GASTRO-INTESTINAL MOTILITY AND EVACUATION

The mechanism by which ionizing radiation impairs gastrointestinal motility has not yet been fully elucidated. Functional and structural damage to the neuromuscular system proper is a definite factor. Also important is radiation injury to the neurohumoral mechanisms regulating gastric and intestinal activity. This particular aspect has been investigated by several researchers. Contractility of intestinal smooth muscle has been extensively studied; Andersen and Kohlmann (1923) were perhaps the first to take up this problem. Their findings, however, did little more than indicate that contractility is impaired by ionizing radiation.

In our opinion, Swann's data (1924) are important. After total-body X-irradiation of rabbits, he cut out a segment of the small intestine and recorded its movements graphically. He noted increased smooth muscle tone within 20 minutes after irradiation. Toyoma's approach (1933) was similar, but, unlike Swann, he irradiated only the excised portion of the intestine. The post-irradiation effect, however, was the same: increased muscular tone and intestinal peristalsis. This effect was abolished by nicotine but preserved by atropine.

Toyoma's findings suggest that total-body irradiation impairs intestinal motility by acting directly on the smooth muscle of the intestine and, possibly, on the intramural nerve plexi which innervate it. On the other hand, Crawer (1947), who also irradiated an isolated segment of intestine, showed that even a dose of 10,000 r under similar conditions has no effect on intestinal contractility.

Radiation, then, clearly does not impair intestinal motility solely by local injury. The phenomenon is evidently more complex than some investigators originally thought. In acute and chronic experiments on rats, rabbits, and dogs, Conard (1951, 1953, 1956) exposed the animals to total-body irradiation and discovered a heightened tone and increased intestinal contractions one minute later. With a dose of 100 r the contractions were brief, with a dose of 200 r they continued for 8 to 10 minutes, and with a dose of 600 r they continued for 20 minutes. The contractions were weakened by atropine, epinephrine, nicotine, curare, and tetraethyl ammonium chloride; conversely, they were strengthened by physostigmine and acetylcholine. Shielding the intestine during irradiation almost completely prevented the effect, while isolated irradiation of the intestinal loop alone produced the same effect as total-body irradiation. The author was thus led to conclude that ionizing radiation causes increased motility by exciting the cholinergic systems in the intestine. We are compelled to agree with Conard because the agents that block the action of acetylcholine (atropine and nicotine) inhibit this reaction of the intestine to ionizing radiation, whereas physostigmine, a cholinesterase inhibitor, increases the radiation effect on the intestine by preventing the destruction of acetylcholine in the tissues. The author also noted the stimulating effect of X-rays on the parasympathetic ganglia of the intestine, causing increased motility for 3 hours. According to Conard, signs of radiation injury to the gastrointestinal tract are less marked in dogs than in rats; in the latter a dose as low as 25 r distinctly retards evacuation of the gastric contents into the intestine.

Conard's views were further developed by Wachtler (1952), who irradiated guinea pigs with various doses of X-rays and then studied the muscular reaction of an isolated segment of intestine to acetylcholine and histamine. He discovered that doses ranging from 140 to 700 r produced a slight weakening of intestinal peristalsis and reduced sensitivity to acetylcholine and histamine the first few days. These phenomena subsequently disappeared and the normal intestinal response to these chemical agents was restored by the second or third week. Doses of 1000 to 2800 r quickly increased both motility and sensitivity to acetylcholine and histamine, sometimes as much as twentyfold or more. This response, however, did not last long and between the third and fifth days both intestinal motility and sensitivity to these substances decreased simultaneously. Intestinal activity became normal two to three months after irradiation.

Irradiation with doses of 3000 to 8400 r caused changes in intestinal motility and muscular sensitivity to acetylcholine and histamine similar to those produced by doses of 1000 and 2800 r, but these were more pronounced and lasted longer. The animals usually died afterwards. The author divided the functional changes in smooth muscle into three periods: (1) enhanced sensitivity to acetylcholine and histamine and increased motility (2 to 3 days), (2) lowered sensitivity to these substances and weakening of contractility (about 3 weeks), and (3) gradual restoration of normal motility and muscle sensitivity to acetylcholine and histamine.

The author sought to explain these phenomena in the following way. Increased motility in the first period is caused by the presence of N-substance, which is responsible for sensitization of the mediators, whereas inhibited motility in the second period is caused by morphological changes in the intestinal muscles. Although this explanation does not fully elucidate the mechanism of radiation injury to gastrointestinal motility, it has been confirmed by the work of several other investigators. Z. I. Poluboyarinov (1957) noted an initial increase in intestinal sensitivity to acetylcholine and a decrease in cholinesterase activity.

L. R. Protas and A. A. Danilin (1957) irradiated guinea pigs with a dose of 300 to 350 r and then, over a period of 7 to 10 days, injected them with acetylcholine, carbachol, atropine, and epinephrine. Gastrointestinal motility was studied by roentgenography. The experiments showed that daily injection of atropine normalized motility but had no effect on the life span of the animals. Epinephrine inhibited gastrointestinal motility considerably and somewhat prolonged the life of the animals. Acetylcholine and carbachol sharply increased motility while shortening the life of the guinea pigs. The authors concluded that radiation sickness involves stimulation of the parasympathetic division of the autonomic nervous system, since the cholinesterase inhibitors intensify the effect of irradiation and atropine abolishes it.

K. V. Smirnov's experiments (1957) also testify to the great importance of impairment to the acetylcholine-cholinesterase system in gastrointestinal motor disorders. By injecting healthy dogs with neostigmine and atropine, Smirnov obtained an effect comparable to that following X-irradiation.

If one assumes that the acetylcholine-cholinesterase system is involved in gastrointestinal motility changes during radiation sickness, with due regard for the data showing cholinesterase inactivation by ionizing radiation (Burn, Kordik, and Mole, 1952), then it is possible to correlate the period of increased gastrointestinal motility after irradiation, at least in part, with increased concentrations of acetylcholine in the tissues; and further, one can correlate the periods of decreased tone and peristalsis with increased cholinesterase levels which produce greater destruction of acetylcholine in the tissues of the intestine and stomach.

Some confirmation of this assumption is provided by the investigations of N. F. Stradyn' (1957, 1960), who studied in vitro the cholinergic effects of physostigmine, pilocarpine, acetylcholine, and atropine, and the adrenergic effects of epinephrine, on the smooth muscle of an isolated segment of the small intestine of irradiated (13) and nonirradiated (11) rats. The animals were irradiated with a dose of 150 r under the following conditions: filter 0.5 mm Cu copper, skin focus distance 30 cm, voltage 180 kv, current 4 ma, field 10 × 15 cm², using a Stabilovol't apparatus. The rats were killed with a hammer blow on the head.

Tests of the cholinergic reactions yielded the following results. Physostigmine in concentrations of 1:100,000, 1:500,000, and 1:1,000,000 caused distinct intestinal contractions in the non-irradiated rats; except in the concentration of 1:100,000, however, it had no effect on the intestinal muscles of the irradiated rats (Table 52).

Table 52

Action of cholinergic, adrenergic, and myotropic substances on an isolated segment of the small intestine of nonirradiated rats.

(Reported by N. F. Stradyn'.)

No. of experiment	Cholinergic substances				Adren-ergic sub-stances	Myotropic substance
	Physos-tigmine	Acetyl-choline	Pilo-carpine	Atropine	Epine-phrine	Barium chloride
1	+++		+++	+++	+++	+++
2	+++		+++	+++	++	+++
3	+++		++	+++	+++	+++
4	+++		++	+++	+++	+++
5	+++	+++	+++	+++	+++	+++
6	+++	+++-	+++	+++	+++	+++
7	+++	+++	+++	+++	+++	+++
8	+++	+++	+++	+++	+++	+++
9	+++	++	+++	++	+++	+++
10	+++	+++	+++	+++	+++	+++
11	+++	++-	+	-++	+++	+++

Note. + = positive effect, - = negative effect.

Since physostigmine inactivates cholinesterase, it is possible that its contractility effect is caused by the action on the smooth muscles of acetylcholine, which is constantly being formed in the cholinergic nerve structures of the intestine. The absence of an effect in the irradiated animals is apparently due to a decrease in cholinesterase activity of the tissues as a result of irradiation, to a decrease in the amount of acetylcholine released, or, finally, to a decrease in sensitivity of the M-cholinergic receptors in intestinal tissue.

The problem was solved by Stradyn's experiments using pilocarpine and acetylcholine. In a concentration of 1:100,000, pilocarpine, which acts on the M-cholinergic receptors in the intestinal walls, caused strong intestinal contractions in nonirradiated rats. In irradiated animals, however, the effect was usually absent or weak, and sometimes the intestine relaxed instead of contracting.

A fairly similar effect was obtained with acetylcholine used in concentrations of 1:50 million, 1:5 million, and 1:2 million. These concentrations were sufficient to cause muscle contracture in the nonirradiated controls. Only in a concentration of 1:2 million, however, did acetycholine cause faint contracture in five out of eight tests with the irradiated rats. Atropine in a concentration of 1:50,000 completely abolished the effect both of pilocarpine and of acetylcholine (Table 53).

Ionizing radiation, then, may work in two ways: it may either reduce the sensitivity of the M-cholinergic systems or it may prevent the muscles from contracting. The latter possibility was investigated by Stradyn' in experiments with barium chloride in concentrations of 1:50,000, 1:25,000, and 3:50,000. Barium chloride in all these concentrations, he found, caused distinct rhythmic contractions both in irradiated and in nonirradiated rats. We conclude from the foregoing that after a dose of 150 r, the smooth muscle of the rat intestine does not lose its contractile properties, although there is a sharp decrease in the sensitivity of its M-cholinergic receptors.

As for adrenergic reactions of the intestine, Stradyn' discovered that epinephrine in a concentration of 1:500,000 halted contractions and decreased the tone of intestinal muscle in both irradiated and non-irradiated rats. Therefore, it is a fair assumption that the adrenergic reactions of the intestine are either not impaired at all by radiation, which is unlikely, or, if they are, they are less impaired than the cholinergic reactions.

We doubt, however, that the mechanism described above is the basic one responsible for the complex and varied kinds of gastrointestinal motor disorders following radiation injury. It is possible that the acetylcholine-cholinesterase system changes, that the activity of the M-cholinergic systems decreases, and that the adrenergic reactions of the smooth muscle are preserved; these and many other things may participate in an inseparable complex of biochemical reactions involved in contraction.

It must be borne in mind that a sharp decrease in the sensitivity of the M-cholinergic systems causes them to lose their ability to react as they should to the acetylcholine accumulating in the tissues of the intestine. But this is not the main thing. It seems to

Table 53

Action of cholinergic, adrenergic, and myotropic substances on an isolated segment of the small intestine of irradiated rats.

(Reported by N. F. Stradyn'.)

No. of experiment	Time after irradiation	Cholinergic substances			Atropine	Adrenergic substance	Myotropic substance
		Physostigmine	Acetylcholine	Pilocarpine			
1	24 hours	- - -	- - -	- - +	- + +	+ + +	+ + +
2	24 hours	- - +	- - ±	- - ±	+ + +	+ + +	+ + +
3	24 hours	- - -	- - -	- - +	+ + +	+ + +	+ + +
4	5 days	- - +	- - ±	Distorted reaction	+ + +	+ + +	+ + +
5	5 days	- - +	- - +	- - -	- - +	- - +	+ + +
6	8 days	- - -	- - +	- + +	+ + +	- - ±	+ + +
7	8 days	- - -	- - -	- - ±	+ + +	+ + +	+ + +
8	8 days	- - +	- -	- - +	+ + +	- - +	+ + +
9	10 days	- - +		- - -	+ + +	- - +	+ + +
10	30 days	- - +		- + +	+ + +	+ + +	+ + +
11	6 months	- - +	- - +	+ + +	+ + +	+ + +	+ + +

Note: + = positive effect, - = negative effect, ± = doubtful effect.

us that while the mechanism described above operates after radiation injury to the organism in general and to the smooth muscle of the intestine and stomach in particular, it must be regarded as one link in the many chain reactions responsible for impairing the complex reflex mechanism that governs the digestive apparatus.

This view of the problem is wholly justified in the light of the available data on radiation injury to autonomic mechanisms regulating gastric motility (A. V. Solov'ev, N. A. Solov'ev, and O. V. Solodkina, 1956; A. V. Solov'ev, and O. V. Solodkina, 1957, 1958; O. V. Solodkina, 1957, 1958, 1960).

Two Solov'ev pouches were formed in each of five dogs, one on the lesser curvature, which is supplied chiefly by the vagus nerves, the other on the greater curvature, which is supplied chiefly by sympathetic nerves. The motility of both pouches was recorded simultaneously for 6 or 7 hours, and the volume of juice secrected after eating food was measured. Radiation sickness was then induced by total-body irradiation from an RUM-3 apparatus—two animals with a dose of 200 r, one with 400 r, and two with 500 r. Pronounced leukopenia followed irradiation; there were also major secretory changes and minor impairment of motility in the pouches.

After a dose of 200 r, the only change in motility was a slight increase in the amplitude of peristaltic contractions, the muscle tone and frequency of contractions remaining normal. Juice secretion, meanwhile, was almost double the original volume. Motility was scarcely affected by a dose of 400 r, although secretion was quite low. It was only after a dose of 500 r that distinct changes were noted. It was also possible to detect a difference between the disorders of the "vagal" and "sympathetic" pouches. During the first week only the motility of the "sympathetic" pouch was impaired, as shown by an increase in muscle tone above the pre-irradiation level. It is interesting to note that in the meantime secretion was impaired in both pouches: there was an increase in the volume and a marked decrease in the acidity of the juice secreted. During the following weeks the tone of the "sympathetic" pouch decreased to the original level while secretion became normal. The amplitude of peristaltic contractions, however, remained substantial, returning to the original level two to three weeks after irradiation. Secretion during this period remained abnormal.

The findings just described are of considerable theoretical importance. If we assume that the functional disorders following irradiation were actually the result of direct injury to the stomach, then motility and secretion should have been impaired equally; however, this was not the case in the different pouches. At a certain stage in the development of the pathological process, motility was impaired only in the region of the greater curvature, while there were no changes in the motility of the lesser curvature, i.e., changes in motility occurred only in the pouch supplied chiefly by sympathetic nerves. The explanation of this phenomenon is to be sought in the innervation of the different pouches. Radiation undoubtedly impairs motility by injuring the reflex mechanism regulating the gastric musculature rather than by injuring the muscles directly. It is significant that in experiments on intact animals, injury to the adrenergic system involved in regulating gastric motility occurred sooner and was more pronounced than in the cholinergic system.

It is also worth noting that motility changes were not always paralleled by secretory changes in the isolated pouch. Secretory changes may originate and develop in the absence of any functional impairment of its muscular elements, even though gastric secretion and motility have a common autonomic innervation.

The secretory cells are evidently more radiosensitive than muscular tissue. This is borne out by the work of A. V. Kantin (1938).

Finally, the available facts indicate that radiation injury disrupts the synergism between the parasympathetic and sympathetic innervation of the stomach. This was demonstrated by G. A. Gusterin, N. M. Okulov, S. V. Strutsovskaya, and P. A. Buzini (1957), who studied gastrointestinal motor disorders in patients receiving ionizing radiation therapy for cancer of the cervix uteri.

It is still debatable, however, whether impairment of any part of the autonomic nervous system, parasympathetic or sympathetic, is a decisive factor in the disruption of synergistic influences on the gastrointestinal tract. According to N. F. Stradyn', ionizing radiation damages mainly the cholinergic system; according to A. V. Solov'ev, it damages both the cholinergic and adrenergic systems. L. R. Protas and A. A. Danilin are inclined to ascribe the increased gastrointestinal tone and motility following radiation to the stimulating effect of radiation on the parasympathetic innervation. In their experiments acetylcholine and carbachol intensified the effect of irradiation, whereas atropine weakened it. The problem requires further study.

The following studies deal with radiation injury to the neurohumoral mechanism regulating gastrointestinal motility. In experiments on rabbits Swann observed the movements of a loop of small intestine drawn from the abdominal cavity but retaining neural and vascular connections with the body. He noted that changes in motility occurred immediately after the start of total-body irradiation; there was heightened smooth muscle tone and an increase in peristaltic contractions. After irradiation was terminated, these changes disappeared and motility became normal.

In experiments on rabbits Toyoma observed different changes in intestinal motility following local X-irradiation of different divisions of the central nervous system: there was decreased tone after irradiation of the central portion of the brain, heightened tone and intensified intestinal peristalsis after irradiation of the medulla oblongata. The first effect may have been due to excitation of the sympathetic nuclei of the central brain, because the application of nicotine to the sympathetic celiac ganglion before irradiation abolished the effect. The second effect may have been caused by excitation of the vagal nuclei, because preliminary atropinization eliminated the intestinal response to irradiation. The important thing in these experiments, however, is that changes in intestinal motility resulted from the local action of ionizing radiation on the brain centers.

In view of this, the experiments of Swann and Toyoma justify the conclusion that changes in intestinal motility following total-body irradiation are caused both by the direct action of radiation on the neuromuscular apparatus of the intestine and by reflex influences. This view is confirmed by the experiments of R. S. Zhur and V. A. Sonkina (1960), who detected changes in exteroceptive reflexes (from the mouth) and interoceptive reflexes (from the small intestine) in response to gastric motility in seven dogs which received total-body irradiation with a dose of 250 r. N. N. Lebedev and E. F. Fofanova (1960) provided additional evidence through the discovery that reflexes from the mechano- and chemoreceptors in the mucosa of the stomach and small intestine, in response to the motility of these organs, were impaired in dogs following total-body irradiation with doses of 200 to 300 r.

This view is also supported by the work of A. N. Kornilov (1954, 1956) on rabbits, some of which had head irradiation, others abdominal irradiation. He discovered that although a single exposure of the abdominal organs to doses ranging from 150 to 300 r caused radiation sickness, it had no effect on gastrointestinal motility, as determined roentgenographically. After being irradiated with doses ranging from 1000 to 1500 r, the rabbits developed radiation sickness with impaired gastric and intestinal evacuation. The initial radiation effect was to weaken and even totally inhibit gastric peristalsis. During the latent period of the sickness, motility was almost normal, but at the height of the sickness dystonia and intestinal dyskinesia appeared. Similar but less pronounced phenomena were also noted after irradiation with doses ranging from 2000 to 3000 r. Daily irradiation of the viscera with doses of 300 r produced chronic radiation sickness accompanied by protracted changes in gastrointestinal motility. After irradiating the head alone with doses of 2000 and 3000 r, the author noted changes in gastric and intestinal motility along with arrested movement of a contrast medium through the intestine. Ether anesthesia mitigated the disorders of gastrointestinal evacuation and motility. The injection of 50 ml of a 0.25% solution of Novocain into the abdominal cavity intensified gastric peristalsis and accelerated evacuation of the contrast medium.

Experimental data on autonomic involvement in radiation disorders of gastrointestinal motility and evacuation have been
supplemented by some clinical observations on persons. For
example, G. V. Shal' (1941) noted accelerated gastric evacuation
in patients receiving irradiation of the hypothalamic region and
spinal ganglia. R. A. Golonzko (1934) observed the disappearance of
pyloric spasms in ulcer patients after X-ray treatments of the
cervical roots of the sympathetic and parasympathetic nerves.
According to M. V. Ol'khovskaya, E. Ya. Bril', and V. V. Zorina
(1934), this effect is attributable to heightened tone of the vagus
nerves.

According to the findings of our colleagues who have studied
impaired gastrointestinal motility in irradiated dogs, the nature and
extent of the motor disorders is largely determined by the functional
disorders arising in the higher divisions of the central nervous
system—above all, in the cerebral cortex and subcortical autonomic
centers. This is well illustrated by the findings of V. N. Zvorykin
(1957, 1960) who observed persons who had come in contact with
ionizing radiation. He noted that increased excitation in the cerebral
cortex was in some instances associated with increased gastric
motility, in other instances with decreased motility. The former
effects may have been caused by the action of cortical excitation
on the autonomic centers of the subcortex and medulla oblongata;
the latter effects, by negative induction of the subcortex and medulla
from the excited cerebral cortex. This relationship emerged very
clearly after simultaneous examination of higher nervous activity
and gastric motility in the patients. Zvorykin observed how increased excitation in the cerebral cortex was associated with
increased gastric motility (the effect of cortical excitation on the
subcortical centers), while increased inhibition in the cortex was
followed by the weakening and total disappearance of peristaltic
and rhythmic contractions in the stomach muscles (the effect of
cortical inhibition on the subcortex).

The gastrogram in the latter case reflected inhibited motility
(Figure 42). In other cases initial inhibition of gastric motility
then gave way to excitation, which occurred after increased excitation in the cerebral cortex. Thus, the early changes in gastric
motility may have been caused by negative induction of the subcortical autonomic centers from the excited cerebral cortex while
the later changes were caused by the action of cortical excitation
on the subcortex. The gastrogram in this case reflected the inert
type of motility.

The cases in which increased gastric motility occurred during
2-1/2 hours of investigation may also be explained by the action
of cortical excitation on the subcortex, and negative induction of
the subcortex may account for the cases in which gastric motility
was either absent or barely perceptible during the course of the

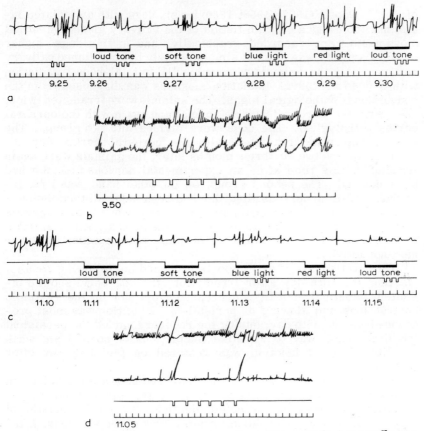

Figure 42. Simultaneous examination of conditioned blinking reflexes and gastric motility in patient B. (Reported by V. N. Zvorykin.) a, c—Conditioned blinking reflexes. Curves, from top to bottom: pneumographic recording of blinking, mark of conditioned stimuli (positive—loud tone, soft tone, blue light; negative—red light), mark of unconditioned stimuli. Time marked at 0.2 and 1 sec intervals. Numbers underneath—hours and minutes. b, d—Gastric motility. Curves, from top to bottom: pneumogram, gastrogram, mark of blinking reflexes. Time marked at 30-sec intervals.

investigation. The latter effect may also have been caused by the influence of cortical inhibition on the subcortical autonomic centers.

The relationship between the nature and duration of impaired intestinal motility and the functional condition of the higher divisions of the central nervous system is demonstrated by the experiments

of A. V. Popov (1957, 1958, 1960) on six dogs with an isolated intestinal loop and a chronic fistula of the salivary gland. Intestinal
movements were recorded graphically, and in five dogs higher
nervous activity was studied simultaneously by conditioned salivary
reflexes. All the animals were subjected to total-body irradiation
with a dose of 250 r. Radiation sickness was diagnosed from the
conventional pathological signs. The animals were irradiated twice,
once with the cerebral cortex normal and again with the cerebral
cortex pathological. The dogs were divided into two groups. The
first group was irradiated with the cerebral cortex normal;
after recovery two to three months later, the animals were again
irradiated, this time after an experimental nervous disorder had
been induced. The second group, on the other hand, was first irradiated after a nervous disorder had been induced; then the sur-
vivors were irradiated again after recovery, when higher nervous
activity and visceral functions had become normal. A few animals
were irradiated a third time after chronic traumatization of higher
nervous activity.

The first series of experiments produced the following results.
Starting the fifth day after irradiation, the dog Seryĭ showed inhibited intestinal motility: decreased amplitude in the rhythmic
contractions and slowing of peristalsis. Inhibition was most pronounced on the 38th day; during the recovery period the persistent
inhibition gave way to wavelike fluctuations of normal and weak
motility. Normal function was restored on the 55th day after
irradiation.

Higher nervous activity became impaired soon after irradiation.
It preceded changes in intestinal motility, and throughout the
radiation sickness it reflected the features characteristic of
cerebrocortical activity during a mild form of the sickness. After
higher nervous activity had become normal, (about the same time
that intestinal motility became restored), an experimental nervous
disorder was induced by overstraining the intensity and mobility
of excitation and inhibition. Then the dog was irradiated a second
time with the same dose. This time impairment of intestinal
motility was more pronounced. The maximum amplitude of rhythmic
contractions decreased from 10-11 to 7-8 mm Hg and there was
considerable lengthening of the intervals between individual peristaltic waves; the height of the peristaltic waves dropped and their
duration became shorter. Intestinal motility became normal after
85 days. Changes in higher nervous activity were likewise more
profound and persistent. When the original level of the functions
under study was restored, the dog was subjected to chronic
traumatization of higher nervous activity and a third irradiation.
This time the inhibition of intestinal motility was very pronounced
from the first few days after irradiation, and it remained so until
the animal died 17 days later (Figure 43).

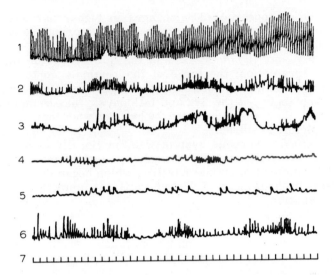

Figure 43. Changes in intestinal motility in the
dog Seryĭ during acute radiation sickness caused
by irradiation with the cerebral cortex normal
and after a nervous disorder had been induced.
(Reported by A. V. Popov.)
Normal jejunogram (1), after first irradiation
with the cerebral cortex normal (2), during
collision (3), during second irradiation with a
nervous disorder (4), after collision (5), and
after third irradiation with a nervous disorder
(6), 7—Time in 5-sec intervals.

On the second day after irradiation, the dog Zhul'bars had
increased intestinal motility. The frequency and force of the rhythmic contractions increased while the intervals between the peristaltic waves became shorter. Between the 7th and 20th days,
intestinal motility decreased, the amplitude of the rhythmic
contractions decreased from 14-15 to 3-4 mm Hg, and the peristaltic waves disappeared. Motility began to intensify on the
28th-29th day, becoming normal on the 50th day. Changes in
higher nervous activity were similar to those noted during mild
radiation sickness.
After restoration of normal cerebrocortical activity, intestinal
motility, and the other functions under study, a nervous disorder
was induced in the dog and he was then irradiated a second time.
Intestinal motility was greatly inhibited at first, and at the height
of the sickness the force of contractions decreased to 1-2 mm and

peristalsis disappeared. The changes in higher nervous activity were more profound. All functions became normal 96 days after irradiation.

Intestinal motility decreased in the dog Dobryĭ on the second day after irradiation; the force of the rhythmic contractions decreased and the number of rest periods grew. Changes in motility were absent between the 3rd and 14th days. They became slightly pronounced thereafter until the 102nd day when normal motility was completely restored.

The animal's nervous system was functionally weakened prior to the second irradiation by repeated "electric clashing". This time, inhibition of intestinal motility, which began on the 10th day, was very pronounced and lasted until the animal died 41 days after irradiation.

The foregoing examples from the first series of experiments suggest that irradiation against a background of functionally weakened higher nervous centers produces more severe injury to intestinal motility than when the nervous system is functioning normally.

The results of the second series of experiments were similar. Impairment of higher nervous activity in the dog Belyĭ caused increased intestinal motility. When the dog was irradiated, the force of individual contractions grew from 14-15 to 30-33 mm Hg. Changes in intestinal motility and higher nervous activity comparable to those associated with moderately severe radiation sickness were observed for several months, after which they disappeared. After higher nervous activity had returned to normal, a second irradiation likewise increased motility. The force of contractions was 21-22 mm. Impaired motility and higher nervous activity lasted 60 days. After prolonged traumatization of higher nervous activity, a third irradiation sharply decreased rather than increased motility. The force of contractions decreased to 2-3 mm and the intestinal muscles became paretic (Figure 44). The animal died on the 18th day after irradiation with signs of profoundly inhibited intestinal motility and higher nervous activity.

In the dog Bars traumatization of higher nervous activity and subsequent irradiation caused a brief increase, and then, starting the 12th day, a weakening of intestinal motility. The force of contractions, meanwhile, decreased from 18-19 to 11-12 mm Hg. Functions became normal 107 days after irradiation. A second irradiation with the central nervous system normal inhibited intestinal motility for 20 days, and the force of contractions decreased from 8-9 to 3-5 mm. Intestinal function became normal 45 days after irradiation, although some changes persisted for 62 days.

The examples from the second series of experiments likewise indicate that the functional condition of the higher nervous centers play an important part in the development of radiation injury to intestinal motility.

Functional traumatization of the brain centers apparently disrupts the defensive and adaptational mechanisms and impairs the complex reflex regulation of intestinal motility, thereby aggravating the radiation injury. Of definite significance in this respect are

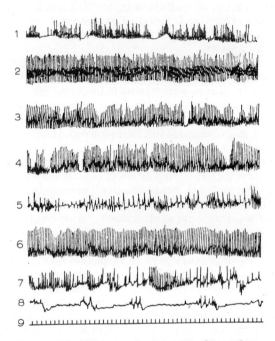

Figure 44. Changes in intestinal motility in the dog Belyĭ during acute radiation sickness caused by irradiation with the cerebral cortex traumatized and normal. (Reported by A. V. Popov.) Normal jejunogram (1); with a nervous disorder (2), the first few days after (1st) irradiation, with an induced nervous disorder (3); at the end of a month after irradiation, with an induced nervous disorder (4); normal (5); after (2nd) irradiation, cerebral cortex normal (6); with a nervous disorder (7), and after (3rd) irradiation, with an induced nervous disorder (8). 9—Time in 5-sec intervals.

the typological characteristics of the nervous system. According
to A. V. Popov, irradiation with a dose of 250 r impaired motility
in dogs with a strong type of nervous system (Dzhul'bars, Belyĭ,
and Bars) for 20 to 50 days and in dogs with a weak type of nervous
system (Seryĭ, Mudryĭ, and Dobryĭ) for 55 to 102 days.

It has also been demonstrated that postirradiation changes in
higher nervous activity usually precede signs of impaired intestinal
motility, the degree and nature of impaired motility being directly
related to the extent of radiation injury to higher nervous activity.
In many cases impaired motility is affected by the activity and
interaction of excitation and inhibition in the cerebral cortex and
the autonomic centers.

We see, therefore, that radiation injury is followed by severe
impairment of gastrointestinal motility and evacuation. It is manifested in different ways, sometimes in inhibited motility with slower
movement of the contents through the gastrointestinal tract, sometimes in increased motility and evacuation, and sometimes in a
combination of both, when inhibition is followed by increased motility
and evacuation, and vice versa.

The nature of the different types of abnormal gastrointestinal
motility and evacuation is highly complex. It may be caused either
by injury to the general neurohumoral mechanism regulating the
activity of the smooth muscles, or by local radiation injury to the alimentary neuromuscular apparatus itself. Most likely both take place.

The typological characteristics of higher nervous activity and
the functional condition of the higher brain centers regulating
motility play an important part in radiation impairment of gastrointestinal motility. In animals with a weak type of nervous system
and with nervous disorders showing weak cerebral tone, impairment
of gastrointestinal motility is more profound and longer lasting.

The functional interrelations between the cerebral cortex and
the subcortical centers are one of the many factors that determine
the particular type of motor disorders in the stomach and intestine.
The spread and reciprocal induction of excitation and inhibition in
these two divisions of the central nervous system frequently determine whether the disorder will be of the hyperkinetic, hypokinetic,
or mixed type.

Another important factor is an imbalance of the parasympathetic
and sympathetic systems, which normally work synergistically
on the smooth muscles of the gastrointestinal tract. Impaired
chemical transmission of excitation from nerve to muscle and
impairment of the mediator mechanism, especially the
acetylcholine-cholinesterase system, also play a part in the process.

Finally, to the functional disorders mentioned above, we must add
the structural changes in the substrate itself which occur both after
local irradiation of the stomach and intestine and after total-body
irradiation.

CHAPTER 9

Morphological Changes in the Digestive System

Following Radiation Injury

Ionizing radiation causes morphological changes as well as functional impairment in the digestive system. These changes have been described in the literature (G. A. Zedgenidze and others, 1936; A. L. Polyakov, 1936; N. A. Kraevskiĭ, 1954, 1957; and others). The most marked changes occur in the intestine. During acute radiation sickness, man suffers from epithelial degeneration in the crypts of the large intestine and hemorrhagic necrosis of the mucosa (Liebow, Warren, and de Coursey, 1949; Bloom, 1947; de Coursey, 1948; Brugge, 1952; Tullis, 1954). Necrosis of intestinal epithelium, multiple hemorrhages in the mucosa, ulcers, scars, and atrophy of the villi and glands also occur in persons given X-ray therapy for diseases of the abdominal organs.

Yu. N. Uspenskiĭ (1956, 1957) observed in the intestinal walls of dogs dying of radiation sickness inflammatory infiltration, proliferation of histiocytes in the intermuscular connective tissue, marked edema, local necroses, and catarrhal (occasionally diphtheritic) enteritis and colitis. In dogs, extensive degenerative changes arise in the intestine both after direct irradiation of the intestine (L. M. Gorovits, 1906; Krause and Ziegler, 1906) and after irradiation of the abdominal region with doses of 500 to 1100 r (Régaud, Nogier, and Lacassagne, 1912); Lieberkühn's glands and the villi appear to be particular sensitive. The radiation dose is a significant factor, because the extent of morphological changes in the intestinal walls varies with the size of the dose.

Martin and Rogers (1923) removed an intestinal loop from dogs, irradiated it with different doses of X-rays, and returned it to the abdominal cavity. The animals were sacrificed three weeks later and the morphological changes that developed during this time were studied. It turned out that small doses had no perceptible effect, whereas large doses caused pronounced scarring with deformation of the walls and atrophy of the mucosa; in some places the epithelium completely disappeared.

A similar relationship between the degree of morphological change and the size of the radiation dose was also noted by Podesta (1925); he applied local irradiation to the belly of animals and found that it caused major changes in the receptors. This is further borne out by the experiments of E. Ya. Gilinskiĭ (1960) on the pancreatic receptors of cats exposed to local abdominal irradiation with a single dose of 600 r. For one or two months thereafter, the receptors exhibited histopathological changes of various kinds and degrees. It was discovered that vacuolization and varicose thickenings were less pronounced in the main fibers of the receptor and its branches; the terminal endings resembled normal, delicately colored fibrils (Figure 45).

Figure 45. An altered pancreatic receptor after single dose local irradiation of the abdominal area. (Reported by E. Ya. Gilinskiĭ.)
Bielschowsky—Gross. Obj. 43, oc. 15.

Histomorphological changes also arise after total-body irradiation. Tsuzuki (1926) observed mucosal hyperemia and lymphatic degeneration in the intestinal wall of rabbits within a few hours after irradiation with a 0.2 to 0.4 erythema dose. More extensive changes followed a 0.6 to 0.8 erythema dose. They were clearly marked on the fourth day.

Major morphological changes are found in the intestine of mice irradiated with a lethal dose of X-rays (1000 r of X-rays or the equivalent in neutron radiation, 230 to 290 r). Within 24 hours after irradiation the cells of the intestinal crypts become swollen (Lawrence and Tennant, 1937). Edema of the villi and degenerative changes in the epithelial cells appear after 48 hours. Marked edema of the villi, epithelial destruction, and diffuse infilitration of the mucosa occur after 72 hours. By the fourth day these changes reach substantial proportions: destruction of intestinal epithelium, hemorrhages, and ulcers of the mucosa.

Similar morphological changes have been described by other authors who irradiated various species of animals (Bloom, 1948; Brecher and Cronkite, 1951; N. A. Kraevskiĭ, 1954). They are characterized chiefly by necrosis of intestinal epithelium, multiple hemorrhages in the mucosa, and ulcers; during the recovery period, the intestine shows scarring and atrophy of the villi and glandular tissue. These phenomena are less pronounced after minor radiation injury.

Irradiation of the head alone causes similar changes in intestinal tissue. For example, doses of 1000 to 3000 r cause necrotic changes in the intestinal mucosa at the beginning of radiation sickness and various trophic changes and scarring at the height of the sickness: atrophy of the mucosa, trophic ulcers, and proliferation of connective tissue.

V. M. Chernykh (1957) made a detailed study of morphological changes in the intestine of dogs and white rats exposed to total-body irradiation with doses of 600 to 2400 r. He discovered that during radiation sickness of moderate and extreme severity, progressive changes occur in the neural, vascular, and connective tissue structures; concomitant changes in intestinal epithelium are comparatively minor and disappear within five to seven days. The number of mitoses in the epithelium of intestinal crypts decreases sharply immediately after the radiation trauma, and the epithelial nuclei steadily swell and their DNA content diminishes. Individual epithelial cells become vacuolized and die as their nuclei undergo lysis and karyorrhexis. In two or three days the goblet cells in the crypts and villi overflow with mucus and diminish in number. By the fifth to seventh days the epithelial cells become normal, although they retain foci of minor degenerative changes. Lysis of the lymphocytes in the lymph nodes sets in a few hours after irradiation. The reticular cells swell and come to resemble epithelioid cells. These changes level off between the fifth and seventh days and the cells become completely normal during the period of clinical recovery of the animal.

Major changes also take place in the neurovascular system of the intestine. Reactive changes are observed in the nerve cells of the plexuses: at the height of the sickness, there is hypochromatism, isolated vacuoles, coarse vacuolization of the protoplasma, and deformation and pyknosis of the nuclei. Meanwhile, some of the cells die. Hemorrhages, necroses, and ulcers appear in the mucosa and deeper coats of the intestine. The walls of the blood vessels swell as subintimal and perivascular hemorrhages increase. According to Chernykh, necroses and ulcers are found in one-third of all cases of radiation sickness.

É. Ya. Graevskiĭ (1955) observed the destruction of crypt epithelium, cell lysis, nuclear hypertrophy, and mycosis in the small intestine of mice irradiated with a dose of 700 r.

Histologic and gastroscopic investigations have shown pathologic changes in gastric tissue also (Lamson and Tullis, 1951; N. A. Kraevskiĭ, 1955).

Of interest in this connection are the data obtained after irradiating swine with a totally lethal dose (about 700 r) during a nuclear test explosion (Tullis, Lamson, and Madden, 1955). The animals were kept in special places so shielded from the blast and heat that they were exposed only to the gamma rays. The first signs of injury were detected 3 hours after the explosion. These included inhibited mitosis of the hematopoietic cells and intestinal epithelium and profound destructive changes in individual lymph tissue cells verging on necrosis. The changes in the intestinal epithelium disappeared within 48 hours, but hemorrhages appeared in the gastrointestinal tract several days later followed by ulcers. A great many microorganisms were found in these areas. There were comparatively fewer hemorrhages in the stomach and duodenum than elsewhere in the alimentary canal.

The data of Tillotson and Warren (1953) are interesting. Using histochemical methods, these investigators found that the RNA and DNA content of the mucosal epithelial cells of the esophagus, stomach, small, and large intestines of rats decreased during the first 10 to 15 days after irradiation with a dose of 700 r.

I. G. Chursin observed focal dilatation of veins in the mucosa of the lesser and larger curvatures of the stomach in dogs dying after total-body irradiation. He also noted hydropic degenerative changes in the neck cells of the glands (Figure 46 A) as well as markedly altered parietal and chief cells in the fundic region of the glands. The parietal cell nuclei were pyknotic, the protoplasm stained weakly, and the cells became vesicular (Figure 46 B).

Gross autopsy observation of persons killed by the atomic bomb in Hiroshima and Nagasaki failed to reveal any unusual anatomical changes except petechial hemorrhages in the pancreas (Tullis, 1954).

N. A. Kraevskiĭ (1955) mentions circulatory disorders and secondary degenerative changes in the pancreas during acute radiation sickness and signs of glandular atrophy during chronic sickness.

Compression of the pancreas, necrotic foci with slight lymphocytic infiltration, and signs of pancreatic degeneration were found

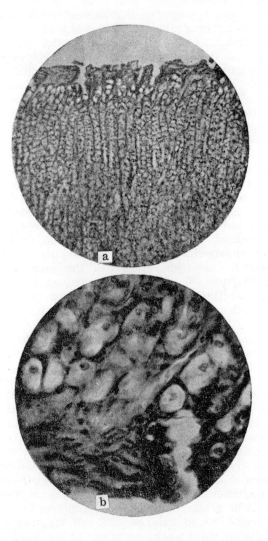

Figure 46. Microscopic view of the gastric mucosa of a dog 16 days after total-body irradiation with a dose of 250 r. (Reported by I. G. Chursin.)
A—low magnification. B—high magnification.

in a man who died of irradiation 207 days after the explosion of a hydrogen bomb over Bikini atoll (A. V. Kozlova, 1957).

According to A. E. Karpenko, who made a histologic examination of the pancreas of four dogs which died of acute radiation sickness, the gland contained both normal secretory cells, with the cytoplasm clearly divided into zymogenic and homogeneous zones, and cells deficient in prosecretin granules. Here and there, especially in the subcapsular lobules, could be seen necrosis, connective tissue proliferation, and degenerated cells whose protoplasm appeared spongiocytic (Figure 47). The epithelium of the efferent duct of the gland was generally sloughed off. The islets of Langerhans were normal, although absent in some places.

E. Ya. Gilinskiĭ (1960) investigated the pancreatic receptors of cats after single total-body exposure to 500 r and found degenerative changes present five months after irradiation. Morphologically, these were varicose thickenings, distentions, and fragmentations both of the main fiber of the receptor and of its branches.

The unusual mottled, mosaic appearance of individual components of the nervous system under identical irradiation conditions is noteworthy. In addition to the markedly argentaffin, varicose, and fragmented nerve fibers, one may also encounter nerve bundles and fibers with no structural changes. The dendritic or free receptors and encapsulated pacinian corpuscles also exhibit an uneven response to radiation. Whereas the former show severe degeneration (Figure 48), the latter reveal an argentaffin quality and marked swelling and thickening along part of its axon. The inner bulb and membrane show cellular hyperplasia (Figure 49).

Morphologic changes also occur in the salivary glands after irradiation (English, 1954); moreover, their nucleic acid content decreases at first, but then increases (A. V. Lebedinskiĭ, 1955).

Major degenerative changes arise in the liver and bile-secreting apparatus after irradiation (Case and Warthin, 1924; G. V. Yasvoin, 1926; N. Chasovnikov, 1928; L. I. Il'ina, V. D. Blokhin, and M. S. Uspenskaya, 1957). According to E. Ya. Graevskiĭ (1955), the liver of mice irradiated with 700 r reveals extensive cytoplasmic vacuolation, enlarged nuclei in the liver cells, and, in some areas, destruction of liver parenchyma. The regenerative processes develop very slowly, ending 30 to 40 days after irradiation.

Local irradiation of the liver of mice with doses of 5000 to 12,000 r, at 1000 r/min, causes the cytoplasm to shrivel and the nucleus and nucleolus to enlarge 29% and 62%, respectively. The nucleus-cytoplasm ratio shifts in favor of the nucleus, the latter approximately doubling, and the lipid content of the cytoplasm decreases from 33.4% to 9.7% (Wilson and Stowell, 1953).

Some investigators are inclined to ascribe the necrotic foci in the liver of irradiated mice to toxic and infectious influences from

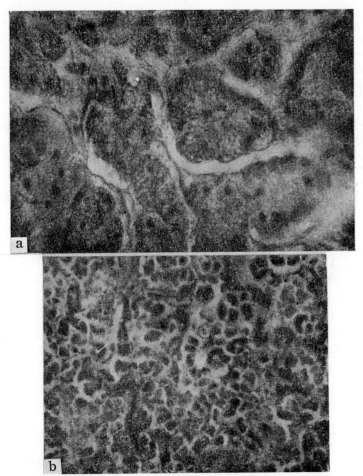

Figure 47. Microscopic views of the pancreas of dogs dying
of acute radiation sickness. (Reported by A. E. Karpenko.)
A—The dog Volk: spongiocytic protoplasm, cells of the
terminal sections reduced in size and deficient in prosecretin. Stained with hematoxylin-eosin. Mag. × 60. B—
The dog Ryzhiĭ: terminal sections of the gland show
dystrophy and disintegration into individual cells; extensive proliferation of connective tissue. Van Gieson's
stain. Mag. × 200.

the intestine, since the permeability of its mucous membrane
increases sharply (Barrow and Tullis, 1952).

Other investigators have discovered that the epithelium of the
biliary tract and gallbladder is more sensitive to X-rays than are

liver cells. Even therapeutic doses cause epithelial necrosis of the biliary tract and cholecystitis (Brams and Darnbacher, 1929).

Histochemical data testify to changes in the liver parenchyma after irradiation (Holtermann, 1924; Fischel, 1941). On the other hand, several investigators (Krause and Ziegler, 1906; Warren and Whipple, 1922) failed to find any morphologic changes in the liver after irradiation; this led others (Desjardins, 1931) to believe that the liver was less sensitive than other internal organs. This erroneous view apparently resulted from the use of imprecise histomorphological methods and from too short a period of post-irradiation observation, because most authors have invariably observed radiation damage to liver tissue.

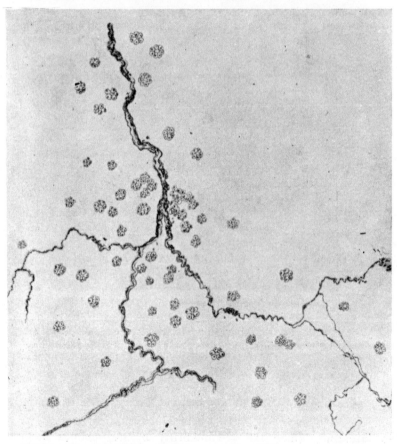

Figure 48. Dendritic or free receptor of the pancreas after single total-body irradiation. (Reported by E. Ya. Gilinskiĭ.) Bielschowsky—Gross stain. Obj. 43, oc. 15.

Internal irradiation also causes morphologic changes in the digestive system. After injecting 2 mc of radioactive gold into the peritoneum of rats, Harel (1953) discovered three months later that the liver had shrunk considerably. Microscopic examination revealed focal atrophy of liver cells, connective tissue proliferation, increased histiocytic and monocytic infiltration, hyperplasia of the Kupffer cells, and regeneration of the blood vessels and bile capillaries. One year after numerous injections of the radioactive gold, the livers of the rats had become atrophied.

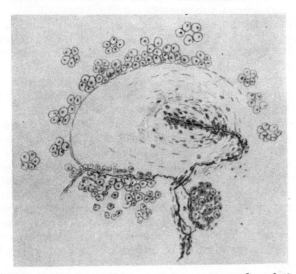

Figure 49. Lamellar pacinian corpuscle of the pancreas after single total-body irradiation. (Reported by E. Ya. Gilinskiĭ.)
Bielschowsky—Gross stain. Obj. 43, oc. 15.

A detailed study of internal ionizing radiation injury to the digestive system was made by V. N. Strel'tsova (1957), who injected rats with the radioactive isotope of lanthanum (La¹⁴⁰). This isotope has a half-life of 40 hours and emits gamma rays with a photon energy of 0.001 to 1.9 Mv. Injecting 40, 20, 14, and 10 μc/g into rats produces a typical picture of acute radiation sickness: rapid atrophy of the hematopoietic tissue of bone marrow, spleen, and lymph nodes; extensive hemorrhages in the mucosa and skin; necrobiotic changes in the gastrointestinal mucosa; and degenerative changes in the parenchymatous organs.

During the acute period of the sickness, the author observed lesions in the gastrointestinal mucosa in about 40% of the animals. The mucosa of the duodenum and small intestine showed dilated crypts lacking in epithelium; the walls were covered in places with a single layer of flattened chromophobic epithelium with watery nuclei; the connective tissue stroma of the intestine was edematous and free of leukocytes, histiocytes, plasma, and mast cells. In the stomach there was destruction of parietal and accessory cells and hemorrhagic erosion in the cervical region of the gastric glands. Destructive processes and extensive areas of necrosis containing masses of microorganisms predominated in the large intestine. The liver showed fatty degeneration and necrosis, marked hyperemia of the central and intermediary parts of the lobules, and liver cells with giant, hypochromatic nuclei.

In addition to the changes in the gastrointestinal mucosa noted above, signs of stromal and epithelial regeneration were clearly evident as early as the sixth or seventh day. In the liver, there was pronounced regeneration of the parenchyma and epithelial proliferation in the bile ducts. Necrotic and ulcerative changes in the large intestine—chiefly in the cecum, sigmoid colon, and rectum—developed slowly without any tendency to regenerate.

Strel'tsova found that radiation injury with La[140] caused subacute hepatitis in 40% of the rats, with 20% of the cases ending in cirrhosis; there were numerous slow-healing ulcers in the cecum, sigmoid colon, and rectum in 25%, and malignant and benign liver and skin tumors in 35%. It is well to keep in mind that injury by La[140] and other rapidly decaying isotopes is characterized by a brief destructive stage with relatively complete restoration of the tissues damaged. After injury by other radioactive substances— e.g., the products of uranium nuclear fission—pathological changes in the digestive system may be more extensive, profound, and longer lasting.

G. A. Lebedeva (1960) made a comparative study of morphologic changes in the gastrointestinal tract of dogs and rats during acute radiation sickness, induced in some cases by intravenous or subcutaneous injection of radioactive strontium or polonium and, in other cases, by external irradiation with roentgen or gamma rays. Such a comparision is very difficult owing to the lack of sufficiently precise criteria by which to measure the biological effectiveness of internal and external ionizing radiation and the selective action of radioactive substances on certain organs and tissues. Lebedeva, however, managed to detect the features of radiation injury common to both internally and externally irradiated animals.

She found that the early morphologic changes in the gastrointestinal tract were essentially the same but differed in degree: isolated dead cells and cells with swollen nuclei were prominent, and there was decreased mitotic activity.

During the latent period of the sickness, whether caused by external or internal irradiation, the early cellular damage was repaired. At the height of the sickness, morphologic changes in the gastrointestinal tract included hemorrhages and degenerative processes in the mucosa, stroma, and neurovascular and lymphatic systems similar in both types of injury.

The sensitivity of the gastrointestinal tract to the action of radioactive strontium and polonium is variable. The reason, according to Lebedeva, is that strontium, an osteotropic isotope, gets into the bones fairly quickly, within three days after it is injected, and remains there a long time. Polonium, on the other hand, is retained for quite a while in the walls of the stomach and intestine; also, it is discharged into the alimentary canal with secretions from the salivary glands, liver, stomach, and intestine. Because of this distribution pattern of the isotopes, polonium injures the walls of the digestive tube throughout the sickness and causes more extensive morphologic changes in the gastric and intestinal cells than does strontium.

Regeneration of the gastrointestinal mucosa proceeds in similar fashion after both internal (G. A. Lebedeva, 1960) and external irradiation (V. P. Mikhaĭlov, K. M. Svetikova, and K. M. Yaroslavt-seva, 1960). Regeneration is usually slow.

Chronic radiation sickness is characterized by the following pathological conditions: in the salivary glands and pancreas, there is epithelial destruction, focal necrosis, and atrophy; the liver shows disorganization of the hepatic cords, pericapillary edema, fatty degeneration, isolated focal necrosis, swelling and desquamation of the reticuloendothelial cells, and cirrhotic changes; in the stomach and intestine, there is atrophy of the lymphatic system, swelling of the epithelial nuclei, cellular disintegration, decreased mitotic activity, and degenerative changes in the intramural nerve plexuses; the plexuses show spherical thickenings, twisted and coarse nerve cells, and chromatolysis with swelling of the nuclei.

In concluding our description of the alimentary tract following radiation injury, we should like to emphasize once again that in addition to morphologic changes in the secretory and vascular elements, there is profound injury to the nerves supplying the digestive organs. We have already commented on changes in the receptors. There is also extensive destruction in the cells of the myenteric and submucous plexuses. This has been observed in rats 26 hours after placing an applicator with 123.2 mg of radium on the belly (Colwell and Gladstone, 1936).

T. N. Oleĭnikova (1957) showed that changes in the peripheral nervous system are alike regardless of the type of ionizing radiation or method of administration, and they appear in the myelinated nerve fibers within 30 minutes after irradiation. At the same time, the staining properties of the fibers change, as shown by the speed and unevenness with which they become impregnated. The axon thickens, becoming oval or round with irregular margins. The fibers of the myenteric plexus frequently become twisted like a corkscrew, and swellings, which eventually turn into vacuoles, appear in the fibers a few days after irradiation. Fragmentation sometimes occurs, and degenerative changes are also noted in the terminal filaments. Numerous argyrophilic granules appear in Schwann's sheath.

The destruction of nerve fibers is particularly marked in rats dying at the height of radiation sickness. Almost all the fibers are fragmented and some of them undergo granular degeneration. The cells of the submucous and myenteric plexuses are rounded, their processes are thickened, and their protoplasm vacuolated. Regenerative processes (e.g., multiplication of the cells of Schwann's sheath) can be seen alongside degenerative processes in the animals that recover.

It is noteworthy that morphologic changes in the nerve plexuses of the digestive apparatus also occur even after the local action of isotopes on the skin. Changes in the nerve fibers of the tongue, esophagus, and stomach, however, are less pronounced than in the cutaneous nerves in the areas of the skin exposed to the radioactive isotope. The former changes develop within 24 hours of exposure; swellings and thickenings are visible along the nerve fibers. Structural changes can be detected in the submucous and myenteric plexuses on the second day: the nuclei are located eccentrically and vacuoles of different sizes appear in the neuroplasm.

Another important fact is that morphologic changes in the gastrointestinal nerve supply of animals surviving radiation sickness last a long time—about a year, according to Oleĭnikova.

Morphologic changes in the gastrointestinal tract after internal irradiation with radioactive strontium (Sr^{90}) are especially interesting. G. A. Lebedeva (1957) discovered that intraperitoneal injection of rats with 0.4 $\mu c/g$ sharply increased the sensitivity of the gastrointestinal tissues and distorted normal regeneration. This specificity of action is probably due to the fact that Sr^{90} not only injures parenchymatous cells, but also has a particularly toxic effect on the nerves.

V. I. Lebedev (1957, 1960) found that injecting dogs with 0.2 $\mu c/kg$ of Sr^{90} induced profound structural changes in the intramural nerves of the stomach and intestine. During the first 14 days after injection, there was liquefaction of the chromophilic substance, swelling of the nuclei, and basophilia of cell bodies. At the height of the sickness, which usually occurred between the 20th and 22nd days, extensive structural changes in the neurons and an increase in the number of altered nerve cells were observed. The myenteric plexus of the duodenum and jejunum was particularly affected.

Similar changes in the nerve elements of the gastrointestinal tract have been observed in dogs injected with doses of 0.005 to 0.1 mc/kg of polonium (Po^{210}).

L. A. Afrikanova (1952) has described structural changes in the intramural nerve plexuses of the stomach and intestine after total-body and local X-irradiation.

It is apparent, then, that radiation injury of the digestive system produces severe morphologic changes in the mucosa, secretory and muscular cells, blood vessels, and local nerve formations. If the dose is sufficiently potent, the changes appear within a few days and progress with the course of radiation sickness, regardless of whether the irradiation was total-body or local, external or internal. They may or (more frequently) may not be reversible, depending on the dose. Typically, degenerative processes develop within the nucleus and cytoplasm. They may be caused by impairment of the trophic function of the nervous system. The morphologic changes in the digestive organs, and in the vascular and nerve formations closely associated with them, are partly responsible for the impaired gastrointestinal secretion, motility, and absorption.

PART II

Mechanisms of Impairment of the Activity of the Digestive Organs during Radiation Sickness

The successful treatment and prevention of radiation injury to the digestive system depends on the extent of our knowledge of the physiological mechanisms involved in the development and elimination of the disease. Our knowledge, however, is far from adequate, and we must first solve some general problems in radiobiology, radiophysiology, and radiopathology. There is as yet no unified theory regarding the action of ionizing radiation on biological tissues, nor is there any generally accepted view on the mechanism by which radiation sickness develops. Theoretical considerations about the origin of radiation sickness, however, have been set forth by many investigators: Jenkinson and Brown, 1944; Warren, 1946; S. A. Nikitin, 1946; Porter, 1952; I. R. Petrov and E. V. Gubler, 1954; P. D. Gorizontov, 1954, 1955, 1958, 1959; E. Cronkite 1954; E. Barron, 1955; B. N. Tarusov, 1955, 1957; A. M. Kuzin, 1956; A. Hollaender, 1959; F. Ellinger, 1952; L. A. Orbeli, 1955; A. V. Lebedinskiĭ, 1955, 1957; I. R. Petrov and V. I. Kulagin, 1957; D. A. Biryukov, 1958. All of these investigations make it possible to conceive of radiation injury as arising in the following way.

It is assumed that direct and indirect action of penetrating radiation on human and animal cells is the primary radiophysiological factor in radiation injury. An important effect of this radiation is the ionization of the liquid medium in the biological substrate; this ionization forms free radicals, various peroxidates, and excited molecules which trigger a succession of organic chemical reactions.

Possessing high toxicity, the free radicals, peroxidates, and proteolytic and lipolytic products are at the same time chemical stimulants of certain reactive substances in the body, chiefly in the receptors. They are thus responsible for numerous reflex responses. When these toxic substances get into the circulatory system, they have a direct effect on all the cells and tissues, causing functional as well as organic injury. Thus, the primary radiation effect develops through a series of complex chain reactions into prolonged radiation injury caused by a nonspecific reaction typical of many pathological processes.

Besides its indirect effect, ionizing radiation also has direct influence on the proteins, lipids, and other molecular substances in the cells as well as on the metabolic enzyme systems. The disruption of metabolism and oxidation-reduction reactions leads to the formation of new toxic substances which, together with the products of nuclear and cytoplasmic destruction, sustain the pathological processes.

The appearance of highly active biological substances, the depolymerization of protein molecules (chiefly nucleo-, and lipoproteins), the spatial disorientation of molecules, and impaired activity of the enzymes adsorbed on the surface of cells—all of these factors cause impaired protein and nucleic acid synthesis, altered cell growth and division, formation of hormones and antibodies, permeability changes in cell membranes and vascular walls, and many other functional and structural changes.

Other important factors are injury to the so-called respiratory enzymes which contain sulfhydryl groups (phosphoglyceraldehyde dehydrogenase, adenosinetriphosphatase, etc.), to the nucleoproteins, and to nucleic acid metabolism. The incompletely oxidized fatty acids, which are highly toxic and are themselves capable of sustaining biochemical chain reactions, also participate in the metabolic disturbances.

It is worth stressing that the direct and indirect actions of ionizing radiation affect not only the organs of the hematopoietic, digestive, cardiovascular, genitourinary, respiratory, and other autonomic systems, but also all the links in the central peripheral nervous systems and endocrine glands—i.e., those vital structures in man and higher animals which regulate and coordinate the activity of the organ systems of the body as a whole. Damage to the defensive and adaptational mechanisms of the central nervous system and neuroendocrine apparatus is largely responsible for the complex of visceral disorders which occur during radiation sickness.

Radiation injury in man and animals, then, is caused by: (a) direct injury to the cells by radiant energy; (b) indirect cellular damage by biologically active chemical substances formed from the ionization of water and the degradation of proteins, lipids, and other substances; and (c) reflexes arising from the direct and indirect (toxemic) effects of ionizing radiation on receptors. (See diagram.)

This is the way in which the over-all process of radiation injury to the digestive functions should be considered. The following basic manifestations should be kept in mind when analyzing this process:

(a) The early appearance of secretory disorders;

(b) The cyclic development of disorders of secretion, motility, and absorption;

(c) Disorders of the hypo- and hyperfunctional types;

(d) The appearance of "spontaneous" secretion and dyskinesia of the gastrointestinal tract;

(e) Changes in the digestive activity of gastrointestinal secretions.

All of these phenomena can apparently be correlated with morphologic changes in the glands, smooth muscle, blood vessels,

Diagram of routes of pathogenic effects of radiant energy
on the body. (After P. D. Gorizontov.)

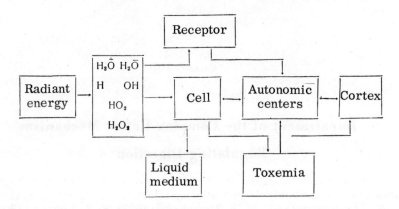

mucosa, and intramural nerve plexuses of the gastrointestinal tract.
Initially, this was the approach to radiation injury taken by certain
pathologists and radiobiologists; however, the mechanisms of impaired digestive function are now looked at more broadly in the
light of recent experimental and clinical material. No one, of
course, can deny the significance of morphologic changes in the
impairment of gastrointestinal function, but one wonders if they
are solely responsible for the impaired digestion seen in radiation
sickness. We think not. First of all, morphologic changes in the
cells and tissues of the digestive organs can arise both as a result
of the direct action of ionizing radiation and as a result of indirect
influences exerted through the nervous system and blood, especially
as radiation sickness develops. Secondly, major digestive disorders
frequently develop even in the absence of clear-cut structural
changes during the latent period of acute radiation sickness and
during mild chronic sickness. We now have enough information to
warrant our correlating radiation injury of secretion, motility, and
absorption both with structural changes in the digestive organs and
with disorders of the general neurohumoral regulatory mechanisms.

In this connection, five fundamental questions arise, each of
which we shall consider in turn:

(1) Impairment of the complex reflex mechanism regulating
digestion;

(2) The significance of functional weakening of the cerebral
cortex in radiation injury to the digestive system;

(3) The role of the vascular factor in secretory disorders;

(4) Impairment of the receptive function of the gastrointestinal
tract;

(5) Impairment of the humoral regulation of digestion.

CHAPTER 10

Impairment of the Complex Reflex Mechanism
Regulating Digestion

Facts about changes in higher nervous activity are highly important in the analysis of radiation injury to the digestive system. I. R. Tarkhanov (1896), M. N. Zhukovskiĭ (1903), E. S. London (1904), E. I. Bakin (1946), P. D. Gorizontov (1955), A. V. Lebedinskiĭ (1955, 1957), N. N. Livshits (1956), D. A. Biryukov (1958), P. F. Minaev (1958), P. I. Lomonos (1959), Yu. G. Grigor'ev (1959), and above all, M. I. Nemenov (1932, 1938, 1944, 1950) and his radiobiology co-workers have clearly demonstrated that the central nervous system is highly radiosensitive.

Using conditioned reflexes and electroencephalography, other investigators have shown that functional changes in the cerebral cortex and subcortical autonomic centers occur within minutes or seconds after irradiation (Yu. G. Grigor'ev, 1954, 1956, 1959; M. N. Livanov, 1957; Z. A. Yanson, 1957; G. M. Frank, 1958; and others).

M. S. Seregin (1959) discovered that conditioned acid-defense reflexes in dogs, formed after stimulation of the gastrointestinal receptors, change within 10 to 15 seconds after the start of total-body X-irradiation (Tables 54 and 55).

The results of these experiments are highly interesting in that they clearly testify to impairment of the complex reflex mechanism regulating salivation immediately after irradiation. It is worth noting that changes in conditioned salivation in the dog Pal'ma were not accompanied by any noticeable deviation in the animal's innate salivary reflex. In fact, prior to irradiation the total value of four conditioned reflexes was 25 drops; after irradiation, this increased to 42 drops. The total value of the unconditioned reflexes both before and after irradiation, however, was 268 and 265 drops, respectively; that is, there was scarcely any change. Ionizing radiation, then, impairs first the cortical mechanism regulating the conditioned salivation and then, as radiation injury deepens, unconditioned reflex activity is also impaired. In other cases,

Table 54

Conditioned salivation in the dog Dzhek before and 10 seconds after
the start of total-body X-irradiation.

(Reported by M. S. Seregin.)

Time (hr and min)	Conditioned stimulus (rhythmic stimulation of the intestine	Duration of the conditioned stimulus (sec)	Latent period (sec)	Magnitude of the conditioned reflex (drops of saliva)	Magnitude of the unconditioned reflex (drops of saliva)
Before irradiation					
10.29	Balloon	20	4	12	93
10.33	"	20	4	18	79
10.37	"	20	5	6	91
10.41	"	20	4	9	92
10 sec after the start of irradiation					
10.45	Balloon	20	—	0	106
10.49	"	20	3	6	117
10.53	"	20	13	2	102
10.57	"	20	—	0	102

however, e.g., in the dog Dzhek, both mechanisms are involved;
therefore, conditioned and unconditioned activity may be impaired
simultaneously.

During radiation sickness injury to the cortical mechanism is
much more pronounced than injury to the subcortical salivary
centers. This early radiation effect on the higher divisions of the
central nervous system is undoubtedly highly significant in radiation
damage to corticovisceral relations in general and to the complex
reflex regulation of digestion in particular. This view has been confirmed by simultaneous study of changes in higher nervous activity
and in gastrointestinal secretion and motility during all phases of
radiation sickness. We presented the pertinent data on this in
our discussion of radiation injury to secretion in the stomach,
pancreas, and intestine and to gastrointestinal tract motility and
bile secretion.

It has been demonstrated experimentally that slight changes in nervous activity are quite often associated with slight disturbances in the digestive organs, and that major impairment of the cerebral cortex is associated with profound changes in digestive activity. Moreover, changes in higher nervous activity often precede impairment of the digestive system. It has been found that ionizing radiation changes both higher nervous activity and gastrointestinal activity, but the question remains, which is primary? It may well be that after total-body irradiation, they change simultaneously in view of the primary radiation effects—ionization, the formation of toxic substances, molecular damage to proteins, enzymes, etc. The question cannot be answered readily, even with the aid of modern physiological research methods. Under the conditions of our experiments, however, when radiation effects were kept under continuous study from the first impact of radiation trauma through the

Table 55

Conditioned salivation in the dog Pal'ma before and 15 seconds after the start of total-body X-irradiation.

(Reported by M. S. Seregin.)

Time (hr and min)	Conditioned stimulus (rhythmic stimulation of the intestine	Duration of the conditioned stimulus (sec)	Latent period (sec)	Magnitude of the conditioned reflex (drops of saliva)	Magnitude of the unconditioned reflex (drops of saliva)
Before irradiation					
9.13	Balloon	20	3	6	63
9.17	"	20	7	6	68
9.21	"	20	5	5	70
9.25	"	20	5	5	70
10 sec after the start of irradiation					
9.29	Balloon	20	3	12	68
9.33	"	20	5	11	69
9.37	"	20	3	6	69
9.41	"	20	3	13	59

ensuing days and weeks until the animals recovered or died, the primacy of higher nervous center involvement could scarcely be doubted. The dose, rate, and radiosensitivity of the animals, of course, were significant.

We kept the dose and the rate constant so that differences in radiation effect were due solely to the degree of radiosensitivity or resistance of the individual animals. As a result, the course of radiation sickness was mild in some cases, but moderately severe, severe, or extremely severe in others. Cerebrocortical and visceral functions paralleled the extent of radiation damage. In cases of moderately severe and especially severe and extremely severe injury, changes in the cerebrocortical and visceral functions appeared and developed simultaneously. It was impossible, therefore, with the methods employed, to determine the primary site of injury. It was another matter, however, when the same dose caused mild radiation sickness. In this case the impairment of higher nervous activity was clearly primary. In support of this view, we should like to supplement the facts given above with the following data.

A. E. Karpenko observed the same phenomenon in experiments on dogs involving the simultaneous study of higher nervous activity and pancreatic secretion. The experiments on Ural and Ryzhiĭ, which were given total-body irradiation of 250 r, are illustrative. Ural developed mild sickness while Ryzhiĭ developed severe sickness and died on the 16th day. Ten minutes after they were irradiated, the two animals were taken into another room for conditioned reflex experiments. It was discovered that higher nervous activity was markedly impaired in both dogs. In Ural this was reflected in a shortened latent period of the conditioned reflexes, an increase in the positive conditioned reflexes, a disinhibition of differentiation, an increase in unconditioned reflexes, and an increase in cerebrocortical activity (Table 56). Ryzhiĭ, however, developed a longer latent period, a decrease in unconditioned reflexes, a disinhibition of differentiation, a slight increase in unconditioned reflexes, a general lowering of cerebrocortical activity throughout the experiment, and a slight increase in the activity of the subcortical salivary centers (Table 57).

The changes in higher nervous activity did not disappear, but continued to develop both during the latent period of the sickness and at its height, although there were features peculiar to each dog.

Impaired pancreatic secretion in Ryzhiĭ was pronounced the second day after irradiation, but in Ural it appeared a week later (Figure 50). There is no doubt that impaired higher nervous activity in Ural preceded pancreatic secretory disorders.

Hypnotic phases were noted in the dogs' higher nervous activity the first few days after irradiation. These are among the early signs of radiation injury to the cortical cells. Experiments involving

Table 56

Higher nervous activity in the dog Ural before and 10 minutes
after total-body X-irradiation with a dose of 250 r.

(Reported by A. E. Karpenko.)

Time (hr and min)	Conditioned stimulus	Duration of the conditioned stimulus (sec)	Latent period (sec)	Magnitude of the reflexes (scale divisions)	
				Con-ditioned	Uncon-ditioned
Before irradiation					
10.49	Bell (+)	20	11	110	730
10.53	Light (+)	20	13	30	720
10.57	Metronome 120 (+)	20	9	120	700
11.01	Metronome 60 (−)	20	—	0	—
11.05	Bell (+)	20	13	80	760
11.09	Light (+)	20	7	50	745
11.13	Metronome 120 (+)	20	11	80	820

Mean magnitude of the positive conditioned reflex - 78.
Mean magnitude of the unconditioned reflex - 746.
Mean magnitude of the latent period of the positive
unconditioned reflex - 10.7 sec.

10 min after irradiation

Time (hr and min)	Conditioned stimulus	Duration	Latent period	Con-ditioned	Uncon-ditioned
10.24	Bell (+)	20	6	150	780
10.28	Light (+)	20	4	130	775
10.32	Metronome 120 (+)	20	13	85	760
10.36	Metronome 60 (−)	20	6	60	—
10.40	Bell (+)	20	8	120	800
10.44	Light (+)	20	12	65	880
10.48	Metronome 120 (+)	20	8	140	820

Mean magnitude of the positive conditioned reflex - 115.
Mean magnitude of the unconditioned reflex - 803.
Mean magnitude of the latent period of the positive un-
conditioned reflex - 8.5 sec.

Table 57

Higher nervous activity in the dog Ryzhiĭ before and 10 minutes
after total body X-irradiation with a dose of 250 r.

(Reported by A. E. Karpenko.)

Time (hr and min)	Conditioned stimulus	Duration of the conditioned stimulus (sec)	Latent period (sec)	Magnitude of the reflexes (scale divisions)	
				Conditioned	Unconditioned
Before irradiation					
9.21	Bell (+)	20	6	145	600
9.25	Light (+)	20	5	120	625
9.29	Metronome 120 (+)	20	6	130	590
9.33	Metronome 60 (−)	20	7	35	−
9.37	Bell (+)	20	5	90	600
9.41	Light (+)	20	4	80	615
9.45	Metronome 120 (+)	20	4	95	610

Mean magnitude of the positive conditioned reflex - 110.
Mean magnitude of the conditioned reflex - 607.
Mean magnitude of the latent period of the positive
unconditioned reflex - 5 sec.

10 min after irradiation					
9.18	Bell (+)	20	7	150	595
9.22	Light (+)	20	5	40	625
9.26	Metronome 120 (+)	20	9	45	625
9.30	Metronome 60 (−)	20	6	70	−
9.34	Bell (+)	20	5	40	630
9.38	Light (+)	20	9	35	630
9.42	Metronome 120 (+)	20	8	50	630

Mean magnitude of the positive conditioned reflex - 60.
Mean magnitude of the unconditioned reflex - 622.
Mean magnitude of the latent period of the positive
unconditioned reflex - 7 sec.

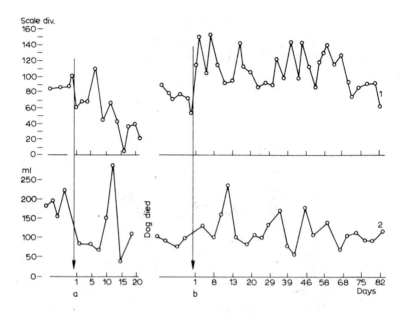

Figure 50. Changes in higher nervous activity and pancreatic
secretion in the dogs Ryzhiĭ and Ural during acute radiation
sickness. (Reported by A. E. Karpenko.)
1—Conditioned salivary reflexes. 2—Pancreatic secretion; a—Ryzhiĭ, b—Ural. Arrows show day of irradiation
(250 r).

the application of unequal stimuli such as meat and milk, showed
that phasic changes occur in pancreatic secretion but later than in
cerebrocortical activity; these phasic changes are most pronounced
at the height of radiation sickness (Table 58).

Similar early changes in higher nervous activity were also observed by several of our co-workers who studied conditioned
salivary reflexes and digestive functions simultaneously. Experimenting on the dog Seraya, I. G. Chursin discovered changes
in higher nervous activity within 30 minutes after total-body irradiation; distinct secretory changes in the Pavlov pouch, however,
became evident only after the fourth day. V. L. Popkov found a 40%
increase in conditioned reflexes above the original level and other
indications of modified higher nervous activity immediately after
a session of total-body irradiation. These deviations lasted throughout the sickness, but changes in bile secretion began only on the
11th day after irradiation.

Investigating radiation injury to intestinal secretion and motility
in the dog Seryĭ, A. V. Popov discovered distinct changes in higher

nervous activity as early as the second day after irradiation; secretion and motility, however, remained normal until the fifth day. He noted decreased positive conditioned reflexes and a disinhibition of differentiation in Dzhul'bars immediately after irradiation, but secretion became impaired only on the ninth day. According to Popov, intestinal disorders generally developed in the dogs between the second and ninth days after irradiation, whereas higher nervous activity became impaired imnediately after irradiation. Although impairment to both systems progressed in parallel fashion throughout the radiation sickness, both functions did not become normal at the same time; normal cerebrocortical activity returned before normal intestinal secretion. The former also preceded normalization of the intestinal musculature and the blood constituents.

In our own experiments we did not attempt to determine the functional condition of the cerebral cortex and the digestive system at the same time. If the dogs' conditioned reflexes were based on acid administration, the digestive experiments were run one or two hours after ending the conditioning experiments. However, when the conditioned reflexes were based on food, the digestive experiments were conducted a day after the conditioning experiments. The functional condition of the cortex was determined from conditioned salivary reflexes; digestive activity was judged from the total secretory volume produced in response to a food stimulus. But radiation injury, as mentioned above, does not necessarily impair secretion equally in the different phases of the secretory process. Glandular activity is frequently impaired in the complex

Table 58

Phasic, parabiotic changes in pancreatic secretion in dogs during acute radiation sickness.

(Reported by A. E. Karpenko.)

Name of dog	Volume of pancreatic secretion (ml)			
	Before the sickness		At the height of the sickness	
	Milk	Meat	Milk	Meat
Ural	54	132	111	89
Volk	129	213	421	221
Chert......	203	284	279	267

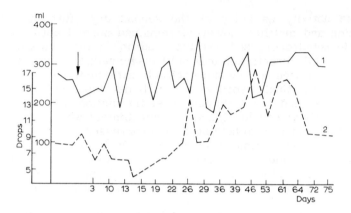

Figure 51. Changes in higher nervous activity and gastric secretion in the dog Chernyshka after total-body irradiation with a dose of 250 r. (Reported by N. A. Yaroslavtseva.)
1—Volume of gastric juice secreted after sham feeding. 2—Magnitude of positive conditioned salivary reflexes per experiment. Arrow indicates day of irradiation.

reflex phase and yet remains unchanged in the second or neurochemical phase. And it sometimes happens that weakening of secretion in the first phase is quantitatively compensated for by intensified secretion in the second phase; however, the total volume of juice secreted per experiment does not exceed the original level. That is why we did not draw a final conclusion on whether higher nervous activity or digestion became impaired first until we had analyzed all the experimental data on both the over-all totals and the individual characteristics of secretion: the latent period, volume and nature of secretion in the complex reflex and neurochemical phases, hourly secretory rate, duration of secretion, etc. Even this fractional analysis, however, which did reveal some earlier changes in several aspects of secretion (e.g., in the latent period of excitation of the secretory cells and in glandular activity in the first or complex reflex phase), clearly showed that radiation impaired higher nervous activity before there were any distinct signs of abnormal secretion in the liver, stomach, pancreas, and small intestine.

For example, in N. A. Yaroslavtseva's experiments on a gastroesophagotomized dog, changes in conditioned activity began immediately after total-body irradiation (250 r), whereas impaired gastric secretion after sham feeding became perceptible only on the tenth day after irradiation (Figure 51). Moreover, the blood constituents changed later than higher nervous activity. The leukocyte count in the peripheral blood, for example began to drop from 11,250 to 3700 only on the tenth day after irradiation; by this time the erythrocyte sedimentation rate had increased from 9-10 to 28 mm per hour.

These results are significant because they reveal 1) that cerebrocortical function becomes impaired before gastrointestinal secretion and motility, and 2) that primary disruption of higher nervous activity is followed by damage to the complex reflex mechanism that regulates digestion. All this provides additional confirmation of I. P. Pavlov's fundamental theory that in man and in higher animals "the most reactive part of the organism is the cerebral hemispheres."*

In view of the evidence on changes in conditioned activity which immediately follow irradiation and on the major role played by the subcortical autonomic centers in the development of radiation sickness (M. I. Nemenov, 1950; D. A. Biryukov, 1958; A. V. Lebedinskiĭ, Z. N. Nakhil'nitskaya, and N. P. Smirnova, 1958; M. N. Livanov, 1959; S. Ya. Arbuzov and others, 1959), we feel that there is no reason to question the significance of radiation injury to the higher divisions of the central nervous system as a cause of digestive disorders during radiation sickness.

---

*Pavlovskie sredy. Izd. AN SSSR, 1949, III, p. 114.

CHAPTER II

Significance of Functional Weakening of the

Cerebral Cortex in Radiation Injury to the

Digestive System

In discussing radiation injury to the various digestive organs, we have constantly emphasized our basic conviction that the functional weakening of the cerebral cortex associated with the disruption of higher nervous activity sharply decreases resistance to radiation sickness, aggravates its over-all course, and causes more severe impairment of gastrointestinal secretion, motility, and absorption. To avoid distracting the reader from our main theme, the characteristics of radiation injury to the digestive system, we have refrained from encumbering the text with clinical details on radiation sickness proper; instead, we have contented ourselves with a brief description of changes in the peripheral blood, the duration and outcome of the sickness, and some other features tending to show that organic injury to the animal is more profound when its defense and adaptation mechanisms are impaired before exposure to irradiation. Therefore, as we describe impairment of the mechanisms regulating the digestive system as a whole, we should like to stress once more the significance of functional weakening of the cerebral cortex both in the development of radiation disease and in radiation injury to digestive functions.

The significance of disrupted higher nervous activity irradiation sickness is graphically illustrated by the fact that total-body irradiation of dogs with doses of 250 to 350 r proved fatal to 57% of the animals with an induced nervous disorder compared with only 25% of the healthy animals. Our co-worker A. P. Myasnikov traumatized the nervous system of cats by means of "electric clashing" either just before or during the first few days after irradiation with 600 r. He discovered that the traumatized animals suffered a much greater and earlier loss in weight, a greater drop in the leukocyte count (down to 400-700/mm³), and a more accelerated erythrocyte sedimentation rate than did the nontraumatized animals. Moreover, they died much sooner after irradiation. For example, of 36 cats subjected to "electric clashing" before irradiation or during the first hour after irradiation, 18 died within 6 to 9 days thereafter; all 18 nontraumatized animals, however, were still alive at this time. The great majority of deaths (12 out of 18 cats) occurred in the cases where "electric clashing" immediately followed irradiation. Traumatization of the central nervous system is particularly effective when it immediately precedes the appearance of clinically pronounced signs of radiation sickness. For example, four cats subjected to "electric clashing" eight days after irradiation died on the 10th, 18th, 19th, and 26th days. In summary, all 40 cats whose nervous systems were traumatized before or soon after irradiation died within 26 days, while the overwhelming majority of irradiated but nontraumatized cats survived throughout the observation period of three to six months. The control group of animals subjected to "electric clashing" but not irradiated also survived.

The aggravating effect of a nervous disorder on the course of radiation sickness has been demonstrated both by experiments involving the digestive system and by experiments on conditioned and unconditioned respiratory reflexes (I. I. Golodov), the optical properties of blood serum (A. G. Kuzovkov), reflexes from the proprio- and interoceptors of the extremities, blood pressure and respiration (D. M. Gzgzyan), and blood circulation and hematopoiesis (M. E. Vasilenko).

The type of nervous system involved is another important factor, as shown by the work of L. I. Kotlyarevskiĭ, L. S. Gorsheleva and L. E. Khozak (1958), P. F. Minaev (1958), P. D. Gorizontov (1954, 1955), R. S. Zlatin, A. F. Makarchenko, V. F. Saenko-Lyubarskaya, and M. F. Sirotina (1959), and others. In our observations of 100 dogs, we found that irradiation caused severe and fatal radiation sickness in 70% of the animals representing the two extreme types, the weak and the impulsive. On the other hand, the same dose killed only 8% of the animals with a strong, balanced type of nervous system.

The experiments of our co-worker P. V. Simonov (1957) on intact and decorticated rabbits are of interest. Total-body irradiation with a dose of 400 r, he found, caused severe radiation sickness in three out of four animals with their cerebral hemispheres removed; the leukocyte count dropped to $3000/mm^3$ before the three rabbits died. The sickness was comparatively mild in four rabbits with intact hemispheres and all survived (Table 59).

If clashing between the food and defense reflexes ("electric clashing") were induced in the rabbits with their cerebral hemispheres removed prior to irradiation, the radiation sickness which followed proved to be exceptionally severe and the animals died four days after irradiation.

Table 59

Effect of extirpation of the cerebral hemispheres on the outcome
of radiation sickness in rabbits.

(Reported by P. V. Simonov.)

Experimental conditions	No. of animals	Outcome of sickness		Day of death
		Sur-vived	Died	
1. Rabbits with intact cerebral hemispheres	4	4	0	
2. Hemispherectomized rabbits	4	1	3	One on 11th day, the others on 17th day
3. Hemispherectomized rabbits irradiated after "electric clashing"	2	0	2	Both on 4th day

These findings corroborate our view that the functional condition
of the cerebral cortex plays a major role in the outcome of radiation sickness and in the development of radiation injury to the
viscera. The figures in Tables 60 and 61 illustrate the aggravating
effect of a nervous disorder on the course of radiation sickness
in dogs.

Radiation injury of the digestive organs, as we have stated
several times, is more profound and longer lasting in animals
irradiated after traumatization of the nervous system. Here are
some additional examples. We have already cited the findings of
N. A. Yaroslavtseva, who showed in experiments on gastroesophagotomized dogs that irradiation with 250 r had a marked effect
on gastric secretion following sham feeding, and that impairment of
conditioned activity was paralleled by impaired glandular activity
in the complex reflex phase. Gastric secretory disorders first
appeared immediately after changes in the conditioned reflexes, and
they paralled the changes in higher nervous activity and disappeared
when the latter became normal. Their depth varied with the degree
of cerebrocortical impairment.

Yaroslavtseva noted the same relationship after irradiating the
same dogs again with 250 r, but this time after inducing a nervous

disorder. After experimental interference with excitation and inhibition and additional overstraining of excitation in the dogs, the magnitude of the positive conditioned reflexes decreased, hypnotic phases appeared, successive inhibition became intensified, and the

Table 60

Effect of functional weakening of the cerebral cortex on changes in the blood, temperature, and weight of the dogs Lis and Medved' during radiation sickness.

(Reported by A. A. Fadeeva, I. T. Kurtsin, and A. D. Golovskiĭ.)

Day of sickness	Leukocytes/ mm^3 of blood (thousands)	Erythro- cytes/mm^3 of blood (millions)	Body tem- perature (°C)	Body weight (kg)
Lis. Before irradiation				
	9.5	5.9	39.0	17.9
Irradiation (250 r) with normal cerebral cortex.				
3rd	9.6	6.2	39.0	17.3
5th	8.1	5.2	39.0	17.2
10th	2.6	4.9	39.5	16.0
15th	0.85	—	39.1	15.5
20th	1.7	3.2	40.5	15.0
The dog died on the 55th day after irradiation from profuse stomach bleeding.				
Medved'. Before irradiation				
	20.0	5.1	38.0	16.0
Irradiation (250 r) after experimentally induced nervous disorders.				
3rd	12.0	5.3	38.5	15.0
5th	3.5	4.7	39.5	14.2
10th	1.4	4.9	40.2	13.1
15th	0.5	3.7	40.5	12.5
The dog died on the 18th day after irradiation.				

Table 61

Effect of functional weakening of the cerebral cortex on blood and weight changes in the dog Don during radiation sickness.

(Reported by A. A. Fadeeva, I. T. Kurtsin, and A. D. Golovskiĭ.)

Day of sickness	Leukocytes/ mm³of blood (thousands)	Erythrocytes/ mm³ of blood (millions)	Body weight (kg)
Before irradiation			
	20.0	4.0	18.1
Irradiation (250 r) with normal cerebral cortex			
3rd	15.8	4.1	18.0
5th	8.0	4.1	17.3
10th	10.0	4.3	17.3
15th	8.3	5.0	17.1
20th	10.7	4.1	17.4
25th	10.1	4.1	18.2
30th	9.7	4.1	18.5
35th	14.7	4.1	18.5
Before irradiation			
	16.1	4.5	18.1
Irradiation (250 r) after experimentally induced nervous disorder			
3rd	8.5	4.5	17.9
5th	7.5	4.5	16.4
10th	5.8	4.4	16.1
15th	4.1	4.3	17.0
20th	6.1	3.0	16.1
25th	11.4	3.9	15.7
30th	16.5	3.5	15.4
35th	13.3	2.4	15.3

latent period of the reflexes lengthened. Against this cortical background, irradiation produced severe sickness. The leukocyte count in the peripheral blood decreased from 10,000 to 1000 and sometimes even $300/mm^3$. The functional capacity of the cortex, meanwhile, was sharply reduced, hypnotic phases were noted in each experiment, and the latent period of the reflexes increased from 3-5 to 15-17 seconds. All the dogs died between the 13th and 33rd days after irradiation. The conditioned reflexes were completely inhibited the day before death. Changes in gastric secretion at this time were even more pronounced. First, "spontaneous" secretion of acid juice appeared. Secondly, secretion after sham feeding fluctuated considerably between high and low levels in a cyclic fashion throughout the sickness. This phenomenon was less pronounced when the animals were irradiated with the cerebral cortex functioning normally (Figure 52).

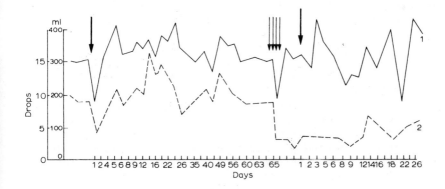

Figure 52. Changes in higher nervous activity and gastric secretion in the dog Belka during acute radiation sickness caused by irradiation first with the cerebral cortex normal, then again after an experimental nervous disorder had been induced. (Reported by N. A. Yaroslavtseva.)
1—Volume of gastric juice secreted after sham feeding following irradiation. 2—Magnitude of the conditioned reflexes after irradiation. Arrows indicate first and last days of irradiation (250 r). Group of arrows indicate clashing.

Secretion was distorted and the period of maximum secretion shifted from the first to the second and third hours after sham feeding with meat. Shortly before the animals died, the total volume of juice secreted after sham feeding dropped to half the original volume.

A. V. Popov (1957, 1958) conducted two series of experiments on the same dogs. The first or control series involved total-body irradiation with 250 r after a nervous disorder had been induced. The second series was performed under the same conditions as the first, but with the use of a number of drugs. These included preparations that improve the functioning of the nervous system, prevent hemorrhage, stimulate hematopoiesis, increase the detoxifying capacity of the liver, and have a broad spectrum of anti-infective action: sodium bromide; vitamins B_1, B_6, B_{12}, P, and K; folic acid; ascorbic acid; Benadryl; potassium chloride; glucose; insulin; and biomycin. In some cases they were administered every day immediately after irradiation for several days. In other cases the drugs were given daily for 10 days prior to irradiation and then throughout the sickness.

Observations were made on changes in higher nervous activity, intestinal secretion and motility, pulse, temperature, body weight, peripheral blood composition, and general behavior of the animals. Here are some of the findings on the dog Dzhul'bars.

Just before irradiation the dog's higher nervous activity was disrupted in a darkened room by the fivefold application of a very strong stimulus (rattle) and triple clashing according to Pavlov's method. This seriously impaired higher nervous activity and gastric secretion and motility and produced changes in blood composition and general behavior.

The magnitude of the positive conditioned reflexes decreased abruptly in several experiments to zero; differentiation was disinhibited; paradoxical and inhibitory hypnotic phases appeared in cortical activity; and the latent period of the conditioned salivary reflexes increased. There was a 30% drop in unconditioned salivation below the original level. Gastric secretion sometimes decreased by 30 to 40% of the original level, while at other times it increased by 60 to 70%. Intestinal motility intensified and the peristaltic waves became longer.

After these severe higher nervous and autonomic disorders were induced, the animal was given total-body irradiation with 250 r. On the next day the magnitude of the positive conditioned reflexes increased while differentiation became considerably disinhibited. The positive conditioned reflexes, however, soon decreased again, to zero in some experiments, and stabilized at this level for 33 days. On some days equalizing, paradoxical, and ultraparadoxical phases were noted in the activity of the cortical cells but with cortical tone now decreased. Differentiation remained disinhibited throughout, especially between the 30th and 45th days after irradiation. Unconditioned salivation during the sickness was generally about 30% below normal. In the recovery period the positive conditioned reflexes gradually increased. These changes in higher nervous activity persisted about 50 days.

Within two days after irradiation, the leukocyte count dropped from 8000 to 4500/mm^3 and, by the 19th day to 600; it returned to the original level on the 56th day. The erythrocyte count dropped from 5.5 to 3.5 million/mm^3. The erythrocyte sedimentation rate rose to 70 to 80 mm/hr.

Changes in gastric secretion began on the fifth day after irradiation; the volume of juice secreted after mechanical stimulation of the intestinal mucosa decreased. By the 21st day secretion had fallen to 20 to 30% of the original volume; it remained on this level until the 43rd day when it began to increase slowly in a wave-like fashion. It became completely normal on the 96th day (Figure 53). Blood was noted in the juice at the height of the sickness.

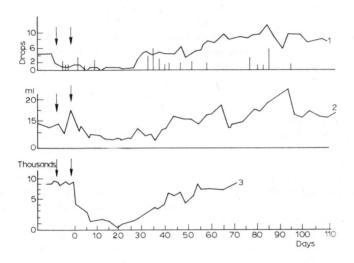

Figure 53. Changes in higher nervous activity, intestinal secretion, and the leukocyte count in the dog Dzhul'bars after irradiation with a nervous disorder.
(Reported by A. V. Popov.)
1—Conditioned reflexes. 2—Intestinal secretion.
3—Leukocyte count per mm³. Arrows: on the left, clashing; on the right, irradiation with 250 r.

Intestinal motility became inhibited almost immediately after irradiation. Rhythmic contractions were markedly weakened at the height of the sickness and peristalsis almost completely disappeared. There was a sharp decrease in intestinal tone. Motility returned to normal on the 90th day after irradiation.

In addition to the foregoing disorders, there was also impairment of the enzyme-forming function of the intestinal glands. Amylolytic activity of the juice rose from 8 to 16 units, proteolytic activity remained 58% below normal for 69 days, and lipolytic activity increased. All these figures testify to the severity of the sickness and to the greatly impaired autonomic function. This is also borne out by the animal's general condition. The dog was sluggish and weak and food excitability was low. At the height of the sickness, body temperature rose to 39.7°C. The dog had lost about 4 kg in weight by the end of the sickness.

After recovery, when the functions under study had returned to normal, the dog was put through another series of similar experiments, except that it was given the drugs mentioned above. The sequence of procedures was the same as in the first series. First, a nervous disorder was induced; it was characterized in the main by the same changes in higher nervous activity, intestinal secretion and motility, blood composition, and general behavior as in the first series of experiments.

Twenty days after traumatization of higher nervous activity, the dog was exposed to 250 r of total-body irradiation. The drugs were administered three days later.

It was found that during the first five days after irradiation the animal's conditioned activity was markedly impaired. But beginning with the sixth day—i.e., three days after the institution of therapy— the first signs of improvement appeared. The magnitude of the positive conditioned reflexes began to increase progressively, the latent period of the conditioned reflexes decreased, and the phasic states of the cortical cells disappeared. On the 15th day the positive conditioned reflexes increased 50% or more above the original level, where they stabilized with insignificant fluctuations from experiment to experiment, even after the course of therapy, which took about four weeks.

Intestinal secretion decreased sharply during the first eight days after irradiation, but on the 11th day, or a week after the start of therapy, it rose considerably, exceeding the original level by 50%. Although there were wavelike fluctuations, the new level was sustained until the animal recovered completely. It is noteworthy that no blood was found in the juice throughout the sickness.

Leukopenia after irradiation developed much later than in the first series of experiments. The leukocyte count did not drop below 2000/mm³. It started to rise on the 24th day and reached the original level on the 36th day.

Immediately after irradiation and up until the 18th day, intestinal motility remained inhibited, but then it quickly returned to normal.

After recovery and the return of normal functions, a third series of experiments were performed, differing from the second in that therapy was started ten days before irradiation (Figure 54).

In this series of experiments, radiation sickness was mild and changes in higher nervous activity and intestinal secretion and motility were minor. Cerebrocortical activity was normal by the 22nd day after irradiation. Juice secretion after mechanical

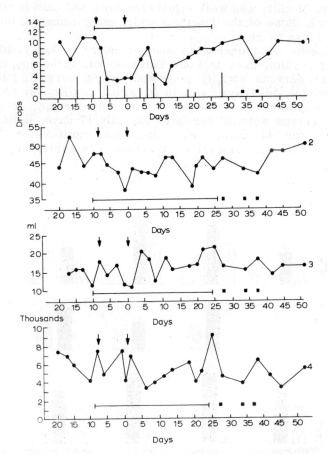

Figure 54. Changes in higher nervous activity,
intestinal secretion, and leukocyte count in the
dog Dzhul'bars after irradiation against the background of a nervous disorder and with administration of drugs. (Reported by A. V. Popov.)
1—Conditioned reflexes. 2—Unconditioned reflexes. 3—Intestinal secretion. 4—Leukocyte
count. Solid horizontal line represents period
of pharmacotherapy. Arrow on the left indicates
clashing; on the right, irradiation (250 r).

stimulation of the intestine was almost equal to the original level
except in three experiments when it increased 25%. The leukocyte
count did not fall below 3800/mm³, and the curve was long and

wavelike. Motility was weak on just a few days, and quickly returned to normal. None of the functions under study remained impaired for more than 28 days.

Analogous experiments on another neurotic dog yielded the following results. In control observations, without therapy, changes in higher nervous activity persisted for 66 days, in intestinal secretion for 107 days, and in intestinal motility for 100 days. In the second series of experiments, with therapy, changes in higher nervous activity persisted for only 17 days, in intestinal secretion for 44 days, and in intestinal motility for 51 days.

The results were similar in experiments on a third dog (Figure 55).

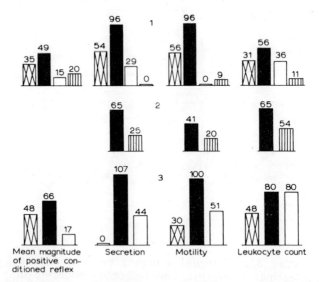

Figure 55. Duration of changes in higher nervous activity, intestinal secretion and motility, and leukocyte count in dogs irradiated with the cerebral cortex normal and pathological, with and without the administration of drugs. (Reported by A. V. Popov.) Columns with diagonal lines indicate irradiation with normal cerebral cortex. Black columns indicate irradiation after an experimental nervous disorder was induced. Blank columns and columns with straight lines pertain to the same, but with the administration of drugs before and during radiation sickness. 1—Dzhul'bars. 2—Mudryĭ. 3—Bars. Figures over the columns indicate number of days.

Use of the drugs mentioned above during radiation sickness complicated by a nervous disorder reduced the time that higher nervous activity and intestinal secretion were impaired by approximately two-thirds and one-half, respectively. They also markedly shortened the duration of intestinal motor disorders.

Although the functional condition of the higher divisions of the central nervous system is highly significant in the genesis of radiation sickness, the evidence of Soviet and foreign investigators indicates that humoral factors are also deeply involved in the process. Our experiments have demonstrated the major role played by the nervous system in the pathogenesis of radiation sickness in general and of radiation injury to the digestive system in particular. This is not to minimize the significance of cellular changes in the digestive organs caused by the direct and indirect action of ionizing radiation. But here also one must keep in mind the injurious effect of radiation on the trophic function of the nervous system.

The views advanced by several authors (A. A. Gorodetskiĭ, 1955; I. B. Bychkovskaya, 1956; Yu. G. Grigor'ev, 1959; P. F. Minaev, 1954; M. A. Movsesyan, S. G. Shukuryan, and A. E. Agababyan, 1954) have not only been confirmed by our investigations, but they have even been expanded. What is most important, in our opinion, is that functional weakening of the cerebral cortex and disruption of the coordinating and integrating functions of the brain severely aggravate radiation sickness and impair the autonomic functions, including digestion, to a greater degree than is observed in radiation sickness without these handicaps.

CHAPTER 12

Role of the Blood Vessels in Secretory Disorders

Evidence that impairment of the complex reflex regulatory mechanism is a significant factor in the digestive changes following injury raises the question of the role played by the blood vessels in the origin and development of these changes. Until recently we had no information on impaired innervation of blood vessels in the alimentary canal during radiation sickness. That such impairment is present can be judged from the pathological and histological changes regularly observed at autopsies in the gastrointestinal walls and glands: these changes include paresis of the vascular walls, major and minor hemorrhages, desquamation of the endothelium of the small blood vessels, fragmentation and degeneration of the vascular walls, and perivascular edema.

This pathoanatomical picture, however, fails to reveal the complex changes that arise in the visceral blood supply and vascular innervation following radiation injury. That is why we thought it would be worthwhile to use the method devised by our colleague A. D. Golovskiĭ (1957) in studying the vascular system of the digestive apparatus and the relation between its vascular and secretory reactions during radiation sickness. By way of illustration we shall describe the results of some experiments in which we recorded gastric and pancreatic vascular and secretory reactions simultaneously.

A. A. Fadeeva, I. T. Kurtsin, and A. D. Golovskiĭ (1957) performed experiments on six dogs with parotid duct fistulas and Pavlov pouches in the greater curvature; electrodes from a Rein thermostromuhr were connected to the left gastroepiploic artery. The authors studied the secretory and vascular responses of the stomach after the ingestion of food, both before and after total-body irradiation with a dose of 250 r. Higher nervous activity was investigated by means of conditioned salivary reflexes.

Experiments were first performed on two dogs irradiated with normal central nervous systems, and then on five dogs (including one

230

animal from the first series of experiments) irradiated after functional weakening of the cerebral cortex.

The dogs irradiated with their cerebral cortex normal developed an acute form of moderately severe radiation sickness. Higher nervous activity in the dog Don, an animal with a strong, impulsive type of nervous system, was characterized before irradiation by stable positive conditioned reflexes to sound and light stimuli with normal intensity relationships between the reflexes. The magnitude of the positive conditioned reflexes in the dog Lis, an animal with a weak type of nervous system, fluctuated considerably from experiment to experiment, but the intensity relationships were preserved.

Acute inhibition of the positive conditioned reflexes was noted in both dogs from the first day after irradiation, but the changes in higher nervous activity at the height of the sickness were not identical. Don's conditioned reflexes returned briefly to the original level two weeks after irradiation, but after that they fluctuated, especially during the third and fourth weeks, when they exceeded the original level two to two and one-half times. Internal inhibition was weak and the magnitude of the reflexes fluctuated considerably. On some days the reaction of the cortical cells to various conditioned stimuli except the first one was absent from the stereotype. Hypnotic phases were persistent. The unconditioned reflexes decreased somewhat during the first 10 days, but then they began to increase when the dog was about to die. Don died on the 55th day after irradiation as a result of gastric hemorrhage. Both Don and Lis, then, suffered serious disruption of higher nervous activity.

A simultaneous study of gastric secretion in Lis revealed hyposecretion during the first month. The total volume of juice decreased, the latent period of secretion lengthened, and total acidity was low. Secretion became normal a month after irradiation, but hypersecretion developed 10 days before the animal died (Table 62).

Analysis of secretion after eating showed that changes occurred chiefly during the first 2 hours of secretion, i.e., in the complex reflex phase.

Secretory changes during radiation sickness in Lis showed a persistent decrease in glandular function followed by a stable rise, but in Don the changes were cyclic, hypofunction giving way to hyperfunction in a comparatively short period of time. On some days, therefore, the amplitude of fluctuations in secretion was substantial, between 3.0 and 20.1 ml per experiment. The nature of the hourly secretion curve also changed (Table 63).

Don exhibited drastic changes in gastric gland activity in both the complex reflex and neurochemical phases.

The differences noted in the dogs' higher nervous activity and gastric secretion during radiation sickness were undoubtedly due to the fact that they had different types of nervous systems.

Table 62

Changes in secretion of the Pavlov pouch in the greater curvature
in the dog Lis after eating 200 g of meat during radiation sickness
caused by total-body irradiation with a dose of 250 r.

(Reported by A. A. Fadeeva, I. T. Kurtsin, and A. D. Golovskiĭ.)

Conditions and days of experiments	Volume of juice (ml) during the					Latent period (min)	Total acidity (%)
	1st hour	2nd hour	3rd hour	4th hour	Entire experiment		
Original level (mean data of 5 experiments)	4.0	4.0	3.9	2.5	14.4	13	0.53
After irradiation:							
1st Day	2.8	4.0	2.7	2.2	11.7	6	0.47
2nd "	2.9	2.7	2.5	2.0	10.1	15	0.46
4th "	2.3	4.0	2.8	2.1	11.2	15	0.45
6th "	2.0	2.5	2.3	2.0	8.8	40	0.43
10th "	3.0	1.0	1.0	1.0	6.0	10	—
12th "	0.0	1.8	1.0	1.0	3.8	110	0.25
31st "	5.5	6.0	0.0	0.0	11.5	4	0.49
35th "	3.5	3.5	3.5	2.3	12.8	50	0.49
38th "	5.5	5.2	3.0	2.8	16.5	9	0.54
42nd "	6.0	4.0	3.5	3.5	17.0	4	0.43
55th "	8.0	7.0	5.0	3.0	23.0	6	0.51

Besides secretory disorders, there was also severe impairment
of the vascular response of the stomach to the ingestion of food. Before
irradiation, eating accelerated the flow of blood in the gastric
vessels within a few seconds. The latent period averaged 27 sec for
meat, 18 sec for milk, and 36 sec for bread. The maximum rate
of flow usually occurred during the first hour after eating. The
flow rate remained high until the end of the secretory period, when
it gradually returned to the original level.

During the first few days after irradiation, the vascular response
changed and remained that way throughout the sickness. For example,
in Lis blood flow was markedly inhibited by the third day.
While the animal was eating meat, the flow rate rose slightly, but
then returned to the original level within 30 seconds. This type of
vascular response occurred for several days. By the end of the
latent period of the sickness and during the first day or two of
clinically pronounced signs, blood flow was virtually normal. It
became inhibited again, however, between the 16th and 20th days
of the sickness. Eating accelerated the blood flow perceptibly, but

Table 63

Changes in secretion in the Pavlov pouch of the greater curvature
in the dog Don after eating 200 g of meat during radiation sickness
caused by total-body irradiation with a dose of 250 r.

(Reported by A. A. Fadeeva, I. T. Kurtsin, and A. D. Golovskiĭ.)

Conditions and days of experiments	Volume of juice (ml) during the					Latent period (min)	Total acidity (%)
	1st hour	2nd hour	3rd hour	4th hour	Entire experiment		
Original level (mean data of 5 experiments)	1.9	3.8	4.0	0.9	9.6	19	0.34
After irradiation:							
1st Day	0.0	1.3	0.0	0.0	1.3	68	0.19
3rd "	1.2	3.2	2.9	0.7	8.0	25	0.36
5th "	1.0	4.6	3.9	3.0	12.5	40	
6th "	1.0	3.9	4.0	1.8	10.7	11	0.41
10th "	0.2	1.0	3.2	3.0	7.4	45	0.47
12th "	0.5	0.5	2.0	2.0	5.0	10	0.37
17th "	1.0	4.3	4.0	1.0	10.3	40	0.27
18th "	1.5	1.8	4.0	2.7	10.0	16	0.27
23rd "	2.7	3.1	2.0	2.0	9.8	20	0.26
25th "	3.0	4.0	2.4	1.4	10.8	21	—
26th "	0.0	0.0	0.0	0.0	0.0	0	0.00
30th "	0.0	1.7	0.0	3.0	4.7	80	—
32nd "	2.5	1.0	2.7	3.6	9.8	—	0.29
33rd "	0.6	1.5	0.5	0.6	3.2	30	0.13
37th "	2.5	2.6	3.0	3.0	11.1	8	0.13
44th "	2.5	5.2	3.0	2.0	12.7	10	0.20
46th "	0.5	0.5	0.3	18.0	19.3	30	0.35
72nd "	2.0	2.0	4.0	2.0	10.0	25	0.26
73rd "	3.0	4.3	2.5	0.9	10.7	20	0.30

the latent period was long and the return to the original level was
slow. At the height of the sickness, eating usually had no effect
on the rate of flow during the entire secretory period. Similar inhibition of gastric blood flow after irradiation was also noted in
Don. Moreover, Don exhibited another, sluggish type of reaction:
delay in acceleration of blood flow after eating (Figure 56).

These experiments showed that there is not only prolonged
secretory impairment during radiation sickness, but also prolonged
impairment of the gastric blood supply caused by injury to the complex reflex mechanism regulating the gastric vessels. Since the
blood supply plays an important role in maintaining the specific
activity of the gastric glands, it is reasonable to assume that the

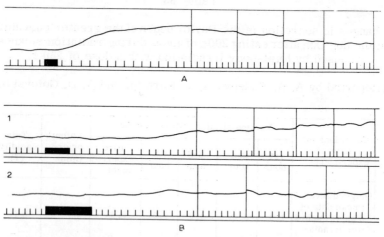

Figure 56. Changes in the rate of blood flow in the gastric vessels of irradiated dogs with normal central nervous systems. (Reported by A. A. Fadeeva, I. T. Kurtsin, and A. D. Golovskiĭ.)
Curves of blood flow rate under normal conditions (A) and during radiation sickness (B). 1—Sluggish type. 2—Inhibited type. Changes in flow rate during eating (dark rectangles) and the first few minutes after eating 200 g of meat; 1, 2, 3, and 4 hours separated by vertical lines. Time marked at 10-sec intervals.

secretory disorders that occur during radiation sickness are caused in part by impaired blood supply to the gastric glands. This can be clearly traced in Lis, in which a decrease in glandular function was accompanied by an inhibition of the vascular response to eating food.

One other highly important conclusion can be drawn from comparing secretory and vascular disorders of the stomach with changes in higher nervous activity. Inhibited secretion and blood flow in the stomach of the dog Lis was paralleled by profound inhibition of the cerebral cortex. In view of the significance of the complex reflex regulation of secretion and gastric blood supply, it would seem that the functional condition of the higher divisions of the central nervous system is largely responsible for the secretory and vascular disorders of the stomach during radiation sickness. Accordingly, the inhibitory type of vascular and secretory reactions are in all likelihood caused by the propagation of inhibition from the cerebral cortex to the subcortical and medullary centers which regulate the secretory and vascular structures of the stomach.

A similar mechanism producing changes in higher nervous activity and in gastric secretion and vascular responses was also observed in the other dog, Don, the first three days after irradiation. On some days of the sickness, however, there was intensified cerebrocortical activity, which was equalled by increased gastric secretion and blood flow; this was caused, perhaps, by the propagation of excitation from the cortex to the secretory and vasomotor centers of the subcortical structures and medulla oblongata.

Secretory and vascular disorders of the stomach in Don also originated by means of reciprocal induction of the cerebral cortex and the subcortical brain centers underneath. This could be seen at the height of radiation sickness when increased conditioned activity was accompanied by decreased secretion and an inhibitory or sluggish vascular response. One possible explanation is the negative induction of the subcortical vasomotor and secretory centers from the cerebral cortex where excitation was sharply intensified at this time. In other cases changes in secretory and vascular responses were caused by the positive induction of the subcortical and medullary centers. The various vascular and secretory disorders, of course, are not caused solely by the propagation of excitation and inhibition and their reciprocal induction in the central structures of the nervous system. Radiation injury to the local regulatory systems, the secretory cells, and the vascular walls apparently plays a definite part here also. So does impairment of the hormonal systems, including the endocrine hormones from the hypophysis, adrenals, etc., and the hormones formed in the gastrointestinal mucosa: gastrin, secretin, enterogastrone, etc. This is partly confirmed by the fact that the dogs—and Don in particular—suffered marked secretory impairment not only in the complex reflex phase but also in the neurochemical phase of digestion.

The soundness of this hypothesis is borne out by the recent findings of our co-worker E. K. Kuznetsova, who studied changes in the humoral mechanism of excitation of the pancreas after radiation injury. In acute experiments on dogs intravenously injected with a 10% solution of urethan, she determined simultaneously the rate of pancreatic secretion and the rate of blood flow in the pancreatic artery after injecting 25 ml of 0.5% HCl into the duodenal lumen. Pancreatic juice was collected through a cannula inserted into the major pancreatic duct. At the same time, the minor pancreatic duct was ligated and the stomach was separated from the duodenum by cutting the mucosa in the pyloric part of the stomach. The rate of blood flow was measured with a Rein thermostromuhr, the electrodes of which were connected to the pancreaticoduodenal artery. The acid solution was introduced into the intestine through a drainage catheter.

Experiments were first run on a number of healthy dogs to determine the normal level of external secretion of the pancreas and its vascular response to the hydrochloric acid in the duodenum. These control experiments showed that the injection of 25 ml of 0.5% hydrochloric acid into the duodenum caused the pancreas to secrete juice within two or three minutes; 30 to 40 seconds before that, it accelerated the flow of blood in the pancreaticoduodenal artery. The secretion and blood flow reached a maximum between 5 and 7 minutes after injection, and then they gradually returned to the original levels. These responses to the acid stimulus lasted about 8 minutes, the vascular response terminating 40 to 50 seconds before the secretory response.

Kuznetsova then performed similar experiments on dogs irradiated with 500 r. The animals were examined immediately after irradiation and on the 3rd, 6th, 7th, and 14th days of radiation sickness. The sickness was evaluated by changes in the peripheral blood composition, weight and temperature, pulse and respiration rates, external appearance, and behavior.

The examination revealed that cyclic changes in pancreatic secretion and blood flow arose immediately after irradiation and during the latent period of the sickness. At the height of the sickness, secretion was meager with the latent period lengthening from 2.5 to 8.5 minutes, and the vascular response, which did not occur until 7 or 8 minutes after the start of stimulation, was almost imperceptible. The duration of secretion at the height of the sickness shortened to 4 minutes. The vascular response set in immediately after irradiation and continued for some time. At the height of the sickness, it developed very steadily and then took a long time to return to the original level (Figure 57).

These experiments show, first, that the responses in the pancreas are similar to those in the stomach, as described previously. Radiation sickness impairs pancreatic secretion and disrupts the blood supply of the gland. Presumably the situation is similar in the other digestive organs and possibly in all organs and tissues. It is logical to conclude, therefore, that the blood vessels play a major role in the mechanism of radiation injury to the specific activity of the digestive organs.

Secondly, these experiments prove that ionizing radiation disrupts the humoral mechanism of excitation in the pancreas, either through damage to the pancreatic cells themselves (whose reactivity to secretin decreases sharply) or by the formation of active secretin in the duodenal mucosa. Or perhaps both of these things occur at the same time. This is a difficult problem, of course, and requires further study with well designed experiments. On the basis of tentative observations made jointly by Kuznetsova and myself, however, it is a fair assumption that impaired synthesis of the hormone secretin in the intestinal mucosa is a major pathological factor. Investigating pancreatic secretion and vascular response simultaneously, we injected extracts of duodenal mucosa

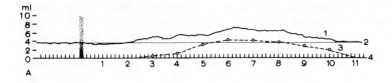

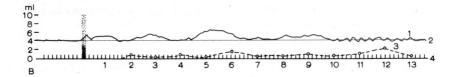

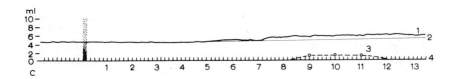

Figure 57. Secretory and vascular responses of the pancreas to
a humoral stimulus (secretin) in irradiated and nonirradiated dogs.
(Reported by É. K. Kuznetsova.)
1—Rate of blood flow in the pancreaticoduodenal artery. 2—
Control line. 3—Rate of pancreatic secretion. 4—Time in
minutes (figures) and seconds (each vertical mark = 10 sec).
a—Healthy dogs. b—In a dog the first few days after total-
body irradiation (500 r). c—In a dog at the height of radiation
sickness. Shaded column indicates time when 25 ml of 0.5%
hydrochloric acid solution was injected into the duodenum.

from irradiated and nonirradiated cats into the blood of healthy
dogs. We then observed that the extracts from the nonirradiated
cats, as we expected, excited pancreatic secretion, whereas the
extracts from the irradiated animals did not stimulate secretion,
especially if they had been prepared from intestinal mucosa taken
from the animals at the height of radiation sickness. We also found
that injecting extracts from the duodenal mucosa of a healthy animal,
or a solution of crystalline secretin, stimulated pancreatic secretion in irradiated dogs, although it differed considerably from normal
secretion.

Accordingly, these two series of observations entitle us to say
that ionizing irradiation impairs the external secretion of the pancreas and depresses the synthesis of secretin in the mucosa of

the small intestine. If this is indeed the case, then this principle can be applied to other digestive glands where hormonal substances play an important part in the mechanism of excitation and inhibition of secretion. However, since the actual synthesis of hormones and their action on the secretory cells and blood vessels involves, according to the modern view, the central and peripheral structures of the nervous system, and since the secretory and vascular disorders vary with the functional condition of the higher brain centers, we are more inclined to ascribe these disorders to changes in the complex reflex regulatory mechanism resulting from functional changes in the cerebral cortex and cortical-subcortical relations.

Evidence of this comes from the following series of experiments on dogs performed by A. A. Fadeeva, I. T. Kurtsin, and A. D. Golovskiĭ. As in the investigations described above, the dogs were irradiated with a dose of 250 r after preliminary traumatization of higher nervous activity by overstraining the intensity and mobility of the nervous processes. Five dogs were used: Atlant and Bob (each of which had a weak type of nervous system), Medved' (a strong, balanced type), and Charley and Don (strong, impulsive types).

Radiation sickness was more severe in all these dogs than in most of the animals irradiated with the same dose but with normal higher nervous activity. This was also apparent from a comparison of changes in various functions in the same dog (e.g., Don) which was irradiated twice: once with the central nervous system normal, then again four months later after a nervous disorder had been induced. Three of the five irradiated animals died: one on the 12th day, another on the 18th day, and the third on the 50th day.

In three dogs (Atlant, Bob, Don) irradiation against a background of weakened cortical activity caused the positive conditioned reflexes to decrease for four to six days, and then it sharply increased them more than twofold. There was also a weakening of internal inhibition. This condition was later followed by exhaustion and profound inhibition of the cortical cells.

Don exhibited a cyclic type of higher nervous activity: brief periods of excitation with disinhibition of differentiation alternated with periods of inhibition accompanied by equalizing, narcotic, paradoxical, and sometimes even ultraparadoxical hypnotic phases. Irradiation with 250 r with the cerebral cortex normal increased active inhibition in Don, but the same dose of irradiation with the cerebral cortex traumatized caused a weakening of differentiating inhibition. Prior to the animal's death, during signs of acute general asthenia, we noted a decrease in the positive conditioned reflexes, lowered food excitability, and a 3-kg loss in weight.

In Medved', which had had radiation sickness twice, a third exposure after a nervous disorder had been induced immediately

Table 64

Secretory changes of a Pavlov pouch in the dog Atlant after eating 200 g of meat, after reflex clashing and subsequent total-body irradiation with a dose of 250 r.

(Reported by A. A. Fadeeva, I. T. Kurtsin, and A. D. Golovskiĭ.)

Conditions and days of experiments	Volume of juice (ml) during the					Latent period (min)	Total acidity (%)
	1st hour	2nd hour	3rd hour	4th hour	Entire experiment		
Original level (mean data of 5 experiments)	6.7	6.3	4.9	3.9	21.8	16	0.25
After clashing	7.0	6.8	5.6	4.0	23.4	9	0.24
After irradiation:							
1st Day	2.5	4.1	3.0	0.5	10.1	35	0.24
3rd "	4.0	7.1	10.0	7.0	28.1	34	0.24
5th "	7.1	7.0	10.2	6.9	31.2	15	0.28
7th "	6.9	7.1	7.0	7.0	28.0	18	0.30
9th "	3.1	5.6	12.2	14.6	35.5	16	0.20
12th "	6.5	7.0	13.0	11.8	38.3	21	0.20
14th "	7.2	6.8	8.1	6.2	28.3	18	0.20
17th "	3.2	4.0	8.0	6.0	21.2	20	0.32
19th "	1.0	2.3	1.5	0.0	4.8	30	0.14

lowered the positive conditioned reflexes and disinhibited differentiation. On the 12th day, when no reflexes could be elicited, the dog died.

The impaired higher nervous activity mentioned above was paralleled by marked changes in gastric secretion which appeared after interference with the cortical processes. These changes were particularly profound and long-lasting after irradiation.

Most of the dogs developed hypersecretion with a 50 to 100% increase in the volume of gastric juice secreted after eating. There was a sharp decrease before the animals died.

We present the results of the experiments on Atlant by way of illustrating the changes in gastric secretion. In this animal, reflex clashing somewhat increased secretion. Then secretion decreased sharply the first day after irradiation. Hypersecretion, however, was clearly in evidence by the third day. Secretion again diminished a few days before death; there was a decrease in total juice acidity and a threefold increase in the latent period of secretion. In addition, the shape of the secretion curve changed as the period of maximum secretion shifted from the first to the third and fourth hours (Table 64).

Table 65

Secretory changes of a Pavlov pouch in the dog Don after eating
200 g of meat, after clashing and subsequent total-body irradiation
with a dose of 250 r.

(Reported by A. A. Fadeeva, I. T. Kurtsin, and A. D. Golovskiǐ.)

Conditions and days of experiments	Volume of juice (ml) during the					Latent period (min)	Total acidity (%)
	1st hour	2nd hour	3rd hour	4th hour	Entire experiment		
Original level (mean data of 5 experiments)	2.5	3.2	3.2	1.4	10.3	14	0.38
After clashing	3.6	3.8	2.5	2.8	12.7	10	0.27
After irradiation:							
1st Day	5.0	3.5	10.0	2.0	20.5	20	0.24
3rd "	6.0	3.0	7.0	3.0	19.0	5	0.20
6th "	2.7	3.0	4.0	1.8	11.5	15	0.27
10th "	7.0	7.0	2.5	2.0	18.5	40	0.24
22nd "	10.0	3.0	0.5	3.5	17.0	3	0.49
25th "	8.0	12.0	1.0	1.4	22.4	30	0.46
34th "	13.5	10.0	5.0	0.0	28.5	—	0.30
49th "	0.7	0.5	0.5	0.3	2.0	—	—
61st "	2.0	0.2	5.5	7.0	14.7	35	0.35
66th "	11.0	6.3	5.5	3.5	26.3	6	0.43
70th "	2.9	2.8	5.8	4.0	15.5	8	0.43
73rd "	9.0	4.0	4.7	5.0	22.7	4	0.35
75th "	4.7	3.5	6.5	6.1	20.8	10	0.49
80th "	4.0	3.3	6.8	2.0	16.1	2	0.38
82nd "	6.7	5.8	5.7	2.2	20.4	2	0.38
97th "	3.0	1.7	2.5	3.0	10.2	50	0.31
103rd "	0.0	6.0	5.4	7.0	18.4	75	0.37

Gastric hypersecretion and shifting of the maximum secretion
period from the first to later hours were also observed in the
dog Don irradiated after a nervous disorder had been induced. On
some days of the sickness, the volume of juice secreted after eating
exceeded the original level of secretion two or more times (Table 65).

Thus, irradiation after functional weakening of the cerebral
cortex produces profound and protracted changes in gastric secretion. Impaired vascular responses in the stomach are also highly
pronounced. They are not only sluggish and inhibited, like the
changes following irradiation with the higher divisions of the central
nervous system normal, but also distorted, as when the ingestion
of food slows down rather than accelerates the flood flow (Figure 58).

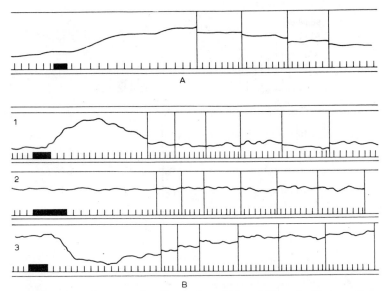

Figure 58. Changes in the rate of blood flow in the gastric
vessels of dogs irradiated with experimental nervous disorders. (Reported by A. A. Fadeeva, I. T. Kurtsin, and
A. D. Golovskiĭ.)
Curves of blood flow rate under normal conditions
(a) and during radiation sickness (b). 1—Asthenic
type. 2—Inhibited type. 3—Distorted type. Changes
in rate of flow during (dark rectangles) and the first
few minutes after eating 200 g of meat; 15 min, 30
min, 1, 2, 3, 4 hours separated by vertical lines.
Time marked at 10-sec intervals.

Total inhibition of the vascular response throughout the 4 hours
of the experiment usually appeared several days before the animals died. Charley and Medved' exhibited distorted vascular
responses with unusual frequency. An asthenic response predominated in Bob for a few days after irradiation. The flow of blood was
very rapid at first, but it soon slowed down, sometimes below the
original rate.
Postirradiation impairment of conditioned activity, secretion,
and vascular response in the stomach persisted in two dogs, Bob
and Charley, for 8-1/2 months; impairment in the animals with
normal higher nervous activity, however, did not exceed two or
three months.
Radiation sickness was often marked by a lack of coordination
between the secretory and vascular responses. Sometimes both

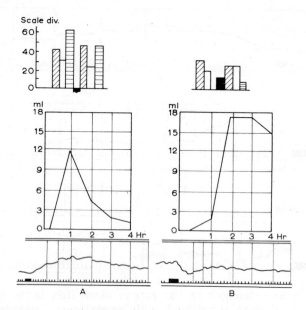

Figure 59. Higher nervous activity, gastric secretion, and rate of blood flow in the gastric vessels of the dog Charley under normal conditions (A) and during radiation sickness (B). (Reported by A. A. Fadeeva, I. T. Kurtsin, and A. D. Golovskiĭ.)
Top: magnitude of conditioned salivary reflexes to stimuli (from left to right), bell (+), light (+), metronome 120 strokes per minute (+), metronome 60 strokes per minutes (-), bell (+), light (+), metronome 120 strokes per minute (+). In the center: gastric juice curve after eating 200 g of meat. Bottom: recording of blood flow in gastric vessels. Same symbols as in Figure 58.

changed at the same time; e.g., hypersecretion would be accompanied by a stimulated vascular response and, conversely, inhibited secretion would be accompanied by an inhibited vascular response. In these cases the reactions were dissociated. Increased glandular activity caused a distorted vascular response with decreased blood flow (Figure 59).

The experimental findings of A. A. Fadeeva, I. T. Kurtsin, and A. D. Golovskii can be summarized as follows. X-irradiation of healthy dogs with a dose of 250 r causes changes not only in conditioned activity and gastric secretion but also in the rate of gastric blood flow throughout the period of acute radiation sickness. The changes in conditioned reflexes in dogs with a weak type of nervous system are generally more marked than in dogs with a strong type. Moreover, there is a dissociation between activity of the cerebral cortex and that of the subcortical centers.

Impaired gastric secretion is mainly hypofunctional and the secretory process itself is somewhat distorted during digestion. Vascular responses in the stomach after eating are sluggish and inhibited. The greatest changes in blood supply occur the first few days after irradiation and at the height of radiation sickness.

Similar irradiation of dogs with an experimental nervous disorder causes more severe radiation sickness and proportionately sharper changes in higher nervous activity, gastric secretion, and vascular responses. Positive conditioned reflexes are inhibited in most dogs immediately after irradiation. This is followed by a sharp increase in the reflexes and a disinhibition of differentiation. Later, especially before the animals die, the conditioned reflexes are profoundly inhibited and stable hypnotic phases are evident.

Secretory disorders are usually hyperfunctional and there are marked changes in the secretory process itself during digestion. The volume of juice secreted after eating falls considerably several days before death.

Vascular responses in the stomach to the ingestion of food are sometimes sluggish and inhibited. More often, however, they are asthenic and distorted.

Conditioned activity and secretory and vascular responses in the stomach are impaired during the period of acute signs of radiation sickness and for a long time afterward. This impairment is manifested by cyclic changes in these three functions.

We conclude from the experimental material cited above that both impaired innervation of the secretory cells and impaired vascular innervation regulating the blood supply of the digestive organs are important factors in the mechanism responsible for gastric secretory disorders during radiation sickness. Changes in the secretory and vascular responses of the digestive glands are caused largely by malfunction of the complex reflex regulatory apparatus and disruption of cortical-subcortical functional relations.

CHAPTER 13

Impairment of Interoception in the Gastrointestinal Tract

In analyzing radiation impairment of digestion, one must bear in mind the functional interrelationship existing between the digestive organs and the higher divisions of the central nervous system, an interrelationship which has been clearly demonstrated, chiefly by K. M. Bykov and his school. We must therefore analyze disruption of the complex reflex mechanism regulating digestion in conjunction with radiation injury both to the brain centers and to the receptors and, consequently, with impairment of the afferent impulses from the digestive organs.

There is now available a fairly substantial amount of experimental data on the severe impairment of the interoceptors during radiation sickness. V. A. Chernichenko (1955, 1956), N. S. Delitsyna (1957), T. V. Popova (1956), T. K. Dzharak'yan (1956), I. T. Kurtsin (1957, 1958, 1960), V. A. Samtsov (1957), and T. K. Dzharak'yan and G. F. Fakhrutdinov (1958) have studied this phenomenon in the gastrointestinal tract.

Our co-workers N. A. Lapshin (1960), V. B. Zakharzhevskiĭ (1957, 1960), and M. S. Seregin (1959, 1960) have thoroughly investigated impairment of the gastric, intestinal, and hepatic receptors during radiation sickness.

Lapshin performed acute experiments with perfusion of an isolated segment of small intestine. The intestinal receptors were stimulated by adding various concentrations of nicotine, acetylcholine, or potassium chloride to the perfusion fluid. The effect was determined from reflex changes in respiration and blood pressure in the carotid artery. The experiments were performed at different times after total-body X-irradiation with doses of 400 to 600 r.

A great many dogs were used. The author discovered an increase in vasomotor and respiratory reflexes from the intestine within two or three days after irradiation. Then inhibition of the reflexes set in and persisted throughout the acute phase of the sickness. If the sickness were severe, the reflexes were totally inhibited. While the symptoms were abating, he observed a gradual restoration of reflexes which reflected the successive development of several parabiotic states in the brain centers: equalizing, paradoxical, and narcotic phases. In these cases, nicotine, for example, had almost the same effect in concentrations of $1:10^4$, $1:10^5$, and $1:10^6$. Or it sometimes caused a lesser effect in a concentration of $1:10^4$ than in a concentration of $1:10^5$. At the height of radiation sickness it usually did not elicit a response even in a concentration of $1:10^4$. After total inhibition the reflexes reappeared approximately 32 to 35 days after irradiation and became completely normal 10 days later.

Thus, three phases in the functional state of the receptors were noted: increased, inhibited, and normal excitability of the nerve endings (Figure 60).

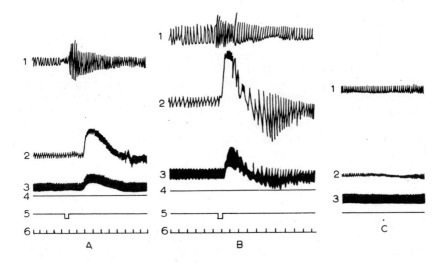

Figure 60. Changes in vasomotor and respiratory reflexes from the receptors of an isolated segment of cat intestine after total-body irradiation with a dose of 400 r. (Reported by N. A. Lapshin.) A—Before irradiation. B—The first few hours after irradiation. C—At the height of radiation sickness. 1—Respiration. 2—Blood pressure (manometric recording). 3—Blood pressure (tonometric recording). 4—Zero line. 5—Stimulus mark. 6—Time in 5-sec intervals.

The first phase did not appear at all when massive doses of ionizing radiation were used; the receptors became inhibited immediately.

E. I. Komarov (1957) and V. B. Zakharzhevskiĭ (1957, 1960) studied changes in receptor excitability. Using the same method of perfusion in a segment of small intestine, they observed an initial increase in the vasomotor and respiratory reflexes after stimulation of the intestinal nerve endings, and then a decrease after direct electric stimulation of the efferent nerves of the intestine.

Zakharzhevskiĭ set out to discover the effect of preliminary traumatization of the central nervous system on radiation changes in interoceptive unconditioned reflexes from the intestine. In acute experiments on 150 cats, he used a segment of intestine with intact nerve connections with the central nervous system and artificially supplied with a nutrient fluid. He investigated changes in the vasomotor and respiratory reflexes from the intestinal receptors 1 hour, 1 day, 7, 14, 21, and 30 days after single, total-body exposure of the animals to 400, 600, and 800 r. The reflexes were checked in 20 cats at each of the indicated intervals, and 10 of these had been irradiated with their nervous systems traumatized by repeated "electric clashing".

The first series of experiments entailed an investigation of reflexes in animals irradiated with normal nervous systems. It was discovered that within 1 to 1-1/2 hours after irradiation, threshold concentrations of the stimulants (potassium chloride, acetylcholine and sodium bromide) were practically normal, although the absolute magnitudes of the reflexes to acetylcholine and sodium bromide were half the normal values. Reflex elevation of blood pressure to the action of 42 mg of potassium chloride decreased insignificantly. During this period the threshold concentrations and absolute magnitudes of the reflexes changed as the experiments proceeded. The vasomotor reflexes were very much drawn out in 80% of the cases. The respiratory responses in this and subsequent periods of radiation sickness were weak, as reflected in an increased frequency and depth of respiration.

The reflexes decreased progressively in the latent period of the sickness; within a day after irradiation, the excitation thresholds rose from 4 to 10 mg of potassium chloride and from 1 μg to 10 μg of acetylcholine. There was also a decrease in the absolute magnitude of the reflexes to these stimulants. Responses to sodium bromide, which is weaker than the other chemical stimulants, were generally absent in the subsequent periods of the sickness. Protracted blood pressure reactions that took a long time returning to the original level were less common (30% of the cases). Three days after irradiation the thresholds of stimulation rose to 42 mg of potassium chloride and to 100-1000 μg of acetylcholine, and the magnitude of the reflexes decreased sharply. Protracted responses were not noted at this time. At the end of the latent period of the sickness, seven days after irradiation, the threshold concentrations of the stimulants dropped to 21 mg of potassium chloride and to 10-100 μg of acetylcholine. The magnitude of the reflexes increased slightly.

At the height of the sickness, 14 days after irradiation, the thresholds fell even more: to 10 mg of potassium chloride and 10 μg of acetylcholine; the magnitude of the reflexes remained the same as in the preceding period. Distinguishing features of this period were the absence of protracted responses and, in 30% of the cases, the presence of balancing and inhibited phases in responses to various stimulant concentrations.

At the beginning of the recovery period, about 21 days after irradiation, reflex excitability again decreased sharply; the thresholds rose to 42 mg of potassium chloride and to 1000 μg of acetylcholine; the magnitude of the reflexes decreased considerably, and the reflexes were generally protracted, an inhibited phase occurring in 30% of the cases. Thirty days after irradiation, the thresholds fell to 4-10 mg of potassium chloride and to 10 μg of acetylcholine; the absolute magnitude of the reflexes increased, but the reflexes to potassium bromide were still absent. There were no protracted reactions at this time.

The author did not continue his observations into the recovery period, but, judging from the experiments of Lapshin, return of the reflexes to normal was probably intermittent.

Zakharzhevskiĭ checked the reflexes at the height of radiation sickness, 7 to 14 days after irradiation, after total-body irradiation with doses of 600 and 800 r. Despite the more severe course of the sickness, the reflexes differed but little from those in animals irradiated with a dose of 400 r. In 90% of the cases, however, the blood pressure responses were protracted and took a long time returning to normal.

This, then, was the pattern of changes in excitability of the intestinal receptors during radiation sickness caused by irradiation of animals with normal central nervous systems.

In the second series of experiments, total-body irradiation was preceded by "electric clashing". The interoceptive reflexes were studied at the same time intervals as in the first series (Figure 61).

The very earliest reactions, within an hour of irradiation, showed a marked decrease in excitability of the receptors; the thresholds were 21 mg of potassium chloride and 100 μg of acetylcholine. The vascular responses were protracted in 40% of the cases. A day later the thresholds dropped to 10 mg of potassium chloride and to 10 μg of acetylcholine. The blood pressure responses were quite protracted in 85% of the cases. Three days later the thresholds were still at the same level, but the absolute magnitude of the reflexes increased somewhat. Protracted responses occurred in 50% of the cases. After a week excitability of the receptors sharply decreased; the thresholds rose to 42 mg of potassium chloride and to 1000 μg of acetylcholine; inhibitory effects were noted in 30% of

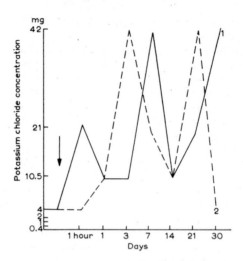

Figure 61. Changes in excitability of the chemoreceptors of an isolated segment of intestine during radiation sickness in cats irradiated after traumatization of the higher divisions of the central nervous system. (Reported by V. B. Zakharzhevskiǐ.) Mean data on the threshold of the intestinal chemoreceptors in cats irradiated with the central nervous system normal (2) and pathological (1). Arrow indicates irradiation with 400 r.

the cases, and the duration of the responses was normal. At the same time, the latent periods of the reflexes were prolonged to 7-10 seconds. Fourteen days later the thresholds fell to 10 mg of potassium chloride and to 10 μg of acetylcholine, while the absolute magnitude of the reflexes increased. Protracted responses were noted in 50% of the cases and phasic phenomena in 30%. Three weeks later the thresholds rose to 21 mg of potassium chloride and to 50 μg of acetylcholine; the magnitude of the reflexes, however, remained the same as before. Phasic phenomena were absent and the duration of the reflexes was normal. After a month the thresholds rose even higher: to 40 mg of potassium chloride and to 1000 μg of acetylcholine. There was a sharp decrease in the magnitude of the reflexes, and an inhibited phase was noted in 30% of the cases. Reflexes to sodium bromide were absent throughout the sickness in half of the cases and were low in the others.

Thus, the results of the two series of experiments just described show that total-body irradiation produces characteristic phasic changes in the interoceptive unconditioned reflexes from the intestine. They decrease on the 3rd and 21st days, but are restored on the 14th and 30th days. Preliminary traumatization of the nervous system alters this pattern. Under such circumstances three phases of decreased reflexes occur—1 hour, 7 days, and 30 days after irradiation—and two phases of restoration—within one to three days after 14 days. Consequently, the maximum deviations are found in the period of early radiation injury and in the period of restoration when the pathological process apparently begins sooner and ends later than after irradiation with the nervous system normal.

The unusual changes in excitability of the receptors during radiation sickness still awaits elucidation. It is possible that the nerve elements are in a parabiotic state. At any rate, the alternating increase and decrease in receptor excitability, which is usually accompanied by inadequate responses to stimuli of varying strengths, is apparently related in some way to parabiotic phenomena in the central and visceral nerve structures. This condition of the nervous system following radiation injury is presumably responsible for the cyclic or wavelike functional changes that are regularly observed during radiation sickness.

Electrophysiologic research has also contributed to our understanding of radiation injury to the gastrointestinal receptors. A thorough study of the problem was made by V. E. Delov, N. A. Adamovich, and O. N. Zamyatina (1957). In acute experiments on cats, they exposed the animals to single and repeated, local and total-body doses of roentgen rays ranging from 100 to 1000 r. Using a cathode-ray oscilloscope to record the afferent impulses in the greater splanchnic and mesenteric nerves, they detected marked intensification of the impulses within the first few hours after local irradiation of the abdominal cavity (Figure 62). Phasic changes, however, set in later: intensification was followed by weakening, which was followed in turn by intensification, etc.

The authors noted the same phasic changes in afferent impulses after total-body irradiation as well. Radiation injury was immediately followed by intensification of the impulses, but the frequency and amplitude were somewhat less pronounced than after local irradiation of the abdominal cavity. The intensification then gave way to inhibition which lasted from the 5th to 20th days (Figure 63). In time the afferent impulses gradually became normal.

N. S. Delitsyna (1957) found that when there was a high initial bioelectric activity in the splanchnic nerve of cats, total-body irradiation with 500 r decreases the amplitude (from 50 to 7 μv) and increases the frequency (from 150-170 to 200-240/sec) of the action potentials; the impulse volleys meanwhile become less pronounced. These changes reach a maximum 30 to 40 minutes after irradiation. Stimulation of the gastric mechanoreceptors increases the frequency and amplitude of the impulses. The impulse volleys

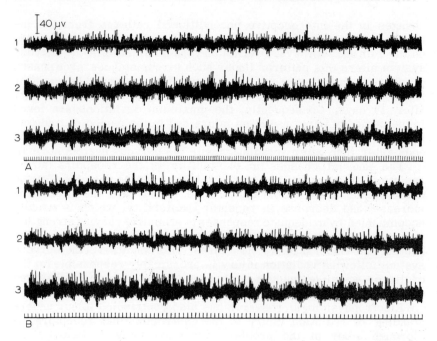

Figure 62. Changes in afferent impulses in the greater splanchnic
nerve of a cat after local X-irradiation of the abdominal cavity.
(Reported by V. E. Delov, N. A. Adamovich, and O. N. Zamyatina.)
   A—After a dose of 500 r. 1—Before irradiation. 2—One hour
   after irradiation. 3—Two hours after irradiation. B—After a
   dose of 1000 r. 1—Before irradiation. 2—Two hours after
   irradiation. 3—Two hours and 30 minutes after irradiation.

become more distinct, and oscillation synchronous with the respiratory rhythm is intensified, thus testifying to increased excitability of the receptor apparatus.

   With a low initial level of bioelectric activity in the splanchnic
nerve, irradiation markedly increases the amplitude and frequency
of the action potentials (Figure 64). Within 24 hours after irradiation, the action potentials are continuous and show no clear correlation with the pulse oscillations. Stimulation of the gastric
mechanoreceptors decreases the amplitude of the discharges, but
brief warming or cooling of the gastric wall changes both the
amplitude and frequency of the discharges; these changes do not
return to the original level for several hours.

   These electrophysiological data provide additional confirmation
of the fact that ionizing radiation causes prolonged injury to the
gastrointestinal receptors, thereby impairing the conduction of

normal afferent impulses. Such impairment naturally has a profound effect on the functional state of the brain centers.

In experiments on 40 rabbits exposed to total-body irradiation of 500 to 1000 r, N. S. Delitsyna (1956, 1957) made the following discovery. Preirradiation stimulation of the mechanoreceptors of the rectum temporarily inhibits the bioelectric activity of the cerebral cortex; this inhibition disappears a few minutes after stimulation is halted. The same stimulation immediately after irradiation causes similar inhibition of cortical bioelectric activity; however, this inhibition persists for a much longer time. Two days after irradiation, cerebrocortical bioelectric activity decreases; stimulation of intestinal receptors at this time produces an even deeper inhibition with a more prolonged after effect. Five days later the after effect is indistinct but at the height of radiation sickness, and especially before the animal's death, the cerebral cortex exhibits signs of deep protective inhibition so that stimulation of the intestinal receptors at this time has virtually no effect on the bioelectric potentials of the brain (Figure 65).

Consequently, as a result of radiation injury to the receptors, abnormal impulses are sent from the viscera to the central nervous system. First, this increases the reactivity of the brain centers; then it induces profound protective inhibition. Further stimulation of the interoceptors then increases inhibition in the brain. Moreover, even weak stimulation, the equivalent of natural physiological

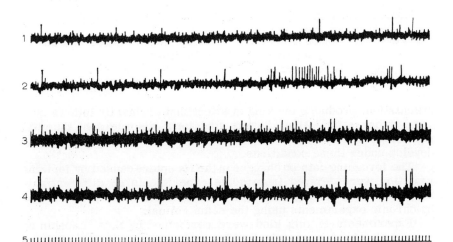

Figure 63. Afferent impulses in the greater splanchnic nerve of a cat on the 5th (1, 2, 3) and 10th (4) days after total-body irradiation with a dose of 300 r. (Reported by V. E. Delov, N. A. Adamovich, and O. N. Zamyatina.)

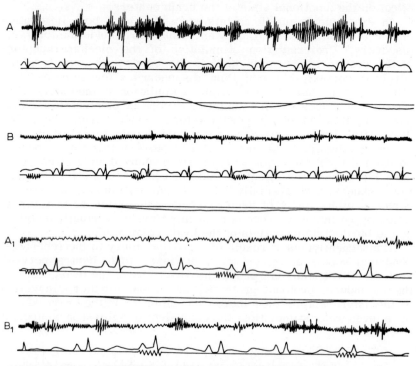

Figure 64. Action potentials of the splanchnic nerve in a cat.
(Reported by N. S. Delitsyna.)
A,A₁—Before irradiation. B,B₁—After irradiation.

stimulation, produces the kind of effect that ordinarily follows only
very strong stimulation. Severe functional disorders of the vital
physiological systems—cardiovascular, respiratory, etc.—clearly
develop under these conditions.

The foregoing data on changes in the receptors caused by ionizing
radiation were derived from acute experiments on different animals. The underlying principles, however, have been confirmed
by chronic experiments using the same animal.

Experiments of this kind were performed by N. A. Lapshin on
dogs with chronic gastric fistulas and with the carotid arteries
exposed by skin flaps. He investigated changes in blood pressure,
cardiac activity, and respiration following stimulation of the
mechanoreceptors of the stomach and rectal ampulla before and
after total-body X-irradiation with a dose of 600 r. He found that
the reflexes from the gastric and rectal receptors increased the

first three days after irradiation; this was shown by an increased pulse rate, an elevation of blood pressure by 15 to 20%, an increase in the depth and rate of respiration, a lowering of stimulus thresholds, and a prolongation of the latent period of reaction. For example, before irradiation the stimulus thresholds corresponded to 70 to 80 mm Hg; the first three days after irradiation, however, the same effect appeared after stimulation of the gastric and rectal receptors by a pressure of 45 to 55 mm Hg. Between the fifth and seventh days after irradiation, the dogs exhibited weakened reflexes which by the 22nd to 25th days were completely inhibited. Normal reactions were restored between the 32nd and 35th days after irradiation. The pattern of restoration was cyclic, the reflexes sometimes increasing, sometimes decreasing. The reactions were distorted in 20% of the cases; e.g., a depressor vascular reflex would develop instead of a pressor reflex.

Thus, three phases of changes in the gastrointestinal receptors were observed under the conditions of chronic experimentation: (a) increased reflexes lasting about two to three days after irradiation, (b) inhibited reflexes coinciding with the end of the latent period and height of the sickness, (c) normalization, characterized by unstable reflexes. This confirms the phasic changes in receptor excitability as demonstrated in the acute experiments on irradiated

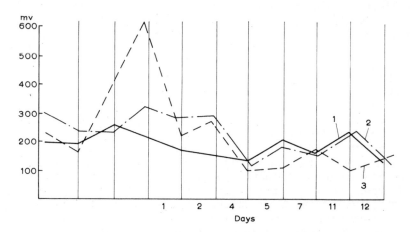

Figure 65. Bioelectric reaction of the cerebral cortex of a rabbit upon interoceptor stimulation before and after irradiation with 1000 r. (Reported by N. S. Delitsyna.) 1—Original level of bioelectric activity. 2—Reaction to the insertion of a rubber tube or balloon into the rectum (dot-dash line). 3—Reaction to thermic and mechanical interoceptor stimulation.

animals, and eliminates the element of individual variations in receptor excitability that may arise in acute experiments on different animals.

N. N. Lebedev (1957) has published some data on changes in the gastrointestinal receptors of dogs during radiation sickness. In chronic experiments, radiation sickness was induced by total-body X-irradiation with doses ranging from 250 to 600 r. The gastric receptors were analyzed from changes in motility and the leukocyte count following stimulation of the gastric mucosa by solutions of copper and barium sulfate. It was discovered that irradiation immediately inhibited the chemoreceptors of the stomach. Sensitivity later increased, but then inhibition reappeared and was particularly pronounced at the height of the sickness. The sensitivity of the receptors increased somewhat during the recovery period.

R. S. Zhur and V. A. Sonkina (1960) observed phasic changes in the interoceptive reflex from the small intestine to the bile-forming function of the liver and gastric motility as a result of ionizing radiation. Changes in the response of the liver were very marked. Like Lapshin, these investigators observed an increased response the first few days after irradiation but a decrease thereafter. Restoration of the normal reflex proceeded in a cyclic fashion, sometimes increasing, at other times decreasing.

Impairment of the gastrointestinal receptors help to explain certain signs of radiation injury, e.g., changes in the acid reflex from the duodenal mucosa to the pyloric sphincter and the reflex from the intestinal mucosa to the musculature of the ileocecal valve, as discovered in the experiments of É. K. Kuznetsova (1957, 1960).

Receptor changes also underlie the vomiting mechanism in radiation injury. Wang, Chinn, and Renzi (1956) found that total-body irradiation of animals with 800 r generally caused vomiting 2 hours later. If, however, the so-called chemoreceptor vomiting center were destroyed prior to exposure, vomiting occurred later. Preliminary destruction of the chemoreceptor vomiting center combined with a vagotomy prevented vomiting altogether.

Data on changes in the interoceptive conditioned reflexes from the gastrointestinal tract are also helpful in elucidating the causes of digestive disorders during radiation sickness. M. S. Seregin (1957, 1959) formed and strongly reinforced a set of positive and inhibitory acid-defense interoceptive and exteroceptive conditioned reflexes in six dogs with chronic gastric, duodenal, and parotid fistulas. A bell, a 25-watt bulb, a metronome (120 beats/min), irrigation of the gastric mucosa with warm water (40 to 42°C), and rhythmic inflation of a rubber balloon in the duodenum at the rate of one inflation per second served as positive stimuli. A metronome (60 beats/min) and irrigation of the gastric mucosa with cold water (16 to 18°C) served as differentiating stimuli. The interoceptive conditioned reflexes were at the end of a stereotype in three dogs but at the beginning in three others. Radiation sickness was induced by total-body X-irradiation with doses of 250 and 350 r. After recovery the animals were irradiated again, this time with a dose of 700 r. Radiation sickness was determined by changes in the blood, weight, temperature, pulse, food excitability, and general behavior.

All the animals developed radiation sickness which varied in severity with individual resistance. The experiments showed that irradiation itself and the ensuing sickness drastically changed both the exteroceptive and the interoceptive conditioned reflexes. On the day of irradiation and for the first two or three days thereafter, there was a decrease in the exteroceptive reflexes and disinhibition of differentiation. A subsequent brief increase was followed at the height of the sickness by inhibition of the conditioned reflexes. The reflexes increased in some dogs during the entire acute phase of the sickness. The latent period of the reflexes was quite often protracted at the height of the sickness. Differentiating inhibition generally increased. Differentiation became disinhibited while the animals were recovering, and, at the same time, the positive conditioned reflexes increased in a cyclic fashion. The cortical cells were observed to be in a hypnotic condition throughout the sickness (Figure 66).

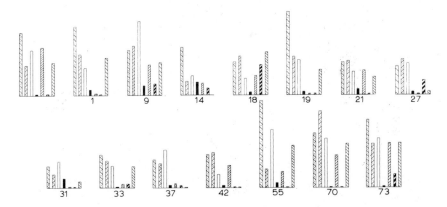

Figure 66. Phasic changes in the cerebrocortical activity of the dog Dzhek during radiation sickness. (Reported by M. S. Seregin.) Columns indicate magnitude of conditioned salivary reflexes to stimuli: bell (+), light (+), metronome, 120 beats/min (+), irrigation of gastric mucosa with water at 40°C (+), irrigation of gastric mucosa at +18°C (-), inflation of a balloon in the duodenum (+). First group of columns pertain to experiment before irradiation, other columns to experiments after irradiation. Figures underneath the columns indicate days after irradiation.

The use of various caffeine and bromine tests, changes in the stereotype, and some other techniques (e.g., determination of the propagation of inhibition in the internal analyzer, changes in the sequence of conditioned stimuli) caused functional weakening of the cortical nerve cells.

Impairment of the interoceptive conditioned reflexes was associated with about the same characteristics as that of the exteroceptive conditioned reflexes (Figure 67).

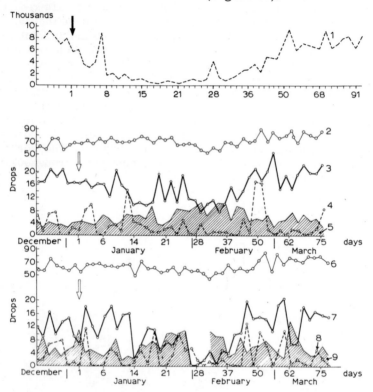

Figure 67. Changes in the exteroceptive and interoceptive conditioned reflexes of the dog Dzhek during acute radiation sickness. (Reported by M. S. Seregin.)
1—Leukocyte count per mm³. Exteroceptive reflexes: 2—Mean magnitude of unconditioned reflexes, 3—Conditioned reflexes, 4—Differentiation, 5—Mean length of the latent period of the positive conditioned reflexes. Interoceptive reflexes: 6—Unconditioned reflexes, 7—Conditioned reflexes, 8—Differentiation, 9—Length of the latent period of the reflexes. Arrow indicates day of irradiation with 350 r.

There were also some unusual features about the interoceptive conditioned reflexes, notably the fact that changes in the interoceptive conditioned reflexes differed in accordance with their position in the sequence of the conditioned-reflex stereotype. When the interoceptive conditioned reflexes were at the beginning of the stereotype, inhibition was less pronounced than when they were elicited at the end. This phenomenon is apparently due to the rapid fatigability of the cortical cells of the interoceptive analyser. Another important feature was the definite relationship observed between the magnitude and nature of the changes in both the interoceptive and the exteroceptive conditioned reflexes. The exteroceptive and interoceptive conditioned reflexes tended to interact. When the former retained their original magnitude, or exceeded it somewhat, the magnitude of the latter decreased. Conversely, when the magnitude of the exteroceptive reflexes decreased, that of the interoceptive reflexes either remained unchanged or exceeded the exteroceptive reflexes.

In other words, Seregin discovered that radiation sickness disrupts both the interoceptive signaling from the gastrointestinal tract and the interaction between exteroceptive and interoceptive signaling. This testifies to the discord in the integrative activity of the cerebral hemispheres.

This fact, which is of exceptional theoretical importance, was confirmed by Seregin in another series of experiments in which an exteroceptive conditioned stimulus (bell) was combined with an interoceptive stimulus (balloon in the stomach or intestine) and, conversely, an interoceptive stimulus was combined with an exteroceptive conditioned stimulus.

In dogs with a strong type of nervous system, the effect of each type of reflex on the other manifested itself at the height of radiation sickness in the form of pronounced inhibition. When interaction occurred, the animal was normal during the recovery period, however, there was invariably an increase in both types of conditioned reflexes.

In dogs with a weak type of nervous system, the interaction between these reflexes during radiation sickness caused inhibition of the reflexes, just as before the sickness, although there was some tendency for the inhibition to increase (Table 66).

Seregin then studied the effect of rectal stimulation on conditioned activity before and after irradiation. He found that distending the ampulla of the rectum with a rubber balloon (150 cm^3 of air with a pressure of 40 mm Hg) for 5 minutes prior to application of the first conditioned stimulus caused increased conditioned reflexes in dogs with strong as well as weak types of nervous system. Applied at different periods of the sickness, this stimulus inhibited the conditioned reflex in two dogs with a strong type of nervous system and in one dog with a weak type (Table 67).

Table 66

Effect of an exteroceptive conditioned reflex on an interoceptive
reflex in dogs before and after irradiation.

(Reported by M. S. Seregin.)

Conditioned stimuli	Magnitude of conditioned reflexes (drops)					
	Before irradiation	After irradiation				
		9th day	20th day	26th day	49th day	65th day
Dog with a strong type of nervous system						
Balloon	47	51	42	31	44	41
Bell	50	50	38	33	44	42
Balloon and bell after 10 sec	53	44	32	44	45	46
Balloon	46	49	44	25	45	26
Difference	+6	-7	-10	+13	+1	+5

Dog with a weak type of nervous system

Conditioned stimuli		After irradiation				
	Before irradiation	7th day	15th day	22nd day	30th day	52nd day
Balloon	20	18	16	24	18	22
Bell	24	12	23	12	11	22
Balloon and bell after 10 sec	14	17	11	7	14	12
Balloon	25	13	9	13	3	10
Difference	-6	-5	-5	-17	-4	-10

Note: + and - designate the difference in magnitude of
the response to the balloon when used alone and in combination with a bell.

Clearly, then, afferent impulses from the gastrointestinal tract
during radiation sickness alter the processes of excitation and
inhibition in the cerebral cortex, chiefly by intensifying the latter.
Four to six weeks after irradiation (sooner if the sickness is mild,

later if severe), higher nervous activity is gradually restored. This occurs after periods of increasing and decreasing conditioned reflexes, thus imparting a wavelike pattern to the return of normal higher nervous activity, which is completed two to three months after irradiation.

The main conclusions to be drawn from Seregin's work are the following. Radiation sickness impairs the exteroceptive and interoceptive signals in the cerebral cortex and disrupts their interoceptive

Table 67

Effect of stimulation of rectal receptors on the conditioned activity of dogs with different types of nervous systems before and during radiation sickness.

(Reported by M. S. Seregin.)

Experiments	Total of positive conditioned reflexes per experiment (drops)				
	Before irradiation	After irradiation			
		5th day	16th day	29th day	39th day
Dog with a strong type of nervous system					
Control	143	163	142	170	168
With stimulation of the rectum	166	139	129	166	183
Difference	+23	-24	-13	-4	+15
Dog with a weak type of nervous system					
Control	54	48	28	45	61
With stimulation of the rectum	60	46	27	41	23
Difference	+6	-2	-1	-4	-38

Note. + and - designate the difference in magnitude of the conditioned reflex in response to a conditioned stimulus by itself and in combination with stimulation of the rectal receptors.

signals in the cerebral cortex and disrupts their interaction; this transforms their mutually reinforcing effect into an inhibitory effect and distorts the function of the visceral analyser. One result of this, among others, is that the afferent impulses from the intestine sharply inhibit rather than increase the exteroceptive and interoceptive conditioned reflexes.

All the experimental evidence on radiation injury to the receptors of the digestive organs indicates that ionizing radiation disrupts the connections between the digestive system and the brain centers. The absence or distortion of information from the powerful receptor field of the gastrointestinal tract and its blood vessels will naturally severely impair the over-all integration of the digestive functions by the higher divisions of the central nervous system. This creates a vicious circle. On one hand, radiation injury to the brain centers distorts the normal activity of the digestive organs; on the other hand, radiation damage to the receptor apparatus of the gastrointestinal tract disrupts the normal afferent impulses and thereby further alter the regulatory activity of the brain centers. The way in which corticovisceral interrelations develop during radiation sickness possibly determines not only the nature and degree of digestive disorders, but also the outcome of the sickness itself.

CHAPTER 14

Impairment of Humoral Regulation of Digestion

In radiation sickness, impairment of the efferent and afferent connections between the digestive system and the brain centers is the main cause of inadequate secretion after eating and of secretion at times other than during digestion. After analyzing the pathology of secretory cells, I. P. Pavlov wrote: "It sometimes starts with hypersecretion; the abnormal excitability of the glands is manifested both in excessive and in causeless secretion of gastric juice."* The same thing often happens in radiation diseases of the stomach. It is also possible that spontaneous and excessive secretion during the neurochemical phase of secretion is caused by impaired nervous regulation of both the secretory cells themselves and the production of secretory hormones—gastrin, secretin, pancreozymin, enterogastrone, etc. Another factor is disruption of the mediator mechanism by which nervous excitation is transmitted across the synapses and the neuroeffector junctions linking the autonomic nervous system and the digestive organs. This assumption is based on the fact that several authors (I. A. Pigalev, 1954; A. V. Lebedinskiĭ, 1955; N. E. Kuznetsova, 1957; T. M. Mel'gunova and K. M. Larionova, 1958) have found phasic changes in the amount of epinephrine, acetylcholine, and cholinesterase present in the blood of irradiated animals. Further, I. A. Lapotnikov, O. S. Nasonkin, Yu. A. Senkevich, G. A. Isaev, and P. V. Kovalev of our laboratory have discovered changes in the activity of the gastric and pancreatic juices of dogs during acute radiation sickness (Figure 68).

These phenomena can also be explained in terms of the humoral theories of radiation sickness pathogenesis; that is, they may be caused by the action of toxins, proteolytic products, histamine, and other biologically active substances on the secretory cells of the digestive glands.

---

*I. P. Pavlov. Poln. sobr. soch. [Complete Writings]. Izd. AN SSSR, 1951, II, 2, p. 193.

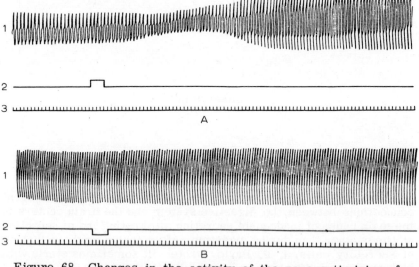

Figure 68. Changes in the activity of the pancreatic juice of a dog during radiation sickness. (Reported by I. A. Lapotnikov, O. S. Nasonkin, and Yu. A. Senkevich.) A—Action of the pancreatic juice of a healthy dog. B—Sick dog. 1—Contractions of an isolated heart. 2—Introduction of pancreatic juice into a perfusate. 3—Time in 5-sec intervals.

The intestine does play a special role in the formation of toxins because radiation sickness is most severe after local irradiation of the abdominal region. Extensive changes in all intestinal tissues are found at autopsy. The humoral view, which is fairly widespread among radiobiologists, is not shared by P. D. Gorizontov (1955, 1957), who found that blood flowing from the intestine after irradiation is virtually identical with the blood of a healthy animal.

We may conclude from the extensive research to date that many substances differing greatly in biological activity, rather than a single substance, are involved in the origin of radiation sickness. It is not likely, however, that the entire dynamics of the pathological process can be correlated with their action.

In this connection the data obtained by our co-workers on the interrelation of nervous and humoral factors in radiation sickness are of significance. I. L. Dzhagiĭka (1958) X-irradiated a perfused spleen which had only nervous connections with the body, and analyzed the perfusate flowing from the spleen for the presence of toxins. At the same time he determined the condition of the splenic receptors from changes in blood pressure and respiration after adding solutions of potassium chloride, nicotine, and other chemical compounds to the perfusate.

The experiments showed that during the first few minutes of irradiation excitation of the sensory nerve endings in the spleen produced a distorted vasomotor and respiratory response; the fluid flowing from the spleen during these minutes, however, preserved its normal biological and physical properties; this was shown by biological tests on the frog heart (isolated by Straube's method) and the rabbit ear (prepared by Kravkov's method) and by determinations of its spectral properties in a spectrophotometer. Qualitative changes in the fluid did not appear until ten minutes after the start of irradiation of the spleen. From this time on, the fluid flowing from the spleen exerted first an excitatory effect on the frog heart, then an inhibitory effect, and a vasoconstrictor effect on the rabbit ear; according to the spectrophotometric data, it had a different optical density from that at the beginning. Similar results were obtained by D. M. Gzgzyan, who irradiated the hind paws of dogs isolated in a similar fashion.

The findings of these investigators suggest that impairment of the receptors arises first during the early radiation effect, or before the toxic products of radiation injury appear in the fluid surrounding them (I. T. Kurtsin, 1959). Yet there is evidence that such products are formed in the irradiated tissue. This has been borne out by other authors who have made special studies of the problem.

Our colleague N. A. Lapshin conducted some special experiments along this line. He took the perfusate flowing from an isolated segment of intestine of a cat given 400 to 600 r of total-body irradiation and, after introducing it into the perfusate of a similarly isolated segment of intestine of a nonirradiated cat, observed the reflex changes in blood pressure and respiration. The changes were particularly marked when the perfusate was obtained 18 to 20 hours after the animal was irradiated (Figure 69). The perfusate obtained from the intestine of the nonirradiated cat, however, did not have the same properties.

A. G. Sverdlov's experiments (1959) produced comparable data. He injected healthy rabbits intravenously with a perfusate obtained while irradiating an isolated ear with 1000 to 3500 r, and he noted changes in the blood reminiscent of radiation injury. They arose three to ten days after the perfusate was injected and remained for two to three weeks. A perfusate from a nonirradiated ear did not have the same effect.

The results of all these experiments are grounds for believing that unidentified toxins are formed in the tissues during the development of radiation sickness. Weber and Steggerda (1949), F. Ellinger (1952), and Lasser and Stenstrum (1954) attach a good deal of significance to the formation of histamine and similar substances. However, Baxter, Drummond, Rose, Stephens-Newsham, and Randall (1954) noted a decrease in the blood content

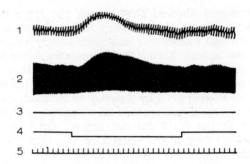

Figure 69. Reflex changes in blood pressure
following the injection of a perfusate from the
intestine of a totally irradiated cat into the
perfusion stream of an isolated segment of
intestine of a healthy cat. (Reported by
N. A. Lapshin.)
1—Blood pressure (manometric recording).
2—Blood pressure (tonometric recording).
3—Zero line.   4—Injection of perfusate.
5—Time in 5-sec intervals.

of histamine in totally irradiated swine. E. I. Krichevskaya (1958)
was unable to find any significant amount of histamine in the blood
immediately after irradiation, although the histamine level in the
tissues of the liver, kidneys, stomach, and skin reached a maximum during the first five minutes after irradiation. This increase
did not last long, and within an hour the histamine content of the
organs dropped below the original level, where it remained until
the animal died.

M. S. Seregin (1959, 1960), after transfusing healthy dogs
with blood taken from dogs with radiation sickness, found that
while 100 ml of blood taken from a donor before irradiation stimulated conditioned activity in the recipient, the same volume of
blood taken from the donor on the fifth or sixth day of radiation
sickness sharply inhibited the recipient's conditioned reflexes
(Figure 70). Blood taken on the 11th or 12th day, however, caused
virtually no inhibition. Blood taken on the 16th day or later stimulated rather than inhibited the recipient's conditioned reflexes;
i.e., it had the same effect as the blood of a healthy animal. These
data agree with those of P. D. Gorizontov (1955), who found increased amounts of histaminelike substances in the blood between
the 5th and 12th days after irradiation. They also agree with the
observations of T. M. Mel'gunova and K. M. Larionova (1958),
who noted a sharp decrease in the histaminase content of the blood

of dogs; the blood level was at a minimum between the third and seventh days.

As for the mechanism causing impaired conditioned activity after the transfusion of blood of an irradiated animal, it is apparent that the toxins entering the vascular bed of the recipient change the internal environment of the nerve cells and thus their functional condition. Then, acting on the vascular interceptors, they stimulate the flow of impulses "bombarding" the cortical cells so that the latter enter a state of protective inhibition and the conditioned reflexes decrease. The data cited above on changes in the gastrointestinal receptors tend to corroborate this view. Regardless of the mechanism underlying this phenomenon, however, it is important at this point to stress the fact that the toxins formed during the development of radiation sickness cannot be a decisive

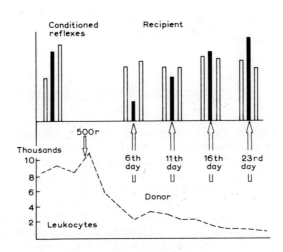

Figure 70. Changes in the exteroceptive and interoceptive conditioned reflexes of the dog Tobik following a blood transfusion from an irradiated dog. (Reported by M. S. Seregin.) Columns show total positive conditioned reflexes per experiment; black indicates day of transfusion. First set of columns—blood transfusion from donor before irradiation; other columns—after irradiation. Arrows and figures underneath indicate days after irradiation. Curve shows changes in the leukocyte count per mm^3 of blood in the donor dog after irradiation with 500 r.

factor in the impairment of gastrointestinal secretion and motility. Furthermore, as we have shown in our experiments (I. T. Kurtsin and I. G. Chursin, 1960) on dogs with two Pavlov pouches—one of which retained its extragastric innervation while the other was completely denervated—impaired secretion during radiation sickness is manifested chiefly by the innervated pouch (Figure 71). This pouch has an increased reaction to histamine, whereas the denervated pouch has a decreased reaction (Figure 72).

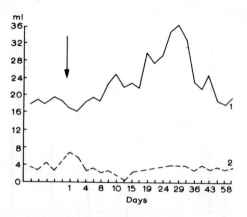

Figure 71. Comparative data on changes in juice secretion from innervated and denervated pouches in the dog Tigr after eating 200 g of meat during acute radiation sickness. (Reported by I. G. Chursin.)
1—Secretion of gastric juice from the innervated pouch. 2—Secretion of gastric juice from the denervated pouch. Arrow indicates irradiation with 350 r.

Among the humoral substances capable of playing a part in radiation impairment of digestion are the hormones of the endocrine glands (epinephrine, insulin, ACTH, the corticosteroids, etc.) and the hormones formed in the mucosa of the stomach and intestine (secretin, gastrin, cholecystokinin, enterogastrone, villikinin, urogastrone, duocrinin, and enterocrinin). The significance of the latter group in digestive disorders of radiation sickness has still not been wholly determined. It has been assumed that the adenohypophyseal-adrenocortical hormones are involved because of the resemblance between the acute radiation sickness syndrome and the intoxication syndrome appearing in rats injected with toxic doses of ACTH and cortisone: e.g., loss of weight; involution of the thymus, lymph nodes and spleen; atrophy of the liver; a slowing

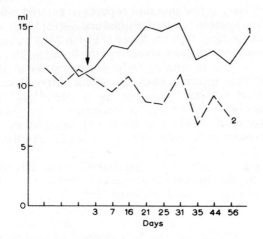

Figure 72. Comparative data on changes in juice secretion from innervated and denervated pouches in the dog Tigr in response to histamine during acute radiation sickness. (Reported by I. G. Chursin.)
Symbols the same as in Figure 71.

of the regenerative processes, and increased sensitivity to infectious agents (Selye, 1952). Involvement of these hormones is confirmed by the following observations: (1) the presence of leukopenia and the disappearance of lipids from the adrenal cortex in individuals irradiated during an atomic explosion, (2) increased reactivity of the adrenals in persons who have undergone radiotherapy, (3) the development of leukopenia in rats during the first 24 hours after local irradiation of the hypophysis, and the prevention of such leukopenia by adrenalectomy, (4) the increased reactivity of the adrenal cortex in animals following irradiation of the hypophysis, (5) the histomorphological changes in the adenohypophysis and adrenal cortex in animals during radiation sickness, (6) the greatly aggravated radiation sickness following removal of the adrenals and increased survival rate when these are shielded. Additional evidence is provided by the favorable therapeutic value of somatotropin (Selye, Solgada, and Procopio, 1952) and desoxycorticosterone acetate (Ellinger, Rosuit, and Glasser, 1949) in treating radiation sickness, and by the experiments of Nims and Sutton (1954), A. V. Tonkikh (1958), E. I. Komarov (1957), L. A. Kashchenko (1958), E. A. Moiseev (1958, 1959), and D. E. Grodzenskii (1957), who noted changes in the hypophyseal-adrenal system caused by ionizing radiation.

There are only a few isolated reports on related humoral effects in the digestive system itself. Leblond and Segal (1942) experimented on rats irradiated locally with doses of 630 to 3600 r, and discovered in the nonirradiated organs atrophy of the thymic-lymphatic system, hypertrophy of the adrenals, fatty degeneration of the liver, and ulceration of the gastric mucosa. Prior adrenalectomy reduced these radiation effects, possibly as a result of changes in the adenohypophyseal-adrenocortical system.

E. M. Kedrova (1957) has observed changes in the content of sulfhydryl groups in soluble liver proteins of irradiated white rats under the influence of ACTH.

E. I. Komarov (1958) has published some information on the part played by the hypophyseal-adrenal system in changes in the interoceptive unconditioned reflexes from the intestine.

Neither these nor similar data, however, are yet sufficient for us to form a clear-cut idea of the role of the adenohypophyseal-adrenocortical system in the development of radiation sickness in general or radiation injury to the digestive tract in particular.

The practical applications of this research have not been fully established experimentally. For example, several investigators have been unable to lower the death rate of irradiated animals by the use of ACTH or cortisone (Smith, Smith, and Thompson, 1950).

Selye's theory of the general adaptation syndrome, with which he explains many diseases, including radiation sickness, has many shortcomings, one of the most important being that the humoral factors in the pathological process are regarded as having no connection with the neural mechanisms.

CHAPTER 15

Some General Conclusions on Radiation Injury to the Digestive System

The experimental and clinical material described in the preceding pages indicates that ionizing radiation severely injures the digestive system. It damages all the basic functions—secretion, motility, and absorption. The extent and duration of the injury vary with the radiosensitivity of the organism and the severity of the sickness, and the resulting impairment invariably appears in the form of hyperfunction or hypofunction, or both, each alternating with the other.

Our own data obtained from experiments on 100 totally irradiated dogs showed that hyperfunction of the main digestive glands is almost as common as hypofunction in acute radiation sickness. Similarly, the efficiency of these glands increases or decreases to approximately the same extent, about 40%. The changes in efficiency of individual glands, however, are not identical. With hyperfunction, the intestinal and gastric glands work most intensively, the liver least so, the pancreas and salivary glands occupying an intermediate position. With hypofunction, the intestinal and salivary glands exhibit the sharpest decrease in efficiency, the liver and pancreas the smallest decrease, the gastric glands occupying an intermediate position (Table 68).

The range of functional variations in the digestive system is of some interest. Compared with the mean deviations from the original levels, the maximum range occurs in the intestinal and salivary glands, the minimum range in the liver and pancreas.

While conceding the tentativeness of these generalizations, which have obscured the individual peculiarities in the changes observed in the various animals and at different stages in the pathological process, we believe we have clearly shown that there is a definite limited range of changes in the efficiency of a particular organ or of the digestive system as a whole during acute radiation sickness. It is obvious that excessively high or excessively low

269

Table 68

Efficiency of the digestive glands in dogs during acute radiation
sickness (mean data).

Organ	Percentage of increase (+) or decrease (-) in the original (normal) volume of juice secreted with various kinds of secretory disorders.		
	Hyper-functional	Hypo-functional	Range of variations in changes
Salivary glands	+35	-55	90
Stomach	+43	-39	82
Pancreas	+37	-25	62
Liver	+17	-29	46
Intestine	+60	-53	113
Efficiency of digestive apparatus as a whole	+38.4	-40.2	78.6

digestive activity following ingestion of the same amount and kind of food cannot be beneficial to the organism. With excessively high digestive activity, there is an unnecessary waste of energy and building material. With excessively low digestive activity, there is insufficient secretion and, consequently, defective digestion.

If we were to express the hyperfunction or hypofunction of the digestive glands in absolute figures, assuming the daily production of the digestive glands in man to be 10 liters, there would be an excess or a deficiency of 4 liters of juice.

Also of interest is the secretory capacity after the disappearance of clinically pronounced signs of radiation sickness during recovery. It infrequently returns to normal, and it is rarely below normal; most often it is above normal. The degree of hypersecretion varies with the different glands, ranging from about 40% above normal in the pancreas and intestinal glands and 70% above normal in the gastric glands.

The data and figures given above, it seems to us, may have some practical value in working out diets for patients with radiation sickness.

There is still another fact worth noting when comparing the different radiation effects on the digestive organs. Experiments have shown that under identical conditions of radiation, the various digestive glands do not become pathologically altered at the same time; e.g., the salivary glands are affected earlier in the disease, the liver and pancreas later. There is also a difference in the severity and duration of secretory disorders in the different organs.

The difference in radiosensitivity of the individual digestive glands is not characteristic of this physiological system alone. The sensitivity of organs and tissues, like the nature, duration and reversibility of the reaction to injury, differs greatly among individual cells, tissues, organs, and organ systems. It varies with their physiological significance, differentiation, stage in evolution, and rhythm of the biochemical processes taking place in the cells. L. A. Orbeli (1955) referred to these factors in his report to a session of the USSR Academy of Sciences considering the peaceful uses of atomic energy. Additional details have been contributed since then by M. G. Durmish'yan (1957) and his co-workers: Ya. I. Azhipa, V. P. Godin, S. I. Gorshkov, M. G. Durmish'-yan, V. M. Zakharov, V. I. Kandror, and K. V. Khomutova, 1959.

Regarding the digestive system, we must bear in mind that the activity of one organ is closely connected with that of another. For example, hyperfunction or hypofunction may arise from the morphologic and functional characteristics of the cells and tissues of the organs, the degree of sensitivity to ionizing radiation, and impaired functional relationships, between the organs. But the most important factor of all, in our opinion, is the nature and extent of injury to the neurohumoral mechanism regulating the activity of the glands; especially important in this regard is the cerebral cortex, which in man and the higher animals controls all functions and their interrelationship with the autonomic centers of the subcortex and the medulla oblongata.

We therefore conceive of the mechanism responsible for the various digestive disorders in the following way. Functional weakening of the cerebral cortex and the development of protective inhibition is followed either by the propagation of inhibition into the subcortical structures or by positive induction. In the former case, the digestive glands are hypofunctional, in the latter case, hyperfunctional. When excitation becomes dominant in the cerebral cortex, however, hyperfunction may be due to the propagation of excitation from the cortex to the subcortical centers regulating digestion, whereas hypofunction may be caused by the negative induction of these centers.

These possible variations in the functional relationships between the cerebral cortex and the autonomic centers which exert direct control over the digestive system, are tentative since this cortical-subcortical relationship is extremely complex, very dynamic, and not always detectable by modern research techniques. Presumably, the same mosaic of excitation and inhibition occurring among the cells of the cerebral cortex may also occur in the functional relations among these lower divisions of the central nervous system. It is quite possible, for instance, that the brain centers regulating digestion are in a state of excitation at the same time that the brain centers regulating gastrointestinal motility or blood supply are in a state of inhibition, or vice versa. The result of this complex interrelationship may be the creation of stable foci of excitation and inhibition in different parts of the brain and medulla oblongata which in principle correspond to dominant foci. As is well known, such centers are capable of blocking the flow of afferent and efferent impulses.

The relationship between functional disorders of the digestive system as a whole, or of its individual organs, and the functional condition of the cerebral cortex and the subcortical autonomic centers does not exclude the involvement of several other physiological systems in the mechanism causing digestive disorders after radiation injury. In this connection, we must consider:

(a) any imbalance between the parasympathetic and sympathetic divisions of the autonomic nervous system, and especially the loss of synergistic action of these systems on the digestive organs;

(b) various degrees of impairment to the synaptic transmission of nervous excitation in the sympathetic and parasympathetic nervous systems and to the acetylcholine-cholinesterase system;

(c) any upsetting of normal endocrine gland balance, especially the adenohypophyseal-adrenocortical system, and disturbances to the digestive hormones formed in the gastrointestinal tract proper: gastrin, secretin, cholecystokinin, villikinin, enterogastrone, etc., and

(d) the changes in physiological responsiveness of the digestive organs following direct radiation injury to the parenchyma and neural structures of the organ.

Since all the functions of the internal organs, including secretion, are controlled, according to K. M. Bykov (1947) and his school, by the cerebral cortex, we can safely assume that among the factors listed above, the functional state of the cerebral cortex and subcortical autonomic centers is definitely involved in the digestive changes caused by ionizing radiation. The type of nervous system is of some significance in this respect because dogs with a weak type frequently suffer from hypofunctional secretory disorders, whereas dogs with a strong type suffer from hyperfunctional disorders or a combination of the the two.

One might wonder if there is any clinical value in determining the condition of the digestive system after radiation injury. To our way of thinking, an investigation of the digestive glands and of the entire digestive system as a whole after radiation injury has both diagnostic and prognostic value, naturally in conjunction with other objective signs, especially the condition of the hemic, nervous, cardiovascular, and other physiological systems. Accordingly, the following clinical and experimental findings can be considered and evaluated appropriately.

With minor injury and mild or moderately severe radiation sickness, hyperfunction of the digestive organs is the commonest disorder; hypofunction generally follows major injury and severe radiation sickness. The latter frequently occurs when the sickness follows a chronic course involving substantial degenerative and atrophic changes in the cells and tissues besides injury to the neurohumoral mechanism regulating digestion. Reflecting profound functional exhaustion of the cells, hypofunction is generally observed on the days before the organism dies. In such cases hypofunction is a grave sign from the prognostic point of view. Moreover, hypofunction soon after exposure, during the latent period of the sickness and sometimes at its height, indicates that the digestive functions are inhibited as a result of injury to the complex reflex regulatory mechanism. The functional condition of the central nervous system is now a matter of particular significance, and it can be determined by conditioned reflexes and electroencephalography. The possibility that the neuroglandular apparatus of the digestive system may be in a parabiotic state must be kept in mind and checked by means of a double functional test including stimuli of different intensities. The results should be of diagnostic value.

A detailed analysis of the function of an organ is important in evaluating its condition. The total volume of juice secreted in response to a stimulus, for example, is sometimes an insufficient basis for judging the changes that may have occurred in the specific activity of the organ. Only a thorough investigation of the secretory process will provide clues to serious functional impairment of the organ. For example, a slight increase in the volume of gastric secretion would apparently indicate mild hyperfunction of the gastric glands, but a comparison of the secretory activity during the first and second phases of secretion would reveal severe impairment to the complex reflex regulatory mechanism. It is quite evident that such disorders of the gastric glands cannot be detected by using a fine tube to introduce various test meals directly into the stomach since this would reveal information only about the second or neurochemical phase of secretion. Nor would a large tube be helpful except for the first or complex reflex phase of secretion, and, moreover, the objective data would be very meager indeed. In our opinion, the most feasible method for this purpose is the Bykov-Kurtsin method, which is effective in making absolute quantitative and qualitative determinations of gastric gland activity in both phases of secretion, and, at the same time, determines the functional condition of the gastric neuromuscular apparatus.

A major element in diagnosing radiation injury to the digestive functions is the composition of the secretion, which in many instances significantly supplements or reveals that which is hidden behind the salient characteristics of an organ's activity. In injuries to the pancreas we saw that the juice secreted possessed weak digestive properties, despite the apparently mild hypersecretion, and that there was a marked disparity in the concentrations of its constituent enzymes, e.g., high concentration of lipase with low concentrations of amylase and proteolytic enzymes. Qualitative changes in the secretion, in the enzymes in particular, is an important sign of degenerative impairment to the glandular apparatus and must therefore be taken into account when appraising the functional condition of the organ.

Spontaneous secretion, which arises quite often in radiation injury to the digestive glands, is another phenomenon worth noting. It occurs during the moderately severe and very severe forms of radiation sickness, chiefly as a result of disrupted nervous regulation of glandular activity. When there is continuous secretion of juice in the fasting organism, food stimuli frequently cause mild secretion, which is also characteristic of the hypofunctional disorders.

A clinical appraisal of digestive disorders, then, must take into account all the signs of radiation sickness. Detection of hyperfunction or hypofunction under these conditions undoubtedly has both diagnostic and prognostic significance.

As for the physiological mechanism causing malfunction of the digestive organs during radiation sickness, a major role is played by changes in the corticovisceral relations which normally coordinate the activity both of the individual organs and of the digestive system as a whole. Impairment of the initiating and correcting mechanisms of the cerebral cortex and the subcortical autonomic centers functionally related to the cortex is another important factor. In such cases impairment of the complex reflex regulation of digestion is extremely marked, as shown by major changes in: (a) conditioned and unconditioned salivation, (b) secretion in the Pavlov pouch, particularly in the lesser curvature, the first few hours after eating, (c) gastric secretion after sham feeding, (d) pancreatic secretion and bile secretion into the intestine the first 2 hours after eating, (e) the movement of food through the gastrointestinal tract, and the tone and rhythmic and peristaltic contractions of the musculature of the stomach, intestine, and gallbladder, and, (f) the vascular reflexes of the stomach and pancreas and their correlation with glandular secretion.

Changes in afferent impulses from the gastrointestinal receptors to the higher divisions of the central nervous system also play an important part, as shown by: (a) changes in conditioned interoceptive reflexes from the gastrointestinal tract, (b) decreased and distorted vascular and respiratory unconditioned reflexes from the intestine, stomach, and liver, and (c) morphologic changes in the receptors, nerves, autonomic ganglia, and intramural nerve plexuses of the stomach and intestine.

Our knowledge of radiation injury to the digestive system enables us to describe its course of development as follows. Ionizing radiation immediately does considerable damage to all the cells and tissues of the body, including those of the nervous system. Weakening of the functional condition of the nervous system and powerful impulses from the internal organs bring about distinct changes in higher nervous activity. At this time there are also pronounced changes in the digestive functions. Later, the high degree of plasticity of the nervous system and its great adaptative capacity, together with a reduced intensity of afferent impulses, mitigate this initial impairment of higher nervous activity and digestive functions; this results in a relative normalization which corresponds to the latent period of radiation sickness.

This normal phase, however, is unstable, as shown by certain changes in the latency and magnitude of the positive and inhibitory food-conditioned reflexes, by the appearance of phasic states in the cortical cells, and by occasional days of impaired gastrointestinal secretion and motility. Tissue and cell injury becomes more profound because of structural degeneration caused by the radiation trauma and because of indirect influences. The over-all cumulative effect of this is severe and prolonged impairment of the nervous system and digestive apparatus. The inadequacy of the protective and adaptational mechanisms at this time is caused not only by functional and morphologic changes in all the links of the central and peripheral nervous systems, but also by the toxic substances formed after the radiation trauma and during subsequent chain reactions in the biological substrate, activity on the secretory and motor cells of the digestive organs and on the organs of neurohumoral regulation.

Impaired hormonal regulation is also of some significance, as shown by: (a) secretory disturbances in the stomach, pancreas, liver, and intestine at the height of secretion and after eating; (b) secretory disorders in denervated salivary glands, pouches, and segments of small intestine; (c) changes in the activity of the gastric and pancreatic juices; (d) considerable changes in the optical density of blood serum during impairment of the gastric glands in the neurochemical phase; (e) an increased content of histamine-like substances in the blood during the first few days after irradiation; (f) inhibited synthesis of secretin at the height of radiation sickness; and (g) functional and morphologic changes in the endocrine glands, chiefly those of the hypophyseal-adrenal system.

The impaired functions return to normal if the sickness is not fatal, and the higher nervous system becomes normal before the digestive system.

All the clinical and experimental material described above clearly indicates that treatment of radiation injury to the digestive system must be based on an individualized approach to the patients; the therapy should include combined measures aimed at overcoming the pathological phenomena both in the digestive system proper and in the higher divisions of the central nervous system regulating its activity.

References

Afrikanova, L. A. Condition of the peripheral nervous system after total-body and local X-irradiation. Author's abstract of dissertation. Moscow, 1952.

Akopyan, S. A., É. Arutyunyan, Zh. Gevorkyan and A. Zakharyan. Study of the gastric physiology of irradiated animals. Ninth Congress of the All-Union Society of Physiologists, Biochemists and Pharmacologists. Izd. AN SSSR, i Belgosuniversiteta, Moscow-Minsk, 1959, I, pp. 20-21.

Andersen and Kohlmann. Röntgenstrahlen u. Mineralstoffwächsel. Fortschr. Geh, Röntgenstrahlen, 1923, 30, Kongressheft, SS. 102-105.rbuzov, S. Ya., A

Arbuzov, S. Ya., V. A. Bazanov, V. P. Korotkova, M. M. Lomkevich, P. I. Lomonos, I. Ya. Nekachalova, V. N. Patalova, V. V. Petelina, A. M. Stashkov and Z. K. Shamova. Pharmacological protection against injury by ionizing radiations. Ninth Congress of the All-Union Society of Physiologists, Biochemists and Pharmacologists. Izd. AN SSSR, i Belgosuniversiteta, Moscow-Minsk, 1959, I, pp. 24-25.

Arnold, I. R. Effects of the recent bomb tests in human beings. Bull. Atomic Scientists 10 (9): 347-348, 1954.

Ashwell, G. and I. Hickman. Effect of X-irradiation upon the enzyme systems of the mouse spleen. Proc. Soc. Exp. Biol. a. Med. 80 (3): 407-410, 1952.

Auer, G. and A. Chechulin. Experimental gastric ulcers induced by radium emanations. Vestn. khir. XVIII (53): 105-112, 1929.

Azhipa, Ya. I., V. P. Godin, S. I. Gorshkov, M. G. Durmish'yan, V. M. Zakharov, V. I. Kandror and K. V. Khomutova. Neuroendocrine system reactions to small doses of internal radiation with radioactive elements. Ninth Congress of the All-Union Society of Physiologists, Biochemists, and Pharmacologists. Izd. AN SSSR i Belgosuniversiteta, Moscow-Minsk, 1959, I, pp. 16-17.

Babkin, B. P. External Secretion of the Digestive Glands. GIZ, Moscow-Leningrad, 1927.

Babkin, B. P. Secretory Mechanism of the Digestive Glands. New York—London, 1944.

Babkin, B. P. The Secretion Mechanism of the Digestive Glands. Medgiz, Leningrad, 1960.

Bagdasarov, A. A. and S. L. Kopel'man. Roentgenology of gastric diseases. Klin. med. VIII (21): 1345-1351, 1929.

Bagdasarov, A. A. and S. L. Kopel'man. X ray therapy of gastric ulcers. Vestn. rentgenol. i radiol. VIII(2): 198-199, 1930.

Bakin, E. I. Effect of radium emanations on the course of conditioned reflexes in dogs. Vestn. rentgenol. i radiol. XXVI(4): 72-74, 1946.

Barbaczy, M. Die Anderungen des Blutcholesteringehalts nach nach Röntgentiefenbestrahlungen. Strahlentherapie. (19): 531, 1925.

Barron, E. S. G. Action of ionizing radiations on biologically important systems (transl.). Radiobiology (main characteristics of the effect of radiation on living organisms). Izd. IL, Moscow, 1955, pp. 249-274.

Barron, E. S. G., W. Wolkowitz and I. A. Müntz. Influence of X-irradiation on metabolic changes in small intestinal and absorption of glucose. Biological Effects of External X- and γ-radiation. Atomic Energy Commission, Document MDDC, 1947, 14 February, 3, 1241.

Barrow, J. and J. L. Tullis. Sequence of cellular responses to injury in mice exposed to 1100 r total-body X-radiation. Arch. Pathol. 53 (5): 391-407, 1952.

Baxter, H., J. Drummond, B. Rose, L. Stephens-Newsham and R. Randall. Blood histamine levels in swine following total-body X-irradiation and a flash burn. Ann. Surg. 139 (2): 179, 1954.

Becquerel, H. Comptes rendus hebdomadaires des séances de l'Académie des sciences, Paris, 1896, v. 122, pp. 420, 559, 762 et al.

Bekkum, D. W. van and others. The oxidative phosphorylation by mitochondria isolated from the spleen of rats after total-body exposure to X-rays. Brit. J. Radiol. 27 (314): 217-130, 1954.

Belovintseva, M. F. and E. N. Speranskaya. Significance of the functional condition of the liver in the development and course of radiation sickness. Radiobiology. Izd. AN SSSR, Moscow, 1958, pp. 251-257.

Belyaev, P. M. Effect of total-body gamma-irradiation with Co^{60} on nucleic acid metabolism in animals. Ninth Congress of the All-Union Society of Physiologists, Biochemists, and Pharmacologists. Izd. AN SSSR i Belgosuniversiteta, Moscow-Minsk, 1959, II, p. 44.

Belyaeva, E. M., V. D. Blokhina, S. S. Vasileĭskiĭ, N. N. Demin, L. I. Il'ina, A. S. Kaĭnova, K. V. Smirnov, L. T. Tutochkina, T. A. Fedorova and V. A. Shaternikov. Ibid. p. 45.

Bennet, L. R., S. M. Chastain, A. B. Decker and I. F. Mead. Effect of roentgen irradiation upon protein absorption in the mouse. Proc. Soc. exp. biol. a. med 77 (4): 715-718, 1951.

Bensaude, R., I. Solomon et P. Oury. Le traitment radiotherapie des affections gastriques non néoplasiques. Le presse Medicale. (49): 841-843, 1925.

Biryukov, D. A. Data on the effect of penetrating radiation on central inhibition. Conference on Problems Relating to the Evolutionary Physiology of the Nervous System. Abstracts. Leningrad, 1958, pp. 31-33.

Bloom, W. Plutonium Project; Histological changes following radiation exposures. Radiology. 49 (3): 344-348, 1947.

Bloom, W. Histopathology of irradiation from external and internal sources. New York, Toronto, London, 1948, chapt. 13.

Bogaevskiĭ, A. Ya. and B. Gol'dshteĭn. Effect of X-rays on the processes of enzyme formation in the cells of an isolated pancreas. Zhurn. eksper. biol. i med. IX (34): 328-334, 1928.

Boĭko, N. S. Electromotive force of the mucosa of an isolated dog pouch following injury by radioactive substances. Scientific Conference on Problems in the Physiology and Pathology of Digestion, celebrating the 40th anniversary of the Great October Socialist Revolution. Abstracts. Tartu, 1957, pp. 28-30; Transactions, Tartu, 1960, pp. 477-484.

Bond, V., M. Swift, A. Allen and M. Fischler. Sensitivity of Abdomen of Rat to X-irradiation. Amer. J. Physiol. 161 (3): 323-330, 1950.

Brams, I. and L. Darnbacher. The effect of X-rays on the gallbladder: experimental production of an X-ray cholecystitis. Radiology. XIII: 103-108, 1929.

Brechler, G. and E. P. Cronkite. Lesions of the alimentary tract of dogs exposed to whole-body X-irradiation of 300 to 3000 r. Amer. J. of Pathol. 27 (4): 676-677, 1951.

Brügel, C. Die Bienflussung des Magenchemismus durch Röntgenstrahlen. Münch. med. Wschr. (19): 9, 670, 1916; (12, 20): 379-380, 1917.

Brugge, C. F. von. Radiation injury following atomic bomb explosion. Ann. Internal. Med. 36 (6): 1444-1458, 1952.

Bryukhanov, O. A. Changes in the higher nervous activity of dogs following the action of injected radioactive phosphorus. Author's abstract. Leningrad, 1954.

Buchwald, K. W. Influence of X-irradiation on small intestinal absorption of glucose. J. Exptl. Med. (53): 827, 1931.

Bunatyan, G. Kh. and G. T. Alunts. Effect of beta-irradiation (P^{32}) on the glycogenic function of the liver. In: Biochemistry of the Nervous System. Izd. AN UkSSR, Kiev, 1954, p. 130.

Burn, I. H., P. Kordik and R. H. Mole. Effect of X-irradiation on the cholinesterase in rat intestine. J. Physiol. 116 (2): 5-6, 1952.

Burn, J. H., P. Kordik, and R. H. Mole, The effect of X-irradiation on the response of the intestine to acetylcholine and on its content of pseudocholinesterase. Brit. J. Pharmacol. (1): 58-66, 1952.

Bychkovskaya, I. B. Significance of the state of the nervous system in the body's response to the action of X-rays following total-body irradiation. Vestn. rentgenol. i radiol. (6): 10-15, 1956.

Bykov, K. M. Secretory fields of the stomach. Klin. med. 19 (7-8): 3-9, 1941.

Bykov, K. M. The Cerebral Cortex and the Internal Organs'. Medgiz, 1947.

Case, I. T. and W. N. Boldyreff, A study of the influence of high voltage roentgen irradiation on salivary secretion in dogs and its effect on the sensibility of the buccal mucosa. Am. J. Roentgenol. 13: 130-139, 1925.

Case, I. T. and W. N. Boldyreff. Influence of roentgen rays upon gastric secretion. Amer. J. Roentgenol. a. Radium Therapy. XIX (1): 61-70, 1928.

Case, I. T. and A. S. Warthin. Occurrence of hepatic lesions in patients treated by intensive deep roentgen irradiation. Amer. J. Roentgenol. (12): 27-46, 1924.

Chasovnikov, N. Effect of X-rays on the delicate structure of frog liver cells. Sibirsk. arkh. med. III (1): 1-6, 1928.

Chernichenko, V. A. Changes in certain interoceptive reflexes following ionizing radiation. In: Use of Radioactive Isotopes in Medicine. Gosmedizdat, Ukr. SSR, 1955, pp. 175-187.

Chernichenko, V. A. Certain changes in the functional state of the nervous system immediately after exposure to ionizing radiation. Author's abstract. Leningrad, 1956.

Chernykh, V. M. Pathological changes in the intestine during acute radiation sickness. Transactions of the All-Union Conference on Medical Radiology. Moscow, 1957, pp. 147-150.

Chursin, I. G. Effect of superstrong sound stimuli on the course of gastric secretion in dogs during acute radiation sickness. In: Problems in Corticovisceral Physiology and Pathology. Leningrad, 1957, pp. 52-60.

Chursin, I. G. Gastric secretion during acute radiation sickness in dogs with functionally weakened cerebral cortex. Author's abstract. Leningrad, 1958.

Colwell, H. A. and R. I. Gladstone. A note on the action of gamma rays on the nerve-cells of Auerbach's and Meissner's Plexus. Brit. J. Radiol. 9 (105): 620-623, 1936.

Conard, R. A. Effect of X-irradiation on intestinal motility of the rat. Amer. J. Physiol. 165 (2): 375-385, 1951.

Conard, R. A. Effect of X-irradiation on weight and contents of rat stomach and small and large intestine. Proc. Soc. Exptl. Biol. Med. 82 (2): 333-337, 1953.

Conard, R. A. Some effects of ionizing radiation on the physiology of the gastrointestinal tract. A Review. Radiation Res. 5 (2): 167-188, 1956.

Crawer, B. N. The effect of X-rays on the in vitro motility of the feline intestine. Amer. J. Roentgenol. a. Radium Therapy. 58 (3): 357-358, 1947.

Cronkite, E. P. Radiation sickness, pathogenesis and therapy. In: Radioactive Decay and Medicine (transl.). Izd. IL, Moscow, 1954, pp. 154-170.

Curie, Marie. Radioactivity. OGIZ, Gostekhizdat, 1947.

Dambrin, L. Le syndrome clinique de "l'atomice"; la victime des armes atomiques. Toulouse med. (9): 579-598, 1955.

Davydov, G. M. Secretory Areas of the Stomach and Their Inter-relations. Oblpoligrafizdat, Arkhangel'sk, 1950.

De Coursey, E. Human pathologic anatomy of ionizing radiation effects of the atomic bomb explosions. Mil. Surgeon. 102 (6): 427-432, 1948.

De Coursey, E. Effect of midlethal doses of total-body ionizing radiations. J. Amer. Med. Ass. 151 (11): 904-905, 1953.

Delitsyna, N. S. Some changes in receptors following X-irradiation. Transactions of the All-Union Conference on Medical Radiology. Medgiz, Moscow, 1957, pp. 28-34.

Delov, V. E., N. A. Adamovich, and O. N. Zamyatina. Effect of local and total-body X-irradiation on the gastrointestinal receptors. Scientific Conference on Problems in the Physiology and Pathology of Digestion celebrating the 40th anniversary of the Great October Socialist Revolution. Abstracts. Tartu, 1957, pp. 65-67.

Denisova, E. A. On the functional state of the liver in persons who have been in contact with radioactive substances. Med. radiol. (6): 44-49, 1957.

Desjardins, A. U. Action of roentgen rays and radium on the gastro-intestinal tract; Experimental data and clinical radiotherapy. Amer. J. Roentgenol a. Radium Therapy. 26 (1-3): 145-190, 335-370, 493-510, 1931.

Detrick, L., H. Upham, D. Highby, V. Debley and T. Haley. Effect of X-irradiation on gastric secretion and the accompanying gross and histological damage in the "Shay" rat stomach. Amer. J. Physiol. 179 (3): 462-466, 1954.

Detrick, L., H. Upham, D. Highby, V. Debley and T. Haley. Influence of X-irradiation on intestinal absorption of glucose in rat. Radiation Res. 2 (5) 1955.

Domshlak, M. P., Yu. G. Grigor'ev, N. G. Darenskaya, L. B. Koznova and G. F. Nevskaya. Complications during radiation therapy and methods of treating them. Transactions of the All-Union Conference on Medical Radiology. Medgiz, Moscow, 1957, pp. 170-174.

Douglas, D. M., W. R. Chent and S. Rowlands. Production of hypochlorhydria by beta-radiation of stomach. Lancet. 1 (IX): 492-495, 1951.

Dunhan, J. L., E. P. Cronkite, le Rey and S. Warren. Atomic bomb radiation injury. JAMA. 142 (1): 50-54, 1951.

Durmish'yan, M. G. Significance of relative radiosensitivity of organs and systems in the pathogenesis of radiation sickness. Abstracts of Reports Presented at the Scientific Conference celebrating the 40th anniversary of the Great October Socialist Revolution. Central Scientific Institute of Roentgenology and Radiology, Leningrad, 1958, pp. 48-50.

Dzhagiĭka, I. L. Effect of X-rays on reflexes from normal and inflamed spleen. Author's abstract. Leningrad, 1958.

Dzharak'yan, T. K. Reflexes from receptors of the spleen and intestine during acute radiation sickness. Abstracts of the All-Union Conference on Medical Radiology. Experimental Pathology Section. Medgiz, Moscow, 1956, pp. 18-19.

Dzharak'yan, T. K. and G. F. Fakhrutdinov. Changes in reflexes from the intestinal receptors after the action of penetrating radiation. Med. radiol. 3(2): 11-18, 1958.

Ellinger, F., B. Rosuit and G. M. Glassner. The treatment of radiation sickness with the adrenal cortical hormone (desoxy-corticosterone acetate). Amer. J. Roentgen a. Radium Therapy. 61(3): 387, 1949.

Ellinger, F. Histamine theory of the biological action of radiation. In: Action of Radiation and Use of Isotopes in Biology. Moscow, 1952, No. 4, pp. 36-38.

Engelstad, R. B. Effect of roentgen rays on stomach in rabbits. Am. J. Roentgenol. 40: 243-263, 1938.

English, J. A. Morphologic effects of irradiation of the salivary glands of rats. Nuclear Science. (14): 8, 1954.

English, J. A. Enzymatic acitivity of irradiated and normal salivary gland tissues. Amer. J. Physiol. 183 (3): 463-474, 1955.

Fadeeva, A. A., I. T. Kurtsin and A. D. Golovskiĭ. Significance of weakening the higher divisions of the central nervous system in secretory and vascular disorders of the stomach during radiation sickness. Abstracts of Reports Presented at the Conference on Medical Radiology celebrating the 40th Anniversary of the Great October Socialist Revolution. Medgiz, Moscow, 1957, pp. 47-49.

Fedorova, T. A. Nitrogen metabolism during experimental radiation sickness in rats. Transactions of the All-Union Conference on Medical Radiology. Moscow, 1957, pp. 103-108.

Fedorovskiĭ, L. L. Some data on changes in the cholepoietic function of the liver in dogs exposed to polonium. Transactions of the Scientific Conference on Problems in the Physiol. and Pathol. of Digestion, in memory of Academician K. M. Bykov. Ivanovo, 1960, pp. 846-849.

Fedotov, V. P. Condition of the carbohydrate function of the liver in dogs exposed to polonium. Author's abstract, Moscow, 1959.

Fenton, P. F. and H. M. Dickson. Changes in some gastrointestinal functions following X-irradiation. Amer. J. Physiol. 177 (3): 528-530, 1954.

Fischel, E. Recherches experimentales sur l'influence des rayons X sur la production ou accumulation de bile et glicogène dans la cellule hépatique. Schweiz. med. Wchschr. (71): 764-769, 1941.

Fox, B. W., A. Littman, M. I. Grossman and A. C. Ivy. Effect of intragastric irradiation on gastric acidity in the dogs. Gastroenterology. 24 (4): 517-534, 1953.

Fox, B. W., A. Littman, J. Lash and M. I. Grossman. Effect of beta-radiation on gastric secretion in dogs. Amer. J. Physiol. 163 (3): 711-712, 1952.

Frank, G. M. Biophysical investigations of radiation reactions. Radiology. Izd. AN SSSR, Moscow, 1958, pp. 14-25.

Friedman, N. B. Effect of radiation on the gastrointestinal tract including the salivary glands, the liver and pancreas. Arch. of Pathology. 34 (4): 749-787, 1942.

Gamaleya, A. N. and M. D. Donskoĭ. Acute radiation sickness. Voenno-med. zhurn. (10): 9-22, 1954.

Gasul', R. Ya. X-ray therapy for gastric ulcer in the light of radiobiological and clinical data. Kazansk. med. zhurn. (3-4): 310-316, 1934.

Gilinskii, E. Ya. Morphological changes in the nerve structures of certain internal organs following total-body and local X-irradiation. Transactions of the Scientific Conference on Problems in the Physiology and Pathology of Digestion, dedicated to the memory of Academician K. M. Bykov. Ivanovo, 1960, pp. 164-168.

Glazunov, I. S. and A. M. Vyalov. Thermoregulation after radiation injury. Abstracts of All-Union Conference on Medical Radiology. Moscow, 1956, p. 7.

Gol'dberg, S. V. Physiological Action of Becquerel's Rays. Diss. St. Petersburg, 1904.

Golonzko, R. A. Treatment of gastric and duodenal ulcers by irradiation of the cervical roots of the sympathetic and parasympathetic nervous systems. Sov. rentgenol. I: 35-39, 1934.

Golovskiĭ, A. D. Secretory and vascular reactions of the stomach in various functional states of the higher divisions of the central nervous system. Author's abstract. Leningrad, 1957.

Goodman, R. D., A. E. Lewis and E. A. Schuck. Effects of X-irradiation on gastrointestinal tract and absorption availability. Amer. J. Physiol. 169, (1): 242-245, 1952.

Gorizontov, P. D. Functional manifestations of lesions produced by external irradiation. In: Biological Action of Radiation and Clinical Radiation Sickness. Medgiz, Moscow, 1954, pp. 107-136.

Gorizontov, P. D. Pathological physiology of radiation lesions. In: Radiation Medicine. Moscow, 1955, pp. 80-173.

Gorizontov, P. D. Processes of inhibition in experimental radiation pathology. Zhurn. vyssh. nervn. deyat. im. I. P. Pavlova. V (3): 318-328, 1955.

Gorizontov, P. D. Changes in the biological properties of blood in irradiated animals. Abstracts of the All-Union Conference on the Application of Radioactive and Stable Isotopes and Irradiation in the National Economy and Science. Moscow, 1957, p. 13.

Gorizontov, P. D. Pathogenesis of radiation sickness caused by external ionizing radiation. In: Pathological Physiology of Acute Radiation Sickness. Medgiz, Moscow, 1958, pp. 5-48.

Gorizontov, P. D. Pathogenesis of acute radiation sickness from the pathophysiological point of view. Med. radiol. 4 (1): pp. 6-12, 1959.

Gorodetskiĭ, A. A. Some information on the part played by the nervous system in the manifestations of radiation sickness. Vestn. rentgenol. i radiol. (6): 3-10, 1955.

Gorovits, L. M. Biological significance of radium rays. Diss. St. Petersburg, 1906.

Graevskiĭ, É. Ya. Investigations of the protection of the animal organism from the harmful effect of ionizing radiations. Session of the USSR Academy of Sciences on the Peaceful Use of Atomic Energy, July 1-5, 1955. Izd. AN SSSR, Moscow, 1955, pp. 34-50.

Graham, J. Radiation Sickness. J. Amer. Med. Assoc. 113 (8): 664-668, 1939.

Grigor'ev, Yu. G. Primary changes in the functional state of the cerebral cortex following radiation action. Vestn. rentgenol. i radiol. (5): 3-10, 1954.

Grigor'ev, Yu. G. Some problems in the classification and clinical symptoms of radiation sickness in man. Klin. med. 34 (3): 12-25, 1956.

Grigor'ev, Yu. G. Primary changes in the functional state of the cerebral cortex in man during radiation sickness. Vestn. rentgenol. i radiol. (2): 3-7, 1956.

Grigor'ev, Yu. G. Data on the Reactions of the Human Central Nervous System to Penetrating Radiation. Medgiz, Moscow, 1959.

Grineva, K. A. Effect of X-rays on the motility and evacuation of the gastrointestinal tract following total-body irradiation of animals. Tr. In-ta fiziol. im. I. P. Pavlova AN SSSR. VI: 479-483, 1957.

Grodzenskiĭ, D. É. Radiation pathology and the endocrine system. Abstracts of the Scientific Conference celebrating the 40th Anniversary of the Great October Socialist Revolution. Central Scientific Institute of Roentgenology and Radiology, Leningrad, 1957, pp. 5-6.

Grodzenskiĭ, D. É. and K. A. Tret'yakova. Biological synthesis of cholesterol and fatty acids in the liver and adrenals of rats in relation to their age and during radiation. Ninth Congress of the All-Union Society of Physiologists, Biochemists, and Pharmacologists. Izd. AN SSSR i Belgosuniversiteta, Moscow-Minsk, 1959, II, p. 93.

Gudkova, E. A. Changes in the external secretion of the pancreas during acute radiation sickness of various degrees of severity. Ezhegodnik, IEM, AMN SSSR, Leningrad, 1957.

Gudkova, E. A. Mechanisms of the influence of ionizing radiation on the external secretion of the pancreas. Transactions of the Scientific Conference on Problems in the Physiology and Pathology of Digestion, in memory of Academician K. M. Bykov. Ivanovo, 1960, pp. 213-219.

Gus'kova, A. K. and G. D. Baĭsogolov. Two cases of acute radiation sickness in man. In: Effect of Irradiation on the Organism. Izd. AN SSSR, Moscow, 1955, pp. 23-42.

Gusterin, G. A., N. M. Okulov, S. V. Strutsovskaya and P. A. Buzini. Changes in the gastrointestinal tract during acute radiation sickness in experiments and in patients who received radiation therapy. Abstracts of the Scientific Conference celebrating the 40th Anniversary of the Great October Socialist Revolution. Central Scientific Institute of Roentgenology and Radiology, Leningrad, 1957, pp. 15-17.

Gvozdikovskaya, E. P. Effect of X-rays on the discharge of bile into the intestine and on the secretory (bile-forming) function of the liver. Abstracts. Kiev State Medical Press, 1937, p. 8.

Haret, J. A propos de l'action sur le foie des injections intra-péritonéales d'or radioactif colloidal (Au[198]). Bull. Assoc. franc. étude cancer. 40 (1): 68-77, 1953.

Hedin, R. F., W. R. Miller and D. G. Ielatis. Effect of beta-irradiation on gastric acidity. Arch. Surg. 61 (4): 748-757, 1950.

Hempelmann, L., H. Lisco, and D. Hofman. Acute Radiation Syndrome (transl.). Izd. IL, Moscow, 1954.

Heuper, W. S. and J. M. Carvajal-Ferero. The effects of repeated irradiation of the gastric region with small doses of roentgen rays upon the stomach and blood of dogs. Amer. J. Roentgenol. 52: 529, 1944.

Hollaender, A. Radiobiology (transl.). Medgiz, Moscow, 1959.

Holtermann, C. Über vitale Gewebefärbung unter dem Einfluss von Röntgenstraheln. Strahlentherapie. (17): 158-174, 1924.

Il'ina, L. I., V. D. Blokhina and M. S. Uspenskaya. Action of ionizing radiation on the proteins of the structural elements of liver cell cytoplasm. Med. radiol. II (4): 23-30, 1957.

Ivy, A. C., I. E. McCarthy and B. H. Orndorf. Studies on the effect of roentgen rays on glandular activity. IV. Effect of exposure of abdominal and thoracic areas to roentgen rays on gastric secretion; Note on roentgen cachexia. J. Amer. Clinical Ass. 83 (25): 1977-1984, 1944.

Ivy, A. C., B. H. Orndorf, A. Jacoby and T. E. Whitelow. Studies of the X-ray on glandular activity. J. Radiology. (1): 189-199, 1923.

Jenkinson, E. L. and M. D. Brown. Irradiation Sickness. A hypothesis concerning the basic mechanism and a study of therapeutics. Amer. J. Roentgenol. a. Radium Therapy. 51 (4): 496, 1944.

Kantin, A. V. Effect of irradiating the neck area with radium and X-rays on gastric secretion and on certain somatic autonomic reflexes. Vestn. rentgenol. i radiol. XX: 20-28, 1938.

Karpenko, A. E. Characteristics of external secretion of the pancreas during radiation sickness. Scientific Conference on Problems in the Physiology and Pathology of Digestion celebrating the 40th Anniversary of the Great October Socialist Revolution. Abstracts. Tartu, 1957, pp. 95-96; Transactions. Tartu, 1960, pp. 336-346.

Kashchenko, L. A. Nature of the reaction of the endocrine system to ionizing radiation. Abstracts of Reports Presented at the Scientific Conference celebrating the 40th Anniversary of the Central Research Institute of Roentgenology and Radiology. Leningrad, 1958, pp. 8-10.

Kedrova, E. M. Effect of the adrenocorticotropic hormone on the survival of white rats irradiated with X-rays and on the content of sulfhydryl groups in the soluble liver proteins. Med. radiol. (2): 42-46, 1957.

Khizhin, P. P. Gastric Secretion in Dogs. Diss. St. Petersburg, 1894.

Khua Guan. Permeability of glandular tissue following impairment of higher nervous activity. Author's abstract. Leningrad, 1955.

Kireev, P. M. Clinical symptoms and treatment of chronic radiation sickness. Med. radiol. 2 (5): 72-79, 1957.

Kiselev, P. N. Changes in permeability of the gastrointestinal tract caused by X-rays and their significance in sensitization of the body. Vestn. rentgenol. i radiol. XXII (1): 38, 1940.

Klimova, E. N. Effect of chronic action of strontium 90 on higher nervous activity. Abstracts of Reports Presented at the

Conference on Medical Radiology Celebrating the 40th Anniversary of the Great October Socialist Revolution. Medgiz, Moscow, 1957, pp. 29-31.

Komarov, E. I. Changes in interoceptive unconditioned reflexes after ionizing radiation. Med. radiol. (3): 3-8, 1957.

Komarov, E. I. The endocrine link in certain interoceptive reflexes and its significance in the systemic reaction to ionizing radiation. Scientific Conference celebrating the 40th anniversary of the Great October Socialist Revolution. Abstracts of Reports Presented at the Society of Physiologists, Biochemists, and Pharmacologists. Leningrad, 1957, pp. 49-51.

Komarov, E. I. Neuroendocrine mechanisms of the reactions to ionizing radiation. Abstracts of Reports Presented at the Scientific Conference celebrating the 40th Anniversary of the Central Research Institute of Roentgenology and Radiology. Leningrad, 1958, pp. 10-11.

Korneeva, Ya. S. Changes in gastric secretion and motility following X-irradiation of the gastric region. Vrach. delo. (5): 377-379, 1928.

Kornilov, A. N. Gastrointestinal motility during radiation sickness caused by external irradiation of the abdominal organs. Author's abstract. Leningrad, 1954.

Kornilov, A. N. Gastrointestinal motility during radiation sickness. Voenno-med. zhurn. (3): 19-25, 1956.

Kothmejer, I. Zur Röntgenbehandlung des Magenschwurs. Strahlentherapie. XIV (1): 145-158, 1922.

Kotlyarevskiĭ, L. I., L. S. Gorsheleva and L. E. Khozak. Effect of ionizing radiation on animals with various types of nervous systems under physiologic and pathologic conditions. Radiobiology. Izd. AN SSSR, Moscow, 1958, pp. 192-196.

Koyama, V. and T. Kumatori. Clinical course of the Bikini patients. National Hospital Japan. (9): 1, 1955.

Kozlova, A. V. Aftereffects of the atomic bomb explosions over Hiroshima and Nagasaki and the hydrogen bomb explosion at Bikini. Report of the International Conference in Tokyo (1955) on the Aftereffects of the Atomic and Hydrogen Bomb Explosions. Medgiz, Moscow, 1957.

Kozlova, A. V. and E. I. Vorob'ev. Clinical Symptoms and Treatment of Lesions Resulting from an Atomic Bomb Explosion. Medgiz, Moscow, 1956.

Kozlova, A. V., V. M. Malenkova, E. V. Karibskaya and T. S. Seletskaya. Clinical symptoms of chronic radiation sickness. Transactions of the All-Union Conference on Medical Radiology. Medgiz, Moscow, 1957, pp. 14-20.

Kraevskiĭ, N. A. Pathological anatomy of radiation sickness. In: Biological Effect of Radiation and Clinical Symptoms of Radiation Sickness. Medgiz, Moscow, 1954, pp. 170-188.

Kraevskiĭ, N. A. Pathological anatomy of radiation lesions. In: Radiation Medicine. Medgiz, Moscow, 1955, pp. 257-275.

Kraevskiĭ, N. A. Essays on the Pathological Anatomy of Radiation Sickness. Medgiz, 1957.

Krause, P. and K. Ziegler. Experimentelle Untersuchungen über die Einwirkung der Röntgenstrahlen auf tierische Gewebe. Fortschr. auf dem Geb. der Röntgenstr. 10: 126-182, 1906.

Krichevskaya, E. I. Effect of X-rays on the histamine content of tissues. Radiobiology. Izd. AN SSSR, Moscow, 1958, pp. 126-129.

Krivchenkova, R. S. Effect of polonium radioactivity on the activity of succinic dehydrogenase of certain rat organs following the injection of unithiole. Scientific Conference on the Problem of "Reparative and Compensatory Processes during Radiation Sickness." Abstracts IEM, Leningrad, 1960, pp. 34-35.

Kurshakov, N. A. Clinical symptoms and treatment of radiation sickness. In: Biological Effect of Radiation and Clinical Symptoms of Radiation Sickness. Medgiz, Moscow, 1954, pp. 137-153.

Kurshakov, N. A. and I. S. Glazunov. Clinical symptoms and treatment of radiation sickness. In: Radiation Medicine. Medgiz, 1955, pp. 191-218.

Kurshakova, N. N. Histochemical investigation of nucleic acids in the tissues of irradiated animals. Abstracts of Reports Presented at the Scientific and Technical Conference on the Use of Radioactive and Stable Isotopes and Radiation in the National Economy and Science. AN SSSR, Moscow, 1957, pp. 47-48.

Kurtsin, I. T. Mechanoreceptors of the Stomach and Activity of the Digestive Apparatus. Izd. AN SSSR, Leningrad, 1952.

Kurtsin, I. T. Principles of Corticovisceral Physiology and Pathology. Leningrad, 1954.

Kurtsin, I. T. Physiology of Digestion. Leningrad, 1954.

Kurtsin, I. T. Activity of the digestive apparatus during radiation sickness. Scientific Conference on Problems in the Physiology and Pathology of Digestion, celebrating the 40th Anniversary of the Great October Socialist Revolution. Abstracts. Tartu, 1957, pp. 120-124; Transactions. Tartu, 1960, pp. 323-335.

Kurtsin, I. T. Disruption of corticovisceral interrelations during acute radiation sickness. Abstracts of the Reports presented at the All-Union Scientific and Technical Conference on the Use of Radioactive and Stable Isotopes and Irradiation in the National Economy and Science. Izd. AN SSSR, Moscow, 1957, pp. 28-29; Radiobiology. Izd. AN SSSR, Moscow, 1958, pp. 211-221.

Kurtsin, I. T. Corticovisceral disruption following penetrating radiation. Transactions of the First Conference of Physiologists, Biochemists, and Pharmacologists of Central Asia and Kazakhstan. Izd. AN UzSSR, Tashkent, 1958, pp. 621-637.

Kurtsin, I. T. Vascular impairment following radiation lesions. Abstracts of Papers Presented at a Scientific Session celebrating the 160th anniversary of VMOLA, Leningrad, 1959, pp. 14-17.

Kurtsin, I. T. and I. G. Chursin. New data on the mechanism of impairment of gastric secretion during acute radiation sickness. Transactions of the Scientific Conference on Problems in the Physiol. and Pathol. of Digestion, in memory of Academician K. M. Bykov. Ivanovo, 1960, pp. 417-420.

Kurtsin, I. T. and A. G. Korobkina. Changes in motility of the gallbladder in dogs during acute radiation sickness. Transactions of the Scientific Conference on Problems in the Physiol. and Pathol. of Digestion, in memory of Academician K. M. Bykov. Ivanovo, 1960, pp. 412-416.)

Kurtsin, I. T., A. G. Kuzovkov and I. G. Chursin. Changes in higher nervous activity in dogs. In: Problems in Corticovisceral physiology and Pathology. Leningrad, 1957, pp. 25-34.

Kusano, N. Atombombenschäden, Berlin, 1954.

Kuzin, A. M. Biochemical principles of the biological action of ionizing radiation. In: Essays on Radiobiology. Izd. AN SSSR, Moscow, 1956.

Kuznetsov, V. I., V. A. Baranov, V. V. Fialkovskiĭ, K. K. Smirnov, G. I. Dovzhenko, G. S. Goryushin, N. I. Shcherbakov, E. G. Zhuk, N. V. Butomo, P. V. Preobrazhenskiĭ and K. B. Tikhonov. Clinical symptoms in persons after prolonged exposure to ionizing radiations. Voenno-med. zhurn. (2): 40-43, 1957.

Kuznetsova, N. E. Changes in the neurohumoral substances in the blood of dogs during chronic radiation sickness. Abstracts of the Reports Presented at the Scientific Conference celebrating the 40th Anniversary of the Great October Socialist revolution. Central Scientific Institute of Roentgenology and Radiology, Leningrad, 1957, pp. 6-7.

Kuznetsova, E. K. Change in evacuation from the stomach and small intestine during radiation sickness. Scientific Conference on Problems in the Physiol. and Pathol. of Digestion celebrating the 40th Anniversary of the Great October Socialist Revolution. Abstracts. Tartu, 1957, pp. 117-118; Transactions. Tartu, 1960, pp. 347-352.

Lamson, B. G. and J. L. Tullis. The progression of morphologic lesions in Swiss mice exposed to 625 r 2000 kvp total-body X-radiation. Military Surgeon. 109: (4): 281-293, 1951.

Lasser, C. E. and K. W. Stenstrum. Elevation of circulating blood histamine in patients undergoing deep roentgentherapy. Amer.

J. Roentgenol. Radium Therapy a. Nuclear Medicines. 72 (6): 985-988, 1954.

Lapshin, N. A. Gastrointestinal receptor functions after ionizing radiation. Transactions of the Scientific Conference on Problems in the Physiol. and Pathol. of Digestion, in memory of Academician K. M. Bykov. Ivanovo, 1960, pp. 421-424.

Lawrence, I. H. and R. Tennan. The comparative effects of neutrons and X-rays on the whole body. J. Exp. Med. 66 (6): 667-687, 1937.

Lebedev, B. I. Condition of the myenteric plexus of the gastro-intestinal tract in dogs exposed to radioactive strontium. Scientific Conference on Problems in the Physiology and Pathology of Digestion celebrating the 40th anniversary of the Great October Socialist Revolution. Abstracts. Tartu, 1957, pp. 127-128; Transactions. Tartu, 1960, pp. 434-440.

Lebedev, B. I. Nervous apparatus of the gastrointestinal tract of dogs injured by polonium. Transactions of the Scientific Conference on Problems in the Physiol. and Pathol. of Digestion, in memory of Academician K. M. Bykov. Ivanovo, 1960, pp. 474-478.

Lebedev, N. N. Data on the pathogenesis of radiation lesions of the gastrointestinal tract. Abstracts of the Reports Presented at the Scientific Conference celebrating the 40th Anniversary of the Great October Socialist Revolution. Central Scientific Institute, Leningrad, 1957, pp. 11-13.

Lebedev, N. N. and E. F. Fofanova. Changes in the interoceptive reactions of the digestive tract to mechanical and chemical stimulation during experimental radiation sickness. Transactions of the Scientific Conference on Problems in the Physiol. and Pathol. of Digestion, in memory of Academcian K. M. Bykov. Ivanovo, 1960, pp. 425-430.

Lebedev, N. N. and M. A. Sobakin. Gastric motility following experimental radiation lesions of the organism. Scientific Conference on Problems of the Physiol. and Pathol. of Digestion celebrating the 40th Anniversary of the Great October Socialist Revolution. Abstracts. Tartu, 1957, pp. 131-133; Transactions. Tartu, 1960, pp. 441-448.

Lebedeva, G. A. Nature of the reaction of the gastrointestinal tract to chemical stimulation following exposure to radio-active strontium. Scientific Conference on Problems of the Physiology and Pathology of Digestion celebrating the 40th Anniversary of the Great October Socialist Revolution. Abstracts. Tartu, 1957, pp. 135-136.

Lebedeva, G. A. Data from a comparative study of gastrointestinal lesions caused by various kinds of radiation. Transactions of the Scientific Conference on Problems in the Phys. and Path. of Digestion, in memory of Academician K. M. Bykov. Ivanovo, 1960, pp. 470-473.

Lebedeva, G. A. Impairment of regeneration in the gastrointestinal tract during chronic radiation sickness induced by the administration of polonium and radioactive strontium. Scientific Conference on the Problem "Restorative and Compensatory Processes in Radiation Sickness". Abstracts. IEM, Leningrad, 1960, pp. 38-39.

Lebedinskiĭ, A. V. The Effect of ionizing radiation on the animal organism. In: The Effect of Irradiation on the Organism. Izd. AN SSSR, Moscow, 1955, pp. 43-77.

Lebedinskiĭ, A. V. Certain neuroendocrine relations in the organism's reaction to the influence of ionizing radiation. Med. radiol. (1): 35-41, 1957.

Lebedinakiĭ, A. V., Z. N. Nakhil'nitskaya and N. P. Smirnova. Involvement of the autonomic nervous system in the reactions of the organism to ionizing radiation. Abstracts of the Reports Presented at the Scientific Conference celebrating the 40th Anniversary of the Central Scientific Institute of Roentgenology and Radiology of the USSR Ministry of Health. Leningrad, 1958, pp. 6-8.

Leblond, C. P. and G. Segal. Differentiation between the direct and indirect effects of roentgen rays upon the organs of normal and adrenalectomised rats. Amer. J. Roentgenol. 47 (2): 302, 1942.

Leopold, R. S. Effects of total-body X-irradiation on salivary components of dogs. J. Dent. Research. St. Louis, 1952, v. 31.

Lepine, R. et Bould. Action des rayons X sur les tissus animaux. Compt. Rend. Acad. des Sciences. Paris, 1904, v. CXXXVIII, pp. 65-67.

Lewin, E., A. Haman and W. L. Palmer. The effect of radiation therapy on the natural gastric secretion in patients with duodenal ulcer. Gastroenterology. 8: 565-574, 1947.

Liebow, A., S. Warren and E. de Coursey. Pathology of atomic bomb casualties. Amer. J. Pathol. XXV (5): 853-1027, 1949.

Littman, A., B. W. Fox, H. M. Schoolman and A. C. Ivy. Lethal effect of intragastric irradiation in the dog. Amer. J. Physiol. 174 (3): 347-351, 1953.

Livanov, M. N. Changes in different sections of the central nervous system after the action of X-rays. Transactions of the All-Union Conference on Medical Radiology. Medgiz, Moscow, 1957, pp. 17-22.

Livanov, M. N. Electrophysiological research on radiation injuries. IX Congress of the All-Union Society of Physiologists, Biochemists and Pharmacologists. Izd. AN SSSR i Belgosuniversiteta, Moscow-Minsk, 1959, Vol. I, p. 275.

Livshits, N. N. Conditioned reflex activity on dogs chronically exposed to ionizing radiation to the head. Biofizika. I (3): 221-231, 1956.

Livshits, N. N. Nervous system and ionizing radiation. In: Essays on Radiobiology. Izd. AN SSSR, Moscow, 1956, pp. 151-232.

Lobasov, I. O. Secretory Activity of the Dog's Stomach. Diss. St. Petersburg, 1896.

Lomonos, P. I. Effect of ionizing radiation on the higher divisions of the dog brain. Author's abstract. Leningrad, 1959.

London, E. S. Physiological and pathological significance of radium rays. Arkh. biol. nauk. 10 (2): 191, 1904.

Lourau, M. and O. Lartique. Influence d'une irradiation générale par les rayons X sur l'utilisation de glucose par le foie. J. de Physiol. 43 (4): 593-603, 1951.

Maĭorov, F. P., M. I. Nemenov and L. S. Vasil'eva. Changes in cortical activity following X-irradiation of the cervical sympathetic nodes. In: Jubilee Session celebrating the 100th Anniversary of the Birth of Acad. I. P. Pavlov. Abstracts. Moscow, 1949, pp. 85-87.

Maĭorov, F. P., B. V. Pavlov and N. Ya. Lipatov. Changes in the higher nervous activity of dogs following X-irradiation of the cervical portion of the autonomic nervous system. Transactions of the AN SSSR I. P. Pavlov Inst. of Physiology. 5: 79-101, 1956.

Makulova, I. D. Clinical symptoms of chronic radiation sickness (external gamma-irradiation) based on dynamic observation of workers. Abstracts of Reports Presented at the Scientific Conference celebrating the 40th Anniversary of the Great October Socialist Revolution. Central Scientific Institute, Leningrad, 1957, p. 68.

Marhefka, E. Gesundeltschäden durch Atombomben. Ther. Gegenwart. 94 (9): 334-336, 1955.

Martin, C. L. and W. H. Moursund. Irradiation sickness. Radiology. 30 (3): 277, 1938.

Martin, C. L. and F. T. Rogers. Intestinal reaction to erythema dose. Amer. J. Roentgenol. a. Radium Therapy. 10: 11-19, 1923.

Martirosov, K. S. Effect of vitamin C on the functional state in the sphere of pigment metabolism following exposure to ionizing radiation. Scientific Conference on Problems in the Physiology and Pathology of Digestion celebrating the 40th anniversary of the Great October Socialist Revolution. Abstracts. Tartu, 1957, pp. 158-159; Transactions. Tartu, 1960, pp. 449-455.

Martland, H. S. Occupational poisoning in manufactures of luminous watch dials; General review of hazard, caused by ingestion of luminous paint with special reference to the New Jersey cases. JAMA. 92: 446-452, 1929.

McDonald, M. R. The effects of X-rays on dilute solutions of crystallin trypsin; Continued inactivation after termination of irradiation. Brit. J. Radiol. 27 (313): 62-63, 1954.

McKendry, I. B. R. Intracavitary visceral radiation. Effect on gastric acid secretion. Proc. Soc. Exp. Biol. Med. 75 (1) 25-27, 1950.

Mead, I., A. Decker and L. Bennet. The effect of X-irradiation upon fat absorption in the mouse. Nutrition. (43): 4, 1951.

Mel'gunova, T. M. and K. M. Larionova. Histaminase content in the blood of dogs during acute radiation sickness. In: Pathologic Physiology of Acute Radiation Sickness. Medgiz, Moscow, 1958, pp. 128-131.

Mel'gunova, T. M. and K. M. Larionova. Vasopressor substances in the blood during acute radiation sickness. Ibid. pp. 131-134.

Miescher, G. Einfluss der Röntgenstrahlen auf die secretion des Magens. Strahlenther. XV (2): 252-272, 1923.

Mikamo, V. a. o. Clinical and hematological studies on Bikini patients. Research in Effects of the Nucl. Bomb. Tokyo, 1956, pp. 1313-1331.

Mikhaĭlov, V. P., K. M. Svetikova and K. M. Yaroslavtseva. Posttraumatic regeneration of the gastric mucosa during acute radiation sickness. Scientific Conference on the Problem of "Reparative and Compensatory Processes during Radiation Sickness". Abstracts. IEM, Leningrad, 1960, pp. 45-46.

Minaev, P. F. Effect of X-rays on the function of the various divisions of the central nervous system. In: Biochemistry of the Nervous System. Kiev, 1954, pp. 171-178.

Minaev, P. F. Role of the nervous system in radiation reactions of the body. Radiobiology. Izd. AN SSSR, Moscow, 1958, pp. 204-209.

Mints, M. M. Picture of the stomach with diseases of the hypophysis cerebri before and after treatment with radiant energy. Vestn. rentgenol. i radiol. VI (1): 57-64, 1928.

Moiseev, E. A. Pathogenesis of endocrine disturbances following radiation lesions. Radiobiology. Izd. AN SSSR, Moscow, 1958, pp. 156-160.

Moiseev, E. A. Role of the endocrine glands in the reaction of animals to gamma- and X-irradiation. Ninth Congress of the All-Union Society of Physiologists, Biochemists, and Pharmacologists. Izd. AN SSSR i Belgosuniversiteta, Moscow-Minsk, 1959, I, pp. 30-303.

Molchanov, S. A. X-ray therapy of gastric and duodenal diseases. Transactions of the 1st Scientific Congress of Turkestan. 1923, pp. 104-109.

Morozov, A. L., E. A. Drogichina, M. A. Kazakevich, N. I. Ivanov and S. F. Belova. State of health of persons exposed to ionizing radiation under industrial and laboratory conditions. Transactions of the All-Union Conference on Medical Radiology. Medgiz, Moscow, 1957, pp. 20-25.

Movsesyan, M. A., S. G. Shukaryan and A. E. Agababyan. Reflex mechanism of action of X-rays. Abstracts of Reports Presented at the Scientific Session dedicated to the 30th Anniversary of the activity of the Central Research Institute of Roentgenology and Radiology. Moscow, 1954, p. 7.

Mulligan, R. M. The lesions produced in the gastrointestinal tract by irradiation. General review with an illustrative case report. Amer. J. Pathol. 18 (3): 515-526, 1942.

Nemenov, M. I. Effect of X-rays on the brain. Vestn. rentgenol. i radiol. XI, (1): 8-10, 1932.

Nemenov, M. I. What have we learned from studying the effect of radiant energy on the central and autonomic nervous systems? Ibid. XX: 3-7, 1938.

Nemenov, M. I. Effect of X-rays on higher nervous activity. Ibid. XXVI (1): 43-53, 1944.

Nemenov, M. I. X-ray Therapy through Action on the Nervous System. Medgiz, Moscow-Leningrad, 1950.

Nesterin, M. F. Effect of total-body X-irradiation on gastric and intestinal secretion. Abstracts of Reports Presented at the Tenth Scientific Session of the Institute of Nutrition. AMN SSSR, Moscow, 1956, pp. 53-54.

Nesterin, M. F. Effect of total-body X-irradiation on the enzyme-secreting processes in the intestine. Vestn. rentgenol. i radiol. (4): 81, 1957.

Nesterin, M. F. Effect of X-rays on gastric and intestinal secretion. Author's abstract. Moscow, 1957. Scientific Conference on Problems in the Physiology and Pathology of Digestion celebrating the 40th Anniversary of the Great October Socialist Revolution. Abstracts. Tartu, 1957, pp. 186-187; Transactions. Tartu, 1960, pp. 456-465.

Nesterin, M. F. Impairment and restoration of gastrointestinal secretion in experimental radiation sickness. Scientific Conference on the Problem "Restorative and Compensatory Processes in Radiation Sickness". Abstracts. IEM, Leningrad, 1960, p. 50.

Nikitin, S. A. Possible development and present knowledge of the biological action of X-rays. Usp. sovr. biol. XXII(2): 277-289, 1946.

Nims, L. F. and E. Sutton. Adrenal cholesterol, liver glycogen and water consumption of fasting and X-irradiated rats. Amer. J. Physiol. 177 (1): 51, 1954.

Oksenov, I. A. Changes in gastric secretion attending radiotherapy of uterine tumors. Vestn. rentgenol. i radiol. X: 340-352, 1932.

Okulov, N. M. Effect of acute radiation sickness on changes in the rate of methionine absorption from the gastrointestinal tract. Med. radiol. (5): 41-45, 1956.

Oleǐnikova, T. N. Morphologic changes in the peripheral nervous system caused by ionizing radiation. Transactions of the

All-Union Conference on Medical Radiology. Medgiz, Moscow, 1957, pp. 61–65.

Ol'khovskaya, M. V., É. Ya. Bril' and V. V. Zorina. Roentgenotherapy of gastric and duodenal ulcers. Sov. rentgenol. I, 1934.

Orbeli, L. A. Effect of ionizing radiation on animals. Session of the Academy of Sciences USSR on the Peaceful Use of Atomic Energy, July 1-5, 1955. Izd. AN SSSR, Moscow, 1955, pp. 3–13.

Palmer, W. L. and F. Templeton. The effect of radiation therapy on gastric secretion. J. Amer. Med. Assoc. 112 (15): 1429–1434, 1939.

Pashkovskiĭ, É. V. Effect of total-body X-irradiation on absorption from the small intestine. Scientific Conference on Problems in the Physiology and Pathology of Digestion celebrating the 40th Anniversary of the Great October Socialist Revolution. Abstracts. Tartu, 1957, pp. 193-194; Transactions. Tartu, 1960, pp. 353-363.

Pashkovskiĭ, É. V. Absorption in the small intestine of dogs X-irradiated with the cerebral cortex normal and in functionally weakened condition. Author's abstract. Leningrad, 1959.

Pavlov, I. P. (1897). Complete Collected Works. Izd. AN SSSR, Leningrad, 1951, Vol. II, Book 2.

Pavlov, I. P. (1927, 1932). Complete Collected Works. Izd. AN SSSR, Leningrad, 1951, Vol. III, Books 1 and 2, Vol. IV.

Perepelkin, S. R. Impairment of gastrointestinal secretion and absorption in dogs during radiation sickness. Eighth All-Union Congress of Physiologists, Biochemists, and Pharmacologists. Abstracts. Izd. AN SSSR, Moscow, 1955, pp. 473–474.

Perepelkin, S. R. Impairment of gastric and intestinal secretion in dogs exposed to the products of nuclear fission of uranium. Scientific Conference on Problems in the Physiology and Pathology of Digestion celebrating the 40th Anniversary of the Great October Socialist Revolution. Abstracts. Tartu, 1957, pp. 195-196; Transactions. Tartu, 1960, pp. 415-426.

Perepelkin, S. R. Effect of certain radioactive substances on gastric and intestinal secretion. Med. radiol. 3 (6): 16-25, 1958.

Perepelkin, S. R. Impairment of Gastric and Intestinal Secretion and Excretion after Poisoning with Radioactive Substances. Medgiz, Moscow, 1960.

Perepelkin, S. R. Nature of impairment of intestinal absorption caused by ionizing radiation. Transactions of the Scientific Conference on Problems on the Physiology and Pathology of Digestion, in memory of Academician K. M. Bykov. Ivanovo, 1960, pp. 651-656.

Petrov, I. R. and E. V. Gubler. Role of the External Environment in the Origin of Disease. Leningrad, 1954.

Petrov, I. R. and V. I. Kulagin. Pathophysiological reactions during acute radiation sickness. Med. radiol. II (2): 3-12, 1957.

Pigalev, I. A. Clinical symptoms of lesions caused by radioactive substances and problems in pathogenesis. In: Biological Action of Radiation and Clinical Symptoms of Radiation Sickness. Medgiz, Moscow, 1954, pp. 76-106.

Piskunova, V. G. and A. M. Vychegzhanina. Cases of radiation sickness. Vrach. delo. (7): 641-642, 1955.

Pobedinskiĭ, M. N. Radiation Complications during Radiotherapy. Medgiz, Moscow, 1954.

Podesta, V. Studi sperimentali sulla lesioni intestinali da raddi x-nella applicazione della radioterapia profonda intensiva Radio. Med. 12: 201-216, 1925.

Polyakov, A. L. Morphologic changes in the gastrointestinal mucosa of white mice after X-ray illumination. Vestn. rentgenol. i radiol. XVII: 365-369, 1936.

Ponomarenko, N. E. Some aspects of lipid metabolism after the action of ionizing radiation. Transactions of the Conference on Medical Radiology. Medgiz, Moscow, 1957, pp. 309-311.

Popkov, V. L. Changes in discharge of bile into the duodenum during acute radiation sickness in dogs with normal and functionally weakened cerebral cortex. Scientific Conference on Problems in the Physiology and Pathology of Digestion celebrating the 40th Anniversary of the Great October Socialist Revolution. Abstracts. Tartu, 1957, pp. 207-209; Transactions. Tartu, 1960, pp. 364-370.

Popkov, V. L. Bile-secreting function of the liver in dogs X-irradiated against a background of normal and functionally impaired higher divisions of the central nervous system. Author's abstract. Leningrad, 1961.

Popov, A. V. Intestinal secretion and motility during radiation sickness in dogs with experimental neurosis. Scientific Conference on Problems in the Physiology and Pathology of Digestion celebrating the 40th Anniversary of the Great October Socialist Revolution. Abstracts. Tartu, 1957, pp. 210-212; Transactions. Tartu, 1960, pp. 371-380.

Popov, A. V. Intestinal secretion and motility during acute radiation sickness in dogs with normal and functionally weakened cerebral cortex. Author's abstract. Leningrad, 1958.

Popova, T. V. Effect of X-irradiating the head of animals on interoceptive unconditioned reflexes. Second All-Union Conference of Pathophysiologists. Abstracts. Kiev, 1956, pp. 313-314.

Porter, E. C. Relationship between the adrenal cortex and radiation sickness. Radiology. 58 (2): 246, 1952.

Portis, S. A. and R. Ahrens. The effects of wave length roentgen rays on the gastric secretion of dogs. Amer. J. of Roentgenol. a. Radium Therapy. (3): 272-280, 1924.

Prokhonchukov, A. A. Changes in solid tissues of the teeth after repeated small doses of ionizing radiation. Med. radiol. (4): 74-78, 1957.

Protas, L. R. and A. A. Danilin. Functional Changes in the Gastrointestinal Tract during Experimental Acute and Subacute Radiation Sickness. Leningrad, 1957.

Protas, L. R. and A. A. Danilin. Mechanism of functional impairment of the gastrointestinal tract during experimentally induced acute and subacute radiation sickness. Abstracts of the Scientific Conference celebrating the 40th Anniversary of the Great October Socialist Revolution. Central Scientific Institute of Roentgenology and Radiology, Leningrad, 1957, pp. 13-15.

Quastler, H., E. Lanzl, M. Keller and J. Osborn. Acute intestinal radiation death studies on roentgen death in mice. Amer. J. Physiol. 164 (2): 546-556, 1951.

Rauch, R. F. and C. W. Stenstrom. Effects of X-ray radiation on pancreatic function. Gastroenterology. 20: 595-603, 1952.

Razenkov, I. P. New Data on the Physiology and Pathology of Digestion. Izd. AMN SSSR, Moscow, 1948.

Regaud, C., T. Nogier and A. Lacassagne. Sur les effects redoutables des irradiations étandues de l'abdomen et sur les lésions du tube digestif déterminés par les rayons de Röntgen. Arch d'élect. med. 21: 321-342, 1912.

Revnivykh, G. A. Functional Changes in the Stomach during Acute Radiation Sickness. Voennoe izd. Ministerstva Oborony Soyuza SSR, Moscow, 1959.

Ricketts, W. S., I. B. Kirsner, E. M. Humphreys and W. I. Palmer. Effect of roentgen irradiation on the gastric mucosa. Gastroenterology. II (6): 813-832, 1948.

Röntgen, W. Uber eine neue Art von Strahlen, Sitzgsbericht physik. med. Ges. Würzburg, 1895, p. 137.

Rother. Uber den Angriffspunkt der Röntgenstrahlen wirkung am biologischen. Object. Strahlentherapie. 27: 197-256, 1927.

Rynkova, N. N. Condition of the digestive organs in patients with radiation sickness. Abstracts of the Sectional Reports of the All-Union Conference on Medical Radiology. Clinical Section. Medgiz, Moscow, 1956, p. 6.

Samtsov, V. A. Effect of ionizing radiation (Co^{60}, P^{32}) on certain mechanisms involved in creating reactivity. First Scientific and Practical Conference on Medical Radiology in the city of Ufa. Abstracts. Ufa, 1957, p. 7.

Sears, T. Role of the Physician in Atomic Defense (transl.). Izd. IL, Moscow, 1955.

Selye, H. The Story of the Adaptation Syndrome. Montreal, Canada, 1952.

Selye, H., E. Salgado and J. Procopio. Effect of somatotrophic hormone (STH) upon resistance to ionizing rays. Acta Endocrinol. (9): 337, 1952.

Seregin, M. S. Interoceptive conditioned reflexes from the gastrointestinal tract and motility of the stomach and duodenum during radiation sickness. Scientific Conference on Problems in the Physiology and Pathology of Digestion Celebrating the 40th Anniversary of the great October Socialist Revolution. Abstracts. Tartu, 1957, pp. 238-241; Transactions. Tartu, 1960, pp. 388-398.

Seregin, M. S. Changes in the interoceptive conditioned reflexes during radiation sickness. Author's abstract, Leningrad, 1959.

Serkov, F. N.   Effect of ionizing radiation on cerebral activity. Eighth All-Union Congress of Physiologists, Biochemists, and Pharmacologists. Izd. AN SSSR, Moscow, 1955, pp. 543-544.

Shal', G. V. Treatment of gastric and duodenal ulcers with X-rays in the light of a control. Transactions of the Central Inst. of Roentgenology and Radiology. Moscow, 1941, V, pp. 74-83.

Shaternikov, V. A. Impairment of the absorption processes in the small intestine following radiation injury of animals kept on various diets. Med. radiol. (4):61-67, 1956; Abstracts of Reports Presented at the Tenth Scientific Session of the Institute of Nutrition. Moscow, 1956, pp. 94-95.

Shaternikov, V. A. Mechanism of impairment of intestinal absorption of glycocoll after total-body X-irradiation. Scientific Conference on the Physiology and Pathology of Digestion celebrating the 40th Anniversary of the Great October Socialist Revolution. Abstracts. Tartu, 1957, pp. 298-299.

Shemyakin, A. I. Physiology of the Pyloric Part of the Stomach of Dogs. Diss. VMA, 1901.

Shlyakhtova, N. F. Effect of X-rays on hepato-pancreatico-duodenal secretion and on duodenal motility. Transactions of the Scientific Conference on Problems in the Physiol. and Pathol. of Digestion in memory of Academician K. M. Bykov. Ivanovo, 1960, pp. 925-929.

Simon, S. L. Suppression of gastric acidity with beta-particles of P^{32}. Science. 109: 563-564, 1949.

Simonov, P. V. Effect of extirpation of the cerebral hemispheres on the course and outcome of radiation sickness. Abstracts of Reports Presented at the Conference on Medical Radiology, celebrating the 40th Anniversary of the Great October Socialist Revolution. Medgiz, Moscow, 1957, pp. 39-40.

Sklyarov, Ya. P. Gastric Secretion. Gosmedizdat UkSSR, Kiev, 1954.

Sklyarov, Ya. P. Secretion of the Main Digestive Glands. Gosmedizdat UkSSR, Kiev, 1958.

Smirnov, K. V. Dynamics of intestinal secretion during radiation sickness in dogs kept on various diets. Abstracts of Reports Presented at the Tenth Scientific Session Institute of Nutrition. USSR Academy of Medical Sciences, Moscow, 1956, pp. 78-79.

Smirnov, K. V. Motility of an isolated segment of the small intestine. Scientific Conference on Problems in the Physiology and Pathology of Digestion celebrating the 40th Anniversary of Great October Socialist Revolution. Abstracts. Tartu, 1957, pp. 255-256.

Smirnov, K. V. Motility in an isolated segment of the small intestine in dogs during acute radiation sickness. Byull. éksper. biol. i med. XL, VI (12): 23-27, 1958.

Smith, W. W., F. Smith and E. C. Thompson. Failure of cortisone or ACTH to reduce mortality in irradiated mice. Proc. Soc. Exptl. Biol. a. Med. 73 (3): 529, 1950.

Smyth, F. S. and G. H. Whipple. Bile salt Metabolism. II. Proteose and X-ray Intoxication. Thyroid and thyroxin. J. Biol. Chem. (59): 637-646, 1924.

Sokolov, A. P. Analysis of gastric secretion in dogs. Diss. St. Petersburg, 1904.

Solodkina, O. V. Changes in gastric motility after total-body single X-irradiation. Scientific Conference on Problems in the Physiol. and Pathol. of Digestion celebrating the 40th Anniversary of the Great October Scientific Revolution. Abstracts. Tartu, 1957, pp. 257-259; Transactions. Tartu, 1960, pp. 427-433.

Solodkina, O. V. New data on the mechanism of impairment of gastric secretion after total-body X-irradiation. Transactions of the AN SSSR I. P. Pavlov Inst. of Physiology. Izd. AN SSSR, Leningrad, 1958, VII, pp. 513-519.

Solov'ev, A. V. New data on Gastric and Pancreatic Secretion. Izd. AN SSSR, Leningrad, 1959.

Solov'ev, A. V. and O. V. Solodkina. Analysis of the effect of X-irradiation on gastric secretion and motility in dogs. Abstracts of Reports Presented at the All-Union Scientific and Technical Conference on the Use of Radioactive and Stable Isotopes and Radiation in the National Economy and Science. Izd. AN SSSR, Moscow, 1957, pp. 22-24.

Solov'ev, A. V. and O. V. Solodkina. Analysis of the effect of X-irradiation on motility and secretion in small pouches formed from the lesser and greater curvatures of the stomach. Radiobiology. Izd. AN SSSR, Moscow, 1958, pp. 222-228.

Solov'ev, A. V., N. A. Solov'ev and O. V. Solodkina. Effect of total-body X-irradiation on secretion of various fields of the stomach. Transactions of the AN SSSR I. P. Pavlov Inst. of Physiology. Izd. AN SSSR, Leningrad, 1956, VI, pp. 509-513.

Stradyn', N. F. Changes in gastrointestinal motility and the pharmacological curve in X-irradiated rats. Scientific Conference on Problems in the Physiol. and Pathol. of Digestion celebrating the 40th Anniversary of the Great October Socialist Revolution. Abstracts. Tartu, 1957, pp. 265-266; Transactions. Tartu, 1960, pp. 472-476.

Strel'tsova, V. N. Pathological anatomy of radiation lesions caused by radioactive lanthanum. Med. radiol. (4): 78-83, 1957.

Sverdlov, A. G. Role of humoral factors in the development of radiation lesions. Ninth Congress of the All-Union Society of Physiologists, Biochemists, and Pharmacologists. Izd. AN SSSR i Belgosuniversiteta, Moscow-Minsk, 1959, v. 1, pp. 348-349.

Swann, M. B. R. A study of the immediate effects of X-rays on the function of certain tissues and organs. Brit. J. Radiol. 29 (237): 195-220, 1924.

Szegö, E. and J. Rother. Über den Einfluss der Röntgenstrahlen auf die Magensaftsekretion. Ztschr. f. d. ges. exper. Med. 24 (144): 270-288, 1921.

Takeda, T. I. and K. Jouen. Über den Einfluss der Röntgenstrahlen auf die Verdauungsorgane. Okayama—Igabbai—Zasshi. (432): 80-94, 1926; Abs. in Zentralbl. f. d. ges. Radiol. I: 185, 1926.

Tarkhanov, I. R. Physiological action of X-rays on the central nervous system. Bol'nichnaya gazeta S. P. Botkina. (33): 753-757, 1896; (34): 785-791, 1896.

Tarusov, B. N. Principles of the Biological action of Radioactive Radiations. Medgiz, Moscow, 1955.

Tarusov, B. N. Primary processes following the action of ionizing radiations. In: Primary Processes of Radiation Injury. Medgiz, Moscow, 1957, pp. 3-29.

The Danger of Ionizing Radiation to Man (transl.). IL, Moscow, 1958.

Tillotson, F. W. and S. Warren. Nucleoprotein changes in the gastrointestinal tract following total-body roentgen irradiation. Radiology. 61 (2): 249-260, 1953.

Tonkikh, A. V. Role of the adrenals in the development of radiation sickness. Radiobiology. Izd. AN SSSR, Moscow, 1958, 11. pp. 148-155.

Toyoma, T. Über die Wirkung der Röntgenstrahlen auf die Darmbewegungen des Kaninchens. The Tohoku J. of Exp. Med. 22 (1-2): 196-200, 1933.

Tsuzuki, M. Experimental studies on the biological action of hard roentgen rays. Amer. J. Roentgenol. a. Radium Therapy. 16 (2): 134-150, 1926.

Tsuzuki, M. Atomic Bomb Injury from Medical Point of View. Tokyo, 1953.

Tullis, J. L. Pathologicoanatomical changes following total-body irradiation. In: Radioactive Decay and Medicine (transl.). Izd. IL, Moscow, 1954, pp. 89-100.

Tullis, J. L., B. G. Lamson and S. C. Madden. Pathology of swine exposed to total-body gamma-radiation from an atomic bomb. Amer. J. Pathol. 31 (1): 41-71, 1955.

Tullis, J. L. and S. Warren. Gross autopsy observation in the animals exposed at Bikini. JAMA. (134): 1155, 1947.

Turel', M. A. Roentgenotherapy of gastric ulcer. Klin. med. XII (6): 896-901, 1934.

Uspenskiĭ, Yu. N. Effect of ionizing radiation on activity of the digestive organs. I (1): 66-68, 1956.

Uspenskiĭ, Yu. N. Mechanism of impairment of the digestive organs during radiation sickness. Abstracts of Reports Presented at the Scientific Conference celebrating the 40th Anniversary of the Great October Socialist Revolution. Central Scientific Inst. of Roentgenology and Radiology of the USSR Ministry of Health, Leningrad, 1957, pp. 10-11.

Uspenskiĭ, Yu. N. Activity of the digestive organs in dogs exposed to ionizing radiation. Fiziol. zhurn. SSSR. XLIII (4): 328-335, 1957.

Uspenskiĭ, Yu. N. Effect of ionizing radiation on the activity of the intestinal glands. Fiziol. zhurn. SSSR. XLIV (3): 225-230, 1958.

Uspenskiĭ, Yu. N. Intestinal secretion and bile formation during experimental radiation sickness. Scientific Conference on Problems in the Physiology and Pathology of Digestion celebrating the 40th anniversary of the Great October Revolution. Abstracts. Tartu, 1957, pp. 282-283; Transactions. Tartu, 1960, pp. 406-414.

Uspenskiĭ, Yu. N. and A. V. Afanas'eva. Dynamics of protein constitution of the blood serum and digestive juices during experimental radiation sickness in dogs. Fiziol. zhur. SSSR. XLIV (6): 565-569, 1958.

Uspenskiĭ, Yu. N., T. A. Timofeeva and I. V. Shvartser. Activity of the salivary glands in dogs following a single massive X-irradiation of the abdominal area. Med. radiol. (6): 37-41, 1957.

Verzar, F. Absorption from the Intestine. London—Toronto, 1936.

Vladimirov, V. G. Effect of cystamine [methenamine] on the nucleic acid content of the liver and spleen of irradiatiated rats. Scientific Conference on "Regenerative and Compensatory Processes in Radiation Sickness". Abstracts. IEM, Leningrad, 1960, pp. 15-16.

Vorob'ev, A. M., E. M. Krasina and N. G. Lesnoĭ. Effect of X-rays on gastric secretion. Byull. éksper. biol. i med. VIII (2): 166-169, 1939.

Wachtler, F. Experimentelle Untersuchungen über die Motorik des röntgenbestrahlten Dünndarms. Strahlentherapie. 87 (3): 415-429, 1952.

Wang, S. C., H. I. Chinn and A. A. Renzi. Role of abdominal visceral afferents in experimental motion and radiation sickness in dogs. XX Congrès International de Physiologie. Bruxelles, 1956, pp. 945-946.

Warren, S. Effect of bomb explosion of Hiroshima and Nagasaki, JAMA. 1946, p. 131.

Warren S. L. and N. B. Friedeman. Pathology and pathologic diagnosis of radiation lesions in gastrointestinal tract. Amer. J. Pathol. 18: 499-513, 1942.

Warren, S. L. and G. H. Whipple. Roentgen ray intoxication. J. Exp. Med. 35: 187-202, 203-211, 1922.

Weber, R. P. and F. R. Steggerda. Histamine in rat plasma, correlation with blood pressure changes following X-irradiation. Proc. Soc. Exp. Biol. Med. 70 (1): 261-263, 1949.

Wetterer. Handbuch der Röntgentherapie. Leipzig, 1908.

Wilson, M. E. and R. E. Stowell. Cytological changes of the liver in mice. J. Nat. Cancer. Inst. 13 (5): 1123-1137, 1953.

Yanson, Z. A. Electrophysiological study of changes occurring in conditioned-reflex activity of rabbits after total-body and local X-irradiation. Transactions of the All-Union Conference on Medical Radiology. Medgiz, Moscow, 1957, pp. 23-27.

Yaroslavtseva, N. A. Complex reflex phase of gastric secretion in acute radiation sickness. In: Problems in Corticovisceral Physiology and Pathology. Leningrad, 1957, pp. 61-69.

Yaroslavtseva, N. A. Complex reflex phase of gastric secretion in acute radiation sickness in dogs with functionally weakened cerebral cortex. In: Problems in Corticovisceral Physiology and Pathology. Leningrad, 1957, pp. 70-74.

Yasvoin, G. V. Effect of radium emanations on frog liver. Vestn. rentgenol. i radiol. IV: 305-310, 1926.

Yugenburg, A. M. Effect of X-irradiation of the gastric region on its secretory activity. Vestn. rentgenol. i radiolog. III (5): 247-257, 1925.

Yugenburg, A. M. and R. G. Gurevich. Does irradiation of the abdominal cavity affect acidity of the stomach? Vestn. rentgenol. i radiol. XII (1-2): 38-42, 1933.

Yugenburg, A. M., E. N. Mozharova and R. G. Gurevich. Results of treating peptic ulcers by Prof. Nemenov's method. Vestn. rentgenol. i radiol. XIV: 38-53, 1935.

Yugenburg, A. M., L. G. Peretts and R. S. Mostova. New data on the pathogenesis of early systemic X-ray reactions. Vestn. rentgenol. i radiol. XII (3): 476, 1933.

Zakharzhevskiĭ, V. B. Chemoreceptors of the small intestine during radiation sickness after functional impairment of the central nervous system. Scientific Conference on Problems in the Physiology and Pathology of Digestion celebrating the 40th anniversary of the Great October Socialist Revolution. Abstracts. Tartu, 1957, pp. 82-84; Transactions. Tartu, 1960, pp. 381-387.

Zakharzhevskiĭ, V. B. Some data on changes in the chemoreceptor apparatus of the cat's small intestine during acute radiation sickness. Transactions of the Sci. Conference on Problems of the Physiol. and Pathol. of Digestion, in memory of Academician K. M. Bykov. Ivanovo, 1960, pp. 281-286.

Zedgenidze, G. A. Functional changes in certain internal organs and systems during radiation sickness caused by external irradiation. Abstracts of Sectional Reports at the All-Union Conference on Medical Radiology. Clinical Section Medgiz, Moscow, 1956, pp. 11-12; Transactions of-the All-Union Conference on Medical Radiology. Medgiz, Moscow, 1957, pp. 30-36.

Zedgenidze, G. A., I. S. Amosov, and L. F. Sinenko. Radiation reactions and radiation sickness. Med. radiol. 3(2): 3-10, 1958.

Zedgenidze, G. A., M. Z. Kotik, L. F. Larionov, Z. K. Pavlova, A. L. Polyakova, E. A. Popova, N. G. Soboleva, L. M. Shabad and G. V. Shor. Morphological changes in the organs of laboratory animals following X-irradiation. Vestn. rentgenol. i radiol. XVII: 356-396, 1936.

Zhoga, N. A. Effect of radioactive phosphorus on the general condition and motility of the gastrointestinal tract in dogs. Fiziol. zhurn. SSSR. 1 (3): 102-107, 1955.

Zhukovskiĭ, M. N. Effect of radium rays on excitability of the psychomotor centers. Obozr. psikhiatr., nevrol. i eksper. psikhol. (11): 801-814, 1903.

Zhur, R. S. and V. A. Sonkina. Effect of X-rays on unconditioned exteroceptive and interoceptive reflexes of the liver and stomach. Transactions of the Scientific Conference on Problems in the Physiology and Pathology of Digestion, in memory of Academician K. M. Bykov. Ivanovo, 1960, pp. 266-270.

Zlatin, R. S., A. F. Makarchenko, V. F. Saenko-Lyubarskaya and M. F. Sirotina. Effect of ionizing radiations on the body. Ninth Conference of the All-Union Society of Physiologists, Biochemists, and Pharmacologists. Izd. AN SSSR i Belgouniversiteta, Moscow-Minsk, 1959, I, pp. 214-215.

Zvorykin, V. N. Some physiological mechanisms governing impairment of the appetite in sick persons. Scientific Conference on Problems in the Physiology and Pathology of Digestion, celebrating the 40th Anniversary of the Great October Socialist Revolution. Abstracts. Tartu, 1957, pp. 84-86; Transactions. Tartu, 1960, pp. 399-405.

Zvorykin, V. N. and I. T. Kurtsin. Interaction of the higher divisions
    of the central nervous system and stomach in man under
    normal and pathological conditions. Transactions of the Sci.
    Conf. on Problems in the Physiol. and Pathol. of Digestion
    in memory of Academician K. M. Bykov. Ivanovo, 1960,
    pp. 287-293.
Zyuzin, I. K., O. S. Vergilesova, I. A. Korovina, and I. A. Shisha-
    kova. Changes in the content of copper, cobalt, and iron in
    the liver of rabbits during acute radiation sickness. Trans-
    actions of the Scientific Conference on Problems in the
    Physiol. and Pathol. of Digestion, in memory of Academician
    K. M. Bykov. Ivanovo, 1960, pp. 294-296.

SUBJECT INDEX

Abdomen, pains, 3
Acetic acid, cholesterol synthesis, liver, 92
Acetylcholine, action on smooth muscles, 174, 176–178
—, increase, gastrointestinal motility, 175
—, intensification of radiation effect, 180
—, intestinal receptors, stimulation, 244, 246
—, salivation, 21
Acetylcholine–cholinesterase system, 272
—, gastrointestinal motility impairment, 175
Acromegaly, radiotherapy, gastric secretion decrease, 28
ACTH, 268
—, digestion impairment, 266
—, liver proteins, sulfhydryl groups, changes, 268
Adenosine triphosphatase, 206
Adenosine triphosphate, glycocoll absorption acceleration, 152
Adrenal, reactivity to radiotherapy, 267
Adrenergic system, impairment, 180
Adynamia, 2, 5, 120
Amino acids, absorption, impairment, 142
Amylase, intestinal juice, 116–118, 128–130
—, pancreatic juice, 78
—, —, cyclic changes, 82
—, —, decrease, with large volume of juice, 80
—, —, —, X-irradiation, abdominal, 77
—, —, neurosis, complicating radiation sickness, 87
—, saliva, 17
—, —, carbohydrate diet (dog), 17

—, —, hypoxia (dog), 17
—, —, mechanism (dog), 17
—, —, parotid (dog), 18
—, —, vascular permeability salivary gland (dog), 17
—, —, synthesis, pancreatic, radioresistance, 76
Anesthesia, ether, intestinal motility disorders, mitigation, 181
Anorexia, 2, 3, 120, 124, 159
—, 20 sec after γ-irradiation, 3
Appetite, loss, see Anorexia
Atropine, effect on small intestine, 176, 178
—, gastrointestinal motility, normalization, 175
—, weakening of radiation effect, 175, 180
Autonomic nervous system, see also Parasympathetic system, Sympathetic system
—, gastric secretion disorders, 28, 58, 70, 72
—, gastrointestinal motility, 182
—, intestinal absorption, 155

Barium chloride, effect on small intestine, 176, 177
Benadryl, see Diphenhydramine
Beta-irradiation, gastrointestinal motility, 161
—, local, see Local irradiation, beta
Bile, capillaries, regeneration, 197
— cholates, after irradiation, 94
— —, —, undulant pattern, 93
— cholesterol, changes, 93
— —, water absorption by gallbladder mucosa, 106
— composition, bilirubin, after irradiation, 93, 94
— —, —, undulant pattern, 93

Evans blue, gastric motility, tracing,
168
Exteroceptive reflexes, 255–257, 265
—, conditioned, effect on interoceptive
reflex, 258
—, —, impairment, 255–257

Fat, liver, 92
— necrosis, pancreas, 77
Fatty acids, incompletely oxidized, toxicity, 206
—, liver, 92
—, —, C^{14}uptake, increase, 92
—, —, toxic, 91
Food, absorption, see Intestinal absorption
— centre, injury, salivation impairment, 20
— processing, chemical, salivation impairment, 25
— —, mechanical, hemorrhages, oral
mucosa, 25

Galactose test, liver function, decrease,
92
Gallbladder, bile secretion, impairment,
101
— contractions, 101
— —, cholecystokinin, 106
— —, end of digestion, 106
— —, hight of digestion, 105
— fistula, 93
—, functional condition, 104
—, motility, asthenic bile secretion, 105
— —, inert bile secretion, 105
— mucosa, water absorption, bile, bilirubin, 106
— —, —, —, cholesterol, 106
— tone, reflex, increase, 101, 103
Gamma-irradiation, flaw detection, 31
—, intestinal,morphological changes,192
—, low dose, gastric secretion, 29, 30
—, maximum permissible dose, 3
—, total-body, anorexia 20 sec after irradiation, 3
—, —, vomiting, 3
Gastric glands, see also Gastric juice,
Gastric secretion
—, accessory cells, destruction, La¹⁴⁰
injection, 198

—, —, radiosensitivity, 35
—, blood supply, impairment, 234
—, chief cells changes, 192
—, —, uranium, 57
—, complex reflex phase, 58
—, disorders, 28, 57
— —, ANS involvement, 72
— —, complex reflex phase, 58
— —, neurochemical phase, 58
—, epithelium, degeneration, uranium,
57
—, excitability, abnormal, 261
—, in intermediate metabolism, 156
—, neck, cells, hydropic degeneration,
192
—, —, hemorrhagic erosion, La¹⁴⁰, 198
—, neurochemical phase, 58
—, —, regulatory mechanism, impairment, 63
—, neuroglandular apparatus, 28
—, parietal cells, 192
—, —, destruction, La¹⁴⁰, 198
—, —, nuclei, shape, uranium, 57
—, —, protoplasm, 192
—, —, pyknosis, 192
—, pyloric, mucous decrease, uranium,
57
—, —, radiosensitivity, 35
—, secretory cells, asthenia,
48
—, —, excitability, complex reflex
phase, 64
—, —, —, in neurochemical phase, 63
—, —, granularity decrease, uranium,
57
—, —, humoral mechanisms, 58
—, —, inhibition, 27, 29
—, —, radiosensitivity, 180
—, —, regulation, complex reflex, 58
— stimulation, enterogastrone, 63
— —, pylorus hormones, 63
— —, secretin, 63
—, uranium effect, 48
—, vulnerability, compared with intestinal glands, 120
Gastric juice, see also Gastric glands,
Gastric secretion
—, acidity, 29, 30, 39
— —, dose of irradiation, 34
— —, greater curvature, 40
— —, —, abdominal irradiation, large
dose, 33

Greater curvature (continuation)
—, secretion, complex reflex phase, 60
—, — disorders, 39, 40
—, — —, bread, meat and milk feeding, 41
—, — —, CNS, 65
—, — —, complex reflex phase, 61, 62
—, — —, cyclic appearance, 39
—, — —, dose of irradiation, 34
—, — —, hypersecretion, 33, 34
—, — —, — in complex reflex phase, 61
—, — —, — during first and second phase, 72, 73
—, — —, — during neurochemical phase, 61
—, — —, hyposecretion, abdominal irradiation, 33, 34
—, — —, —, complex reflex phase, 61
—, — —, —, β-irradiation, mucosa, 34
—, — —, —, neurochemical phase, 61, 62
—, — —, —, radium, 33
—, — —, —, ruthenium, 33
—, — —, —, Sr^{90}, 33
—, — —, latent period, 40
—, — —, neurochemical phase, 61, 62
—, — —, phasic, 41
—, — —, radon, submucosal, 33
—, — duration, response to stimulus, 39
—, —, higher nervous activity, 39
—, —, neurochemical phase, 60
—, —, sham feeding experiments, 65
—, — volume, 39
—, secretory cells, morphology, 37
—, sympathetic system, tone increase, 72, 73
—, veins, dilatation, 192

Head irradiation, gastric contractions, 167
—, salivation impairment, 19
Hemorrhages, oral mucosa, food processing, 25
Hepatitis, subacute, La^{140}, 198
Higher nervous activity, see also Cerebral cortex, Conditioned reflexes, Subcortical centres, 36, 37, 42

—, bile discharge into intestine, 97, 110, 111
—, bile formation, 96, 107, 108, 110, 111
— disorders, bile secretion, 107–109
— —, complex reflex impairment, 217
— —, digestion, regulation impairment, 217
— — as early radiation effect, 209
— —, induced, see also Cerebral cortex, functional weakening, 218, 223
— —, —, bile secretion, 107, 110–113
— —, —, intestinal secretion, drug administration, 225–227
— —, —, pancreatic secretion, 211, 214
— —, intestinal inhibition, 119
— —, intestinal motility impairment, 188
— —, nature and degree, intestinal absorption, 145
— —, primary, before complex reflex mechanism impairment, 217
—, functional condition, bile, 114
—, —, gastric motility, 183, 184
—, —, gastric secretion, 31, 39, 64–66, 242
—, —, intestinal secretion, 229
—, intestinal absorption, 146, 147, 155
—, — regulation, 149–151
—, intestinal juice, composition, 121, 122
—, pancreatic secretion, 78, 84
—, —, "cross" experiments, 84–86
—, radiosensitivity, 208
—, salivation, 212, 213
Histaminase, 264
Histamine, gastric secretion, stimulation, inhibition, 63
—, increase, direct after irradiation, 264
—, smooth muscles, intestinal, sensitivity, 174
Histamine-like substances, 263–265
—, pathogenesis, toxic, of radiation sickness, 63
Hormones, digestion impairment, 266, 267
—, formation, impaired, 206
—, gastrointestinal mucosa, 235
Humoral mechanisms, disruption,

Intestinal juice (continuation)
—, digestive activity, cyclic changes, not identical for the different enzymes, 126
—, —, —, proportion to volume changes, 126
—, enterokinase, 119, 121
—, —, quantitative changes, 120
—, enzymatic activity, 120
—, —, cortex weakened, 131, 138
—, —, impairment, 119
—, enzymes, dissociation, 126
—, invertase, 119, 121
—, lactic acid, 157
—, lipolytic activity, 119, 139
—, —, cortex weakened, 128–130, 140, 225
—, —, Po²¹⁰ oral, large dose, 124
—, peptidase, 119
—, phosphatase, 120, 121
—, —, alkaline, 119
—, polypeptidase, 119
—, protein, high-molecular-weight, 157
—, proteolytic activity, 139
—, —, cortex weakened, 128–130, 140, 225
—, sugar, 157
—, trypsin, Po²¹⁰, oral, large dose, 124
—, urea, 157
—, volume, 121, 139
—, —, cortex normal, 134, 137
—, —, cortex weakened, 130, 134, 135, 140
—, —, cyclic changes, proportional to digestive activity, 126
—, —, decrease, 120
—, —, increase, 120
—, —, Po²¹⁰, 125
—, —, radiation dose, 119
—, —, uranium 124–126
Intestinal secretion, see also Intestinal juice, 116
—, abdominal irradiation, 116, 117
—, cortex, functional state, 127
—, cyclic changes, 120
— disorders, 116, 119, 120
— —, cortex weakened, 127, 130, 132, 140, 217
— —, —, drug administration, 225, 226, 228
— —, humoral factors, 229
— —, hypersecretion, 120

— —, —, inhibition of gastric secretion, 119
— —, —, Po²¹⁰ oral, large dose, 123
— —, hyposecretion, 120, 127
— —, —, increase of amylolytic activity, 116, 117
— —, —, Po²¹⁰, 122, 123
— —, internal irradiation, 116
— —, repeated irradiation, 128
— —, wave-like, uranium, 124
—, higher nervous activity, 122, 125
—, mechanical irritation of mucosa, 117, 118
—, regulation, neurohumoral, impairment, 126
—, "spontaneous", 118
Intestine, activity, neurohumoral regulation, impairment, 173
—, cholinergic system, excitation by irradiation, 174
—, connective tissue changes, 191
—, —, histiocytes, proliferation, 189
— crypts, epithelium degeneration, 191
— —, sensitivity, 189
— —, uranium, 123
— —, vulnerability, compared with gastric glands, 120
—, epithelium, degeneration, 191
—, —, DNA decrease, 191
—, —, mitosis, decrease, 191, 192
—, —, nuclei, swelling, 191
—, function, 270
—, interoceptive reflex, 268
—, Lieberkühn glands, see crypts
—, lymph nodes, lymphocytes, lysis, 191
—, —, reticular cells, swelling, 191
—, M-cholinesterase receptors, sensitivity reduction, 177
—, morphological changes, dose, 190
—, mucosa, atrophy, 189
—, —, hemorrhages, 189, 191
—, —, hormones, 266
—, —, hyperemia, 190
—, muscles, acetylcholine effect, 174, 176–178
—, —, sensitivity to histamine, 174
—, nerve cells, hypochromatism, 192
—, —, protoplasm, vacuolation, 192
—, nerves, intramural, Po²¹⁰ effect, 200
—, —, —, Sr⁹⁰ effect, 200

PRINTED IN THE NETHERLANDS